HOTSHOTS

F.N.G.

by
Stephen Petretti

To Glenn:
Good Talking to you AGAIN
Good Luck with your
Theme PArks

Steve P

Hotshots

F.N.G.

Copyright © 2002 by Stephen Petretti

ISBN 0-9724558-0-9

Flying Dutchman Publishing Co.
1350 Mulberry Dr.
San Marcos, CA 92069
760-744-0562
www.flyingdutchmanpub.com
www.hotshotsusfs.com

printed in America

A special thanks and acknowledgments to:

Dennis Marchuk of Western Image Production for graphic digitizing and layout assistance;
Richard Brown for input typing;
L. W. for editing and consulting;
Bob Dotterer for his input and consulting, Phoenix Rural-Metro FD;
Darryl Atchison for fire technical consulting, USFS.

AND most of all, the guys on the crew who made this story possible and real.

This story is very real, real names, (except two) were used, there were no innocences to protect. Only one occurrence was out of chronological order. All names, times, dates and occurrences are true as to the best of my recollection and journal scribbles.

Make sure you read the back pages for a special tribute and dedication.

Prelude

So, you want to be a hotshot?? Sounds glamorous, doesn't it? Before you accept the job, perhaps you should really know what a Hotshot crewman is, for those who might be erroneously informed, or those better equipped both mentally and physically to apply for less demanding, but equally important work with the United States Forest Service. And we do many jobs that pay the same, and are equally challenging, equally rewarding.

The very term "Hotshot" means many things to many people. But to those of us who recruit, train and work hotshots, the job title is anything but glamorous. From experience, we know that firefighting is 90 percent physical for the Hotshot crewmen. The nature of the work is so demanding that only those of unusual strength, agility, coordination, and stamina can cope with the sustained work required of even the average Hotshot crewman.

Hiring on and passing the Step Test is easy; most people under the age of 60 can do that.

As a Hotshot crewman, you will be required not only to produce physically, but also to live together, eat together, sleep together in close, crowded conditions. Complete compatibility is in itself a difficult challenge.

You must take orders, and carry those orders out at all times, day after day, even when **you** are having a bad day. The emotional strain is extreme, and the competitive pressure of your peer group is always present, for a crew is only as good as its weakest member.

When not on fire duty, you will be required to engage in daily, structured physical fitness training that consists of a two mile run, coordination exercises, push-ups, sit-ups, chin-ups, rope climbs, squat thrusts, abdominal stretching, and obstacle courses.

Regular testing is conducted continually (beginning on the first day of the job) and consists of a battery of exercises to be completed at one time with a five-minute rest between exercises. Run one and one-half miles in 11 minutes or less (or carry a 60 pound pack over a two mile course in 27 minutes or less); pick up a 125-pound dead weight, place it on your shoulder and carry it up a 10 percent slope for a distance of 100-feet, and return to the starting point; 25 push-ups; 8 chin-ups (palms out); 50 sit-ups; climb a 20 foot rope (the first 12 feet using arms only); and 40 squat thrusts.

The rest of your day will be like every other day – hard labor using hand tools, (axe, shovel, saw) and usually piling brush, digging holes, picking up garbage, cleaning toilets, sharpening tools, and similar mundane tasks.

On the fire line, the Hotshot crews are singled out for the most hazardous, difficult assignments. It is normal for Hotshot crews to be on the first shift, 32 hours, before relief is available; succeeding shifts of 14-18 hours for 5 to 15 days straight are necessary. You will normally be "spiked" out away from the main fire camp, thirsty, hungry, and sleeping on rocky ground, too often even without even paper sleeping bags. You'll hardly have the luxury of washing your hands, much less the facilities to bathe. You'll be filthy, exhausted, underfed, and hurting. There will be no privacy, no sanitation, no shelter, no laundry, no ride to work, no doctors or shopping centers.

The Hotshot crew is so-named because of the need for tough, knowledgeable, hard firemen who can be sent ahead of the main contingent of the ordinary labor crews, and independently drive holding lines around critical segments of the fire; they hold their line and survive. You will be required to pack heavy loads for hours on end, up and down extremely mountainous terrain (hose packs of 70 pounds); fell large trees with either power saws or crosscuts saws, buck trees into shorter lengths; haul blocks of logs, dead falls and brush out of the fire path; dig (3 feet to 10 feet wide) fire lines to mineral soil; chop roots out; excavate rocks in the line to construct retaining walls; haul hose; pack heavy portable pumps and tanks; and burn out your line before the fire gets there; and then start extinguishing spot fires over your line. And that's not the end of it

– then the hard work begins – the dirty work of "mop-up." Mop-up is digging and scraping all hot spots out and extinguishing the heat source. Other features of the job are living in and breathing smoke for days on end, contending with poison oak, poison ivy, poison sumac, cactus, thorns, ticks, gnats, flies, snakes, scorpions, spiders, rolling rocks and falling debris. It's dirty, hot and freezing cold; it's dusty, and in short – it reduces all to animal survival. There's no Chaplain, no medication, no union steward, no happy hour, no novelty.

This statement may appear a bit overdone. Don't believe it. I haven't truly captured the reality of what it is to be a Hotshot fireman, and if someone tells you otherwise, better check his or her credentials, because obviously they haven't been there.

Obviously, we're looking for superior individuals to fill our Hotshot crews. If you can live and excel with the job I've described, then we want you. We care not about your sex, color, race, or religion; but if for any reason you cannot live up to these standards, then I encourage you to do yourself and the rest of the crew a favor and apply for other than Hotshot work.

Bill Buck
Fire Management Officer
Coconino National Forest
signed by James Bedlion

Introduction
April 18, 1979

Ring. Ring. Six times. Seven times. The phone is ringing early, way too early for me. I reach for the receiver and mumble a tired "Hello" to whoever is on the line.

"Hello. Is Mr. Steve Petretti there?"

"This is he."

"I'm Michael Reamer from the Forest Service Blue Ridge Ranger District, would you like a job working on a Hotshot crew?"

"A what? A hotshot crew? What do they do?"

"Well, it's a 20 man fire suppression crew."

"Sure, I'll take anything if this is with the Forest Service."

"Yes, it is."

"Where is this place?"

"About 70 miles from Flagstaff, Arizona and 45 miles from Winslow. How soon can you be out here? We would like for you to be here no later than Monday the 2nd of May."

"Well, I should give Litton a two week notice. I'll try to be there on the second."

"You should have a physical before getting here. We'll send you the forms by certified mail today."

"Okay, I'll try to be there by then."

"Sounds like you just woke up."

"I did, I had to work pretty late last night. What's your phone number so that I can call you back when I'm more awake?" As I lean half out of bed to reach a pen I notice the clock. "'You know that it's 7:30 A.M."

"It's 8:30 here."

"Oh, what's your number? I'm ready." I scribble down the number with one hand and hold the phone with the other. "I'll call you back later. Bye." I put the phone back on the hook and jump back into bed. In seconds I'm asleep again, the phone intrusion seemed little more than a dream.

At Litton I worked both swing nights over the weekend. Last night was really boring. I got a lot of goals met though, and it was easy money. It's more the thought of being there on the weekend night shift that I dislike. You're the only Production Control Expeditor available so you have to stick around all night. You are the problem solver in the plant. Keith, a mechanic assembler, was working, too, so it wasn't too bad. At least I had a friend there to keep me company.

After work I waited around until he got off so we could munch out on our favorite Truck Stopper sandwich from 7-11 and our after work nightcap, an every night occurrence. After a few beers and bongs, we'd be well primed for a good laugh. Get Smart, our favorite TV show, comes on at 2:00 in the morning. It's actually aired five times a day, but the 2:00 A.M. showing is the best somehow. After that I'd go to bed about 3 A.M. Except on Friday bowling nights. We'd be up until the sun peeked through the Denny's windows for our breakfast sober-up time. You swing-shifters know what I mean.

I'm not too crazy about this part of my life. I just turned 25. My best friend was found dead seven weeks ago in his cabin in Big Bear. I just broke up with my girlfriend, Kathryn Ann Castleberry. I'm in a dead end job and the fluorescent lights I work under all week are getting to me. Why am I even here? I just got my BA in Philosophy and don't know what to do with it.

There are no listings in the "Help Wanted" sections of the newspaper for Philosophers. Anyway, no one wants to hear what philosophers have to say. I went through 72 units as a chemical engineer before I switched my major. I believe Philosophy is what higher education is all about, not mindlessly being programmed to work out three-hour calculus equations. Chemistry still fascinates me. I figure that if one were to know everything about the physical world, and everything about the metaphysical world, it would be the next best thing to Godliness.

Then there's the fact that I live in Los Angeles, or more specifically the San Fernando Valley part of it. I was born and raised here, in Lake View Terrace. Smell A, that's what I really think of this fucking city, or any big city for that matter. But it's not the city, its buildings, streets, or hurry-scurry! It's not the blacks, the whites, the illegal aliens, lawmakers, and enforcers. It's the labyrinth that they all, as an aggregate, put you through whether you like it or not. If you were born here, brought up here, and lived here all your life, the city is in your face from day one without waiting for you to accept it. Decisions made by others, long before you grew up, set you running through this maze like a confused rat. Your real identity is the smell of cheese just over the wall, cheese you can't see, but just imagine. Cheese that's always just out of reach.

The trap is that the city offers goodies... money and obtainable pleasures. So you take the easy way, enjoy what there is to enjoy, and sell out the dreams of your better self. Next thing you know, you're 65 and locked into a lifestyle you always thought was temporary. You don't know what you've lost, but it doesn't matter any more because it's too late.

Happily, it didn't turn out that way for me. That early morning phone call was about to change my life. What you are about to read is my true life adventure with the firefighting Blue Ridge Hotshots of the Coconino National Forest in Northern Arizona. I hope you enjoy it. I certainly did.

This is the first of three books from the 1979 season.

Book one "Hotshots: F.N.G.," Oct. 2002
ISBN 0-9724558-0-9

Book two: "Hotshots: The Big One," Jan. 2003
ISBN 0-9724558-1-7

Book three: "Hotshots: Seasons End," April 2003
ISBN 0-9724558-2-5

Also there will be a pictorial coffee table book of the season, May
2003 ISBN 0-9724558-3-3.

All above books will be printed in Spanish under different ISBN's.

May 2, 1979

Doug, my brother-in-law, woke me up early. He had already taken his shower and blow-dried his hair. Come to think of it, I remember hearing the high-pitched whine of the drier motor in the background of my last dream. Still coming to from an indifferent sleep, I hear Doug tell me that there are towels in the bathroom. "Oh," he adds, "try not to be too noisy because the baby is still sleeping."

"O.K. Thanks," I say. I just lie there, still trying to realize what I'm about to go through. "I'm crazy, what am I doing here?" I think. I get up for a shower to bring myself back to reality. The shower feels good. I'm pulling on my thermal underwear when I hear sister Laura's voice in the kitchen. I take my time getting my clothes on. I'm feeling shy and sort of nervous about going right out there for the morning greetings. I haven't seen them since shortly after their honeymoon a couple of years ago. They used to live in Seattle where Doug served as the personnel officer for the BLM. After that he transferred to Flagstaff as the personnel officer for the Coconino National Forest. I stall a little more by making my bed, then I join them in the kitchen.

"Good morning," Laura says. She's always smiling. Even has permanent crinkles around her eyes from her frequent, good natured grin. But this morning her smile is especially big.

"Are you ready for your big day?" Doug asks.

"I hope so," I reply. "Is this the usual time you get up?"

"For me it is," Doug replies. "Lori has to go to work today, too." He turns to her and confirms, "Don't you, honey?"

"Yeah. I hate driving two and a half hours to Phoenix, then getting on a plane to Denver. But that's what I've got to do just to get to work. This winter I almost died driving back from there. The roads were icy, and I must have hit some black ice because I started spinning out. I was lucky no one was around me to hit."

"Did anyone stop?" I ask, concerned.

"No. I quit spinning facing the traffic, and I straightened out and parked on the side of the road until my heart stopped racing. Every time I drive on that stretch of highway it scares me. It was supposed to be below freezing last night and there are always icy spots on the road."

I look out the window. "It doesn't look like it's that cold outside, "I remark. "All I can see is pine trees and blue sky. Not a single cloud."

"Don't let that fool you. It gets pretty cold up here," Doug says.

"I should be all right. I got my thermos on."

"Well, do you want some breakfast?" Laura asks.

"Uh, no thanks. I usually don't eat breakfast. By the time I get out of bed it's lunch time and all I have is coffee. If you've got some coffee I'll take it." I scan the kitchen, looking for a coffee pot but don't see one.

"We got that," chirps Laura as she goes to the kettle, dumps out the old water, and fills it back up. "We don't drink coffee here. When we have company I'll make it, but otherwise all we have is this." She pulls out some freeze dried stuff.

"That's fine," I say. "That's all I drink at home."

We all get ready for our journey to work. At least mine is a journey, theirs is mostly a routine. Laura gets the baby ready for the baby sitter. He's still groggy and not too thrilled to see me.

"Alan, this is your uncle Steve from Los Angeles," Laura coos. No soap. Alan hugs his mother closer, hides his face in her bosom and whimpers like a puppy. "He doesn't like men," Laura explains. "Especially ones with beards. His doctor has one and he gave him a shot yesterday. Alan didn't like that doctor sticking him, no-o-o-o." She goes to kiss him and he buries his face even deeper.

"I guess he just needs time to get used to me," I reach out to touch him, but he squirms away, seeking his mother's protection. "He'll get over it," I say with confidence.

It's quiet again and I'm noticing how nice the house looks... more open then last night when the curtains were drawn. Now the morning sun fills and compliments the interior. I see the maps on the dining table where we left them last night, and walk over to them. Doug follows me. I want to inspect them again to check out my route to Blue Ridge. He shows me one more time. He points out the gas station store. "After you make your turn, it's only nine and a half miles," he says. I wonder how he knows that.

Laura comes walking out from the back. Alan is all ready to go. "Remember to tell the sitter not to give him any milk," she cautions Doug as he receives his instructions. "Why don't you want him to have milk?" I inquire. "Because, dear, he comes home and messes his pants up real bad and I don't like changing them." She turns to Doug with a warning, "If you forget," shaking and pointing her finger, "I'll make you change them."

"I'll try to remember," he responds, mentally reflecting the unpleasantness in his expression.

"You better," she says... a stern warning.

"Lori, Steve is going to follow you down I-40," Doug says. He turns to me. "She'll get off first, but don't follow her. Your exit is the next one, right after. If you follow her, you'll be on your way to Phoenix. Just follow the curve around and the Lake Mary Road signs like I told you last night."

"I'm sure I'll find them," I say. "I'm pretty good with directions."

Laura jumps in and adds, "I'm not. I'm always getting lost in town, small as it is."

"What time are you leaving for work today?" Laura asks Doug.

"In about 15 minutes. I like to get there early."

"Well, thanks a lot," I say as I extend my hand.

Doug grasps it and shakes it firmly. "Bye and good luck." I see his eyes water up. "You better go so you aren't late on your first day." I guess he feels somewhat responsible because it was his doing that got me up here working for the Forest Service.

Laura breaks into the moment. "Well, we better go. I'll get the rest of Alan's things together." Doug leaves with Alan and it's just me and Laura. She continues with the good-byes where Doug left off.

I'm putting on my riding suit when Laura notices something wrong. "Don't you have a helmet?"

"No. I don't like to wear one."

"Well, be careful then."

"I will. I always drive carefully," I say reassuringly.

"Yes, but one of these days," she replies.

"I know, I know, dad is always after me to wear one. He doesn't even like me riding the darn thing."

Out on the road I find the turnoff O.K. It's only 15 miles from the house, down on Lake Mary Road. I can feel the freezing air work its way under my clothes. A small chill tries to get me, but I shake it off. My chin and cheeks, directly exposed to the air, know how cold it really is. My fingers, in thin leather gloves, start to feel pre-numbness pain. On my head are just my beanie and goggles. My hair's still damp, and I'm beginning to wish I had never taken that shower. I remember seeing the hair dryer in the bathroom. If I had known how cold it was, I would have blow dried my hair. That whining of the hair dryer that I heard in my half sleep now haunts me. I am thinking that I hope it is not the high pitched tone one hears as a beginning symptom of hyperthermia. It must be below freezing, and with the chill factor on this bike, brrrrrr, unbearable to think about it. This is the coldest weather I've been in. Another chill works through me. This one shakes my body uncontrollably. Oh, God, 45 more miles to go!

The ride isn't even the slightest bit enjoyable. In fact, it's plain miserable. There are some lakes on my right, some trees and slowly winding roads, but I can't enjoy the scenery. I'm afraid even to move, because each time I do, a spot on my body that has finally gotten warm will now feel the cold. The parts that were already numb are doing just fine. The nerve endings in my skin have shut down to escape the cold. My whole body is rigid. My hands freeze on the handlebars and the next chill shakes the bike. I have to slow way down to avoid crashing.

You know, Plato talks about hot and cold. He says we live in a world of opposites. Heat is the absence of cold and cold is the absence of heat. This ties into the laws of Thermodynamics. Energy or heat cannot be created or destroyed. It can only be transferred. So when energy leaves matter, it is in a state of being absent, the absence of heat. That is my state, the absence of heat.

For years, when I watched the Weather Channel, I used this as an example: You don't know how many times that the hot and cold extremes in the nation are in California. You have the Mojave Desert area with the heat energy and the Truckee area with cold. Truckee with the absence of heat because it is just to the south in the heat of the desert. I always found that fascinating. But philosophic talk is not making me feel any warmer. Right now heat is leaving my body faster than I can generate it.

Time to get off this bike and warm up a little. I pull over at the first convenient spot. My knees ache as they peel off the gas tank. I put the gloves behind the warm motor to get the stiffness out of them and rub my numb hands together, close to the engine to soak up the heat. When I finally get some slight movement into them I reach up and feel my hair. It's frozen stiff from the little moisture still left there from my shower. Standing around, however, isn't doing a bit of good. The early sun is too new to offer a warming ray. I loosen up my frozen hair and wipe my runny nose so my mustache won't freeze, too. That being done, it's time to get going and head on out.

I figure I'll lie low and hug the engine to get whatever heat I can absorb, and think about the sunny Southern California beaches. It works for most of the way, except for the stretches through the open meadows where the coldest air lies.

When I get to the tee for the left turn towards Blue Ridge, I stop at the gas station store to see if they have any coffee, but it looks like it had just opened. Thoughts of a cup of coffee tease me. I imagine how I'll open the door and have the smell of fresh brewed coffee hit me in the face. I'll stretch out my cracking fingers to a steaming mug of Java. Back to reality, I push open the door.

"Good morning," says the unshaven, toothless clerk.

"Hello," I respond, trying not to shiver.

"It's a bit cold out there," he says without making eye contact.

"You'rrrrrrre not kidding." I couldn't hold back that one. "Got any coffee?"

"No, the water hasn't heated up yet. I just put it on."

"You got the time?"

He doesn't bother to look up. He's counting his cash drawer, and just points to the wall. I wait until he's finished with the count. "How much further to the Blue Ridge Ranger Station?"

"About ten miles up the road." He looks at me for the first time. "You going to work there?"

"Yeah. I'm supposed to start today. In fact, ten minutes from now. Guess I'd better go."

"New faces been coming by all week going to work there." He adds in a friendly voice, "The water won't take much longer to heat up."

"No, thanks, I'd better go. Bye." I turn around and wobble my unthawed body out the door, catching a quick glimpse of his farewell gesture. As I walk out, I know he had to look up to see the back of me, and he's probably right now calling me a fool for riding in this freezer they call Northern Arizona. He probably knows I'm from out of state. Just hanging around inside his store warmed me up slightly. I didn't really want to leave, but I can't afford to be late on my first day of work. Work... oh, yeah. The realization hits me. I'm really here.

The next ten miles are more comfortable. I'm starting to feel nervous, but the trees and surroundings seem to welcome me in and tell me to relax. Maybe it's their duty to do so as the welcoming committee. Their long limbs stretch out like arms to greet me in this beautiful wonderland.

The Ranger Station has its own welcoming committee, a heavyset timekeeper who was expecting me. What I wasn't expecting was a whole bunch of government forms that I had to fill out. That takes me an hour and a half. Then it's a full set of fingerprints, my signature a dozen or more times, and a five minute physical step test. They set a metronome and I have to keep pace, stepping up on a step and then down. Up and down, up and down. I can feel myself breaking into a sweat. They take my pulse. It has to be below a certain level to pass.

I'm still wiping the sweat off when a man comes into the room. He's dressed in an official looking Forest Service shirt, green pants, and black high-laced boots.

"The Hotshots are out planting trees," he announces crisply. "They started at 6:00 A.M. We'll keep you busy testing hose with the tankers." I notice the name on his name tag. It's Michael Reamer, and the name *rings* a bell.

"You're the one who called me," I say.

"Yeah, that was me," he confirms. "You can go put your things away and find a room. Just follow this road around and you'll see the Hotshot trailers. They're in a horseshoe formation. I'll be down in a little while and get you working on something." I see the three trailers as soon as I step out of the office.

I roam around and poke my nose into all the bedrooms of each trailer. Some are messy, some neat. Each room has 2 bunks, enough for five to six people in each trailer. It's going to be crowded. I pick the trailer with the television, stereo, and microwave, and take the top bunk in the back bedroom. I figure it's the party trailer. I don't have much stuff to put away, everything I brought was in two milk crates bungeed to the back seat. I make a thorough inspection of the other guys' stuff inhabiting this white trash housing unit. I hope I don't start to feel like trailer trash. I want to know a little more about the people I'll be living with. Just as I start to seriously snoop a green truck pulls up. Time to go to work.

Testing hose with the tankers goes pretty good. The men make me feel comfortable and welcome. They seem like good people to work with. There's Mike Hopkins, Denny Nelson, Steve Nickle, and Buck Wickham. They keep me entertained about the different kinds of personalities around the station. All along I'm checking them out. They're probably doing the same with me.

I could have worked for the tankers for the rest of the season. They even offered to cross me over to the tanker crews, but I feel obligated to go with the Hotshots. That's what I was hired for. I still don't know exactly what I'm getting myself into. I have no clue what a Hotshot does.

Finished my first workday and still didn't know where the Hotshot crew is. It takes a while before they all get back. I stay in the trailer as they walk over the circular gravel driveway. They pile in, about six or seven of them, turn on the T.V., and grab a beer. They all seem to be talking at the same time, carrying on with their own business. It reminds me of scenes at Charles Maclay Junior High School in Pacoima. I always got a kick out of how small groups of black kids would walk by. They would all be talking at the same time, just flop jawing away. No one is really listening to any other.

It takes the men a while to actually notice me. We introduce ourselves. I probably won't remember all their names, but it feels comfortable, a good icebreaker for me. My nervousness has mostly disappeared by the time introductions are finally over. Now the conversation turns as they talk about the day's work and the work to come. From the crowd in here I can tell my first impression was right... this is the party trailer. Suddenly, as I notice people shoving food in their face, getting some groceries becomes my number one priority.

"Where can you get food around here?" I ask.

"There's two places to go, Payson or Winslow."

"Or you can go up to Flagstaff," someone adds.

"Nah," I interject. "That's too far to go. I just came from there this morning." "Well, Payson is about 50 miles and Winslow is about 45 miles. Payson is a winding road in the mountains. Winslow is a straight shot. It's mostly desert and a little quicker. I expect that's the best bet for what you want... just groceries."

"Yeah, that's all. I'm not in for sight seeing right now, I need to get dinner for tonight."

"I could give you something."

"Uh, no thanks. I need stuff for the rest of the week. Better hurry up and go so I can get back before I freeze my ass off again. This morning was the coldest I ever felt."

"Welcome to Northern Arizona."

"Yeah, thanks," I say sarcastically as a leftover morning shiver tries to work itself out.

"It still gets pretty cold here at night. And that's when the critters come out."

"What critters? " I ask inquisitively.

"Oh, just some deer or elk. They're dangerous out here. People are always hitting them. They jump out in front of your car and there's nothing you can do about it. People get killed. I've seen cars totaled hitting a deer."

"No way! Come on, Darryl. You have to be going pretty fast to total your car. Even then you wouldn't mess it up much unless you wrapped it around a tree or something."

'Well I'd better go now," I say, cutting the discussion short.

"Watch out for them critters," someone adds as a final bit of caution.

"Later." I get into my full-body riding suit. I can tell the guys think it's funny looking. It does look kind of spacey, but it's the best thing you can have for riding in the cold weather. Still, when I get to Winslow I buy a sweatshirt, some extra protection from the cold air. Winslow is a very dead town. All the way there I run that Eagles song "Taking it Easy" in my head. "Standing on the corner in Winslow, Arizona, such a fine sight to see." I don't know what the hell they were singing about. There are no fine sights to see here. No action at all. Winslow's just a pass-through town with two one-way main streets. There are a lot of Indians here, too. Most of the businesses are already closing down, and it's not even sunset.

I get my groceries and get out. The ride back to Blue Ridge gets frigid pretty damn quick. There's only 15 more miles to go when the sun disappears behind the hills. Darkness comes up fast here. I had forgotten all about the "critters." It never even crossed my mind. Just a few miles from the station there's a big horse, or what looks like one, a few hundred feet ahead, standing just off the pavement. It scares the hell out of me. I can feel my heart banging in my chest. If that thing was out in the road I never could have stopped in time. From now on I sure will "watch out for the critters."

May 3

I'm still half asleep, but I can hear the stereo come on. Getting up early will be the hardest part of this job. The job. I still don't know what I'm in for. Today, planting trees will be the only activity on the agenda. The Hotshots have been doing this for the past two weeks. This will be their last day at it. I can hear more people getting up and walking around the hollow floors of the trailers. Their heavy boots shake the trailer as they scurry around getting ready for work. The bathroom gets a lot of the traffic. I just wait in bed until it's cleared out enough to enter without waiting in a long line. By this time, my six-o'clock morning-hard-on piss is ready to go, limp enough so the straight stream won't hit the seat or rim. After taking a leak, I walk back to the bedroom without greeting anyone.

As I dress I try to listen to the conversations. I'm hoping a name is mentioned that I can remember. So many names were thrown at me last night. I can remember most of them, but am still not sure which face and voice they belong to. I listen carefully to get to know the personality of each voice. I hear someone walking down the hall towards my room. His heavy boots echo down the hallway, loud enough to rattle the door. The door stops rattling when his hand grasps the doorknob. I watch, with curious eyes, as it slowly turns, opens, and some guy walks right in.

"Hi." I greet him, not making any judgments for the moment.

"G' morning. Just came to see if you were awake yet," my early intruder says.

"Yeah. It just takes me awhile to get going in the morning. I'm not used to waking up this early. I fell right to sleep last night, though. I usually don't get to bed until after Get Smart."

"Get Smart?" He asks, surprised. "When is that on?"

"2:00 A.M. They show Get Smart here?" I ask.

"Not that I know. Flagstaff only gets one channel."

"That's weird," I say.

"No, it isn't. It's just Flagstaff."

"I forgot your name," I say, a little embarrassed.

"Darryl, and yours is Steve."

"Yep."

End of conversation. He turns around and walks out to join the commotion in the living room. I follow him out there hoping to learn everyone's name again. Time to head to work. All three trailers seem to empty simultaneously. A casual group walks slowly up to the shop. The cold, morning mountain air condenses their breath, mixing with the steam rising from their tightly held coffee mugs. They meet at the shop. A big green bus is parked outside, clearly labeled with routed letters "BLUE RIDGE HOTSHOTS, COCONINO N.F." Introductions continue with the old timers from the station. I mostly keep quiet. I'm still getting to know people from their conversations with others. An official looking man pokes his head through the shop door, "We got to finish up today. Let's get started."

We pile onto the bus. I find a seat second from the back that suits me. The two-year-old vehicle has personal touches and practical modifications for firefighting. I'm thinking about today's trip. I haven't a clue about how much time I'll be spending on this bus in the days, weeks, and months to come. This big green cocoon will be my ride to adventure, to discover what it is like to be "macho". It will be a retreat for introspection, and a time for replenishing good memories.

On the bus ride I get the first real concept of the new environment I now live in, *the forest*. My first reaction is astonishment as I gaze at the colors, breathe in the odors, and enjoy the sensual pleasures they provide. The privacy and quiet of the forest envelops me and cloaks me with a feeling of serenity. Absorbed in my surroundings I also notice new features that tantalize my senses. I am an alien here, feeling lost, yet not alone. I'm feeling accepted in this place as I take in its beauty with emotional involvement.

People are still talking... conversations and war stories about old times. These hold little interest for me and I concentrate on familiarizing myself with the forest landscape. Someone up front spots deer running through the trees. The deer are on the same side of the road as my bus window, but I can't see them right away. Two of them stop to look at the bus. I see them first. When they notice us they take off. The others join the fleeing herd. Six of them hop together over obstacles and through the trees. Everyone is pretty jazzed over the deer sighting. The novelty and excitement wake me from my daydream. I relished how gracefully they leaped over the barbed wire fence.

With talk buzzing all around me, I take a new interest in the conversation. I must amuse the others with my minor contributions... the offerings of a naive city boy.

Planting trees allows me the time to get acquainted with the people I'll be working with. I know they're checking me out. The fact that Doug is my brother-in-law is brought up more than once. By the end of the day, I'm feeling more comfortable about work, and start to ask my share of the questions. A tall, slender guy comes over to where I'm planting trees. He looks like Ridley, the one who gave me my step test.

"Hello. So I hear you're Doug's relative."

"Yeah. He's my brother-in-law. Do you know him?"

"No, not really, I just know who he is. He's in the personnel office isn't he?"

"Yes, I'm not quite sure what he does. He's supposed to be someone important up there."

"That's right," Ridley replies.

"I guess he's the personnel officer."

Ridley smiles at me and nods confirmation.

"Hey, how come you're planting all these trees? Do you usually start out the year this way?"

"No, not really. We have to do this because the Hotshots let a control burn get out of control last year. It happens once in a while," Ridley says matter-of-factly.

"What do you do with the Hotshots?"

"As little as possible, I'm in timber," Ridley responds.

"Oh, so you're just out here helping?"

"Yes. And to make sure they plant them right." He makes his point by planting one perfectly so I can see it. "I got to make sure they don't put two into one hole. The seedlings need to be spaced evenly. There isn't much more to do. I'm trying to get a good survival rate," Ridley explains.

"I bet it takes a long time." Ouch! That sounds, even to me, like a stupid statement. Ridley must think so, too. He doesn't bother to respond.

"Where do they get these little trees?"

"These actual seedlings were grown in Albuquerque. We had to send the nursery hundreds of pinecones last year so they could propagate them. When the trees get to this size the growers send them back for us to plant. See, it makes for a better survival rate when the seedlings are put back into the same environment the cones came from."

"What's in Albuquerque that they can't do here?"

"The Regional Office. They want it that way."

"Do all the ranger offices do it that way?" I ask.

"Yes, all the national forests in this region have to do it that way. They have the specialist in Albuquerque who takes care of them. That way the seedlings get the special attention they need. All the facilities are there, too."

"How big is this region?" I ask. I want to know this stuff.

"It covers all of Arizona and New Mexico."

There are more questions I'd like to ask, but we're interrupted before I can get them out.

"Hey, Bill, come here," someone yells.

"See you later," Ridley says in closing.

Darryl is close by, maybe trying to listen in on our conversation. "What did Ridley have to say?" he queries.

"We were just talking about planting trees and where they come from."

"HAW, HAW!" He seems to think that's pretty funny. "Where they come from. HAW, HAW. They grow here." He shakes his head. "You really are from the city."

"No, not the ones already here, I'm not that much out of touch. I grew up in a country environment, at least as much of one as you're going to get around L.A. I didn't know where they got these ones we're planting. OK?"

Darryl tries to look serious. "Oh, they come from the R.O."

"You mean the Regional Office in Albuquerque."

"Yeah."

"Well, that's what we talked about."

"Did Ridley tell you why we were planting them?"

"Yes. Something about how the Hotshots fucked up last year."

"Did he say that? 'Fucked up?'"

"No, he didn't say that, just that a control burn the Hotshots were on got out of control last fall.

"I didn't think he would say that. He and his wife are super religious. In fact we did kind'a fuck up, you know. We shouldn't have let it happen. He don't like us too well."

"Why's that?" I ask.

"No one likes the Hotshots. We're outcasts and delinquents. There's a lot of rowdy people on our crew. We don't get along with the timber service, or better, they don't get along with us."

"Are you guys rowdy?"

"I'll say! You know where the trailers are now?"

"Yeah."

"Well, they never used to be there. They were up in the circle where the permanents live."

"I'm not sure I know where you mean."

"Where the paved driveway goes around that one-way part."

I nod my head, and Darryl continues, "See, we were always too noisy up there, and getting into trouble. We play our music too loud and stay up late. They didn't like it. Notice how there's no one living around the trailers? They stuck us way out there so they wouldn't have to hear us. Me, I like it better down there. We can make as much noise as we want now. Besides, we got the whole forest for our backyard."

Darryl motions to me and we walk back to the truck together. There aren't many bundles of seedlings remaining.

"All we have to do is finish these few that are left," Darryl says. "When we do, we will have planted 2500 trees."

"Is that a lot?" I wonder aloud.

"You bet!!! We'll probably not get any overtime today, it's only about two o'clock." He checks his watch quickly. "Not even that, about twenty till two."

"There aren't anymore somewhere else?"

"Nah, I put all we had in this truck. Some people have probably planted two or three trees in one hole."

"That's what that guy I was talking to said. He was out here to see that we didn't do those things."

Darryl heaves a sigh. "He doesn't know anything," he remarks, disgusted.

"Looks like it's going to rain," I say changing the subject.

"You think so?" Darryl looks up, stretching out his double chin, and nods while inspecting the clouds scudding by.

We grab one of the few remaining bundles and rejoin the others. In half an hour we're finished. It's still too early to go back to the station, so we take advantage of the only break of the day before returning.

No one has noticed, but the clouds above us have gotten much darker. The rain begins to fall, lightly at first, not enough to make you run for cover. Then, blam! Within an instant we're pelted with hail. We gather the diggers and "vamoose" back to the bus. The hail thunders on the bus roof, and there is a lot of it. We take our time driving back to the ranger station on roads that have gotten slick and muddy. We get a good example of the hazardous road conditions when our driver, Dennis, one of the squad bosses, slows down on a curve. The brakes lock up while the wheels are at an angle. The bus hydroplanes straight for the edge of the road. The roads out here are very dangerous. These are logging truck roads. A cloud of dust is kicked up with every passing. This blankets a fine layer of dust on the roads. When it mixes with rain, it becomes very slick. There are no safety railings out here, not even a big pine or two that might stop you from going all the way to the bottom, and East Clear Creek is 150 feet straight down. Last year the crew had an even a closer call in a similar situation. That time Kyle Penick jumped out the emergency window. What makes this experience so scary is that the bus is moving on its own, momentarily out of control. Everyone is holding his breath when suddenly the bus wheels grab the road and steering is restored. Now everyone's acting like nothing happened. You know, like the way the Get Smart guy falls and gets up looking nonchalant. We're all back to normal when, further down the road, one of those funny looking horses with spikes on their heads runs across the meadow and up a small ridge. I find out soon enough it's an elk, the biggest one seen this year.

The guys are planning a poker game tonight in our trailer. So far, poker is the only thing I can do well up here. I have to make some phone calls first, and have to sneak off to smoke a joint. Greg tells me where the only phone is and asks if he can come along. I agree.

"Your name is Greg. Right?"

"Yes, and yours is Steve."

"That's it."

"Want to see the obstacle course?"

"Sure. Have you had a chance to run it?"

"Not the whole thing. We've haven't done much P.T. yet. We're supposed to wait until everyone gets here."

"Who's everyone?" I ask.

"Uh, well, some are in school still. Bob Smith, he's the crew boss. They are still going to hire some more Hotshots. There's twenty on each crew. The guy I'm supposed to be roommates with is still in school, they tell me."

"He's in a Forest Service school I understand," I add as I step over a large log used as a tire stop near the office, "Have you seen him yet?"

"Yeah. I was the first one here. Dale came ten minutes after me."

"Dale? Who's Dale," I ask.

"You know, Dalery."

"Oh, you mean Darryl," I say trying to straighten out his accent. "Where are you from anyway?"

"I went to high school in Korea and lived there for four years. I was born in Massachusetts."

I cut him off with my response. "So that's why you talk funny."

Greg takes no offense at my rudeness. "Where are you from?" he asks.

"L.A,." I respond defensively. "I refer to it as Smell A."

"Oh, yeah?"

"What's your last name?" I continue.

"Leveque, Gregory Leveque."

"That's French?"

"Name is, but I'm not really."

"What are you... really?"

"Dunno." I think he looks Polish. "Hey do you smoke dope?" He asks right out.

"Why, do you?" I respond. I'm not confessing anything yet.

"Sure. But I ran out about a week ago. Wish I would have brought more with me."

"That's one thing I didn't forget."

Greg perks up. "You got some now, a joint?"

"That's why I'm taking this walk, that and to make some phone calls. We'll smoke one after I make my calls. I don't want to sound stoned over the phone."

"Great! I've been dying to get stoned. I had a little, but smoked it all when I got up here."

Greg is looking up at the sky and trips over a small log. What a klutz! This guy is a real goofball. I look up the sky, too. It's nice, but I've seen stars before.

"Hey look! There's one." Greg says, pointing up.

"One what?" This guy is easily amused I think.

"Look past the end of my finger. See that thing that looks like a star moving?"

"No, I can't see it, all I see is stars."

"Just look. You'll see something moving up there."

"What is it?"

"A satellite. You see them all the time up here."

"Wow, I can't believe it. I didn't think you could see satellites in orbit from down here."

We stop to watch it. I notice that there are a lot of stars out. More than I had ever seen before. The clear air makes the stars appear large, crisp and glittering. The Milky Way illuminated its path across the sky. In fact, it looks like there are two Milky Ways up there.

Greg pokes my arm. "Hey, look, there's another satellite," he says.

"Where?"

"By that bright star. Oh, wait, I lost it. There it is again."

"I see it now. Bitchin!"

"There's a lot that's going on up there that most people never get to see. You ever wonder what's up there that we don't know about?"

I'm starting to like this guy. "All the time," I say.

The phone is in front of the office. The light supplied by the phone company flickers as the moths home in on it. I pick up the phone and make an interesting discovery... you don't need a dime to reach the operator. I pass this good news on to Greg.

"You didn't know that?" he asks.

"No. In L.A. you have to put money into something to get anything out."

"Some people up in the woods here don't have money and need to make a call, like in an emergency. Darryl said that they just got phones here two months ago."

"I believe that, alright. This is the most remote place I've ever been in."

While I'm on the phone, Greg is busy playing with the moths and June bugs. Must be nice to be so easily amused. He's a big guy, standing six foot two and about two hundred and thirty pounds. His hair is long, wavy and frizzed out. His facial features are unusually large, and his body, while generally in proportion, features a large, overhanging gut. He is the youngest guy on the crew so far. I could tell that he needed to do a lot of growing up. I learn later that he's from a military family, and has lived in a lot of places. I expect he had a well-protected life, but his education in school was broken up a lot, and it showed. His vocabulary was limited and his accent, from the Boston area, was definitely not Back Bay. He's probably as dumb as he looks. Still, he's a nice guy... maybe overly nice with a big heart, but I will find he can sure get on your nerves when he's around too long. I finish my call and get off the phone. "I'll call you back when I get up to Flagstaff... OK... OK... Bye now."

Greg stops playing with the bugs. "Who did you have to call?" he asks.

"My sister, and a girl in Scottsdale I met awhile back."

"Have you ever been to Scottsdale?"

"Nope."

"Then how'd you meet her?"

"I met her and her sisters at this campground in Mission Bay. That's in San Diego."

"Oh." I can see him putting it all together. "I've been to San Diego. We use to live in Torrance a couple years ago before we moved to Sierra Vista in Arizona... not far from Tucson."

"Is that where you came from when you came up here?"

"Yeah. My parents drove me up. Ever been there?"

"Nope." I reach up behind my ear. "You ready to smoke this joint?"

"Sure am."

"We better clear away from the office area before we light up. Let's walk toward the obstacle course."

We stroll into the surrounding dark of the trees and I pause, light up, and take a deep drag. I wait a beat or two, savoring the sensation. "You know, I think I'm going to like it up here. I feel better already." I pass the joint to him, blowing out a long stream of smoke. Greg takes a hit, holds it, exhales the smoke, "Me, too." He waits to notice an effect. "Hey, what are you going to do tomorrow night?"

"We get off don't we?"

"Sure do. And if you want we can drink some peyote tea. My friend that goes to school at Northern Arizona University might have some. I can get almost anything from him."

"No fooling? I never tried peyote, eating or drinking it. But I could be interested. This pot ain't going to last forever. I'll need a good connection up in town if I'm going to be going up there. Whoa... I'm really starting to get buzzed now."

Greg's feeling it, too. I can tell. He shoots me an appreciative grin. "This is really good pot. What is it?"

"Colombian."

"It's mellow, man."

I'm noticing how good it is myself. Feels like I'm getting off better in this high altitude. Or is it attitude? "What is the altitude here anyway?" I ask Greg.

"Like Flagstaff, I think."

"Well Flagstaff is about 7,000 feet. So this is the highest altitude I've ever been at for any length of time. I used to go to Big Bear mountain when I visited my friend Richie. It's 4700 feet high. The trees are similar to what I've seen here, but the thin air here is more noticeable. I still find it hard to believe that I'm really up here."

"It was easy for me to get used to being in the mountains," Greg asserts proudly.

"Well, it might take me awhile. I wanted a change in my life but I didn't expect it would be this major... a complete one hundred eighty degrees from city life." I take a moment to let the gravity of that announcement sink in. "Well, they said they were going to play cards tonight. I'm going to see if I can still get in the game. Are you coming?"

"Naw, I don't have much money. I guess I'll just go to bed early tonight."

"Well, OK, see you later."

"See you later, and thanks for the joint."

Geez, he didn't have to blurt it out! "Sure. 'Night."

The poker game is already in progress, and I get invited to play right away. It's a good opportunity to get to know more people on the crew. There's David Grimwood, nicknamed Drifty, who talks with a lisp. He's a scruffy looking guy with a half-grown beard, a chipped tooth that compliments his full lipped smile, and short, stubby legs. Doesn't look like much on the surface. He could be your everyday bum, but he is a very knowledgeable person. He has a chemical engineering degree and plans to enter that field after this fire season. I was surprised to meet someone of his caliber up here in the middle of nowhere.

I respect him, too, for his accomplishments. I went through 72 units as a chemical engineer before I said that was enough. When I was in school I felt like I had no life. All I did was study, work, and attend classes. When I realized that I had two more years of Chemistry, Physics, and Calculus, I knew I'd had it. Chemical Engineering is a hard major to complete, and I struggled to make 'C's. I loved chemistry, but I didn't like the way they taught the other comprehensive class material. You do these math problems that take two to three hours per problem. You don't know why you are doing it, but you are just doing the mechanics without the reason. I wanted to know the "why" and there was no time in class to learn it. Everything was rush, rush, rush.

It's going to be interesting to get to know my new crewmates. For now I'm playing poker conservatively, losing a little to keep on everyone's better side.

May 4

Seven A.M. already! I groan. Doesn't help to get drunk and play poker when you have to drag yourself out of bed this early. The sun is shining one hundred percent this morning. From what I can see out of a small window, it looks beautiful outside. The bright morning puts some sunshine in my usual bitchy morning mood. We are going to stay around the station today to do some maintenance around the Hotshot trailers. Jake, Greg, and I volunteer to put up the shirting around the trailers since no one else wants to do it, and we're the three new guys on the crew this year.

Though there are still more people to come, I know Jake will end up the oldest member of the crew. He is a thin, soft spoken man with a small build... a grandfather at 44. To offset his encroaching baldness he sports a full length mustache and lets his hair grow over his collar line. He wears round wire eyeglasses that give his face a kind of innocent look. He speaks softly, never seems to have a reason to bellow. Jake has a whole assortment of degrees ranging from philosophy to art. He was head of an art department that he had set up in one of the many schools where he taught in the central and western states. He quit his teaching temporarily because of disputes at the last one about how the department should be run. This job at Blue Ridge is a break in the action for him, and comfortably familiar as he had done some firefighting up around Boise, Idaho about 23 years ago. For now he just wants to get away for a while in a non- conventional environment.

A man with that kind of education will treat this job as a sabbatical experience. It was a relief to know that someone like Jake was on the crew. There's going to be someone up here that I can have some heavy conversations with. Ever since Richie died there has been no one with whom I can share my own philosophical thoughts... thoughts that might turn out to be tomorrow's truths. Jake could be that guy. Even though he is 44, an old man from my standpoint, he acts and communicates like the rest of us. He even found points of interest in Greg's ignorance and was always careful not to utter criticism of Greg's personality. Jake was a fair man in his own right.

Someone pulls up in a car and a hound dog jumps out. The dog is busy scurrying around, sniffing stuff and generally checking out the area. Some people who know the man in the truck walk over and greet him. Soon a half dozen huddle around, talking to him. I'm with Jake and Greg, and they're as curious as I am about what's happening. Jake stops what he's doing and notes that it's almost breaktime.

"I'm ready for one," Greg says and nods his head in the direction of the car. "Who's that?"

"Can't tell from here. Looks like a popular guy. Let's go see."

I ask, "Could it be our crew boss?"

"Bob Smith? No, he's up in Flagstaff, still going to school," Greg remarks. "I saw him once before and that doesn't look like him. They say he's pretty tough."

I think to myself, ummm, pretty plain name for such a tough guy. We walk over to the gathering. The dog runs up to us and sniffs around. The man in the car calls to her, "Betsy, Betsy, come here. Leave them alone."

I reach out to pet her but she is cautious and retreats a little while still trying to get a few whiffs of me. Darryl's standing at the truck and calls to me. "Hey, Steve, come on and meet your new roommate, Russ. He's one of the squad bosses."

I step up and provide my own introduction. "Hi, Russ, I'm Steve."

Darryl continues "And this is Gregory."

"Call me Greg. I think I met you last week."

Jake takes his turn. "I'm Jake Brookins. Glad to meet you."

The dog Betsy noses her way into the crowd. Her friendly wet nose brushes my hand. I wonder if she does that on purpose. Dogs seem to have people figured out before we humans do.

Russ makes the final introduction. "And this is Betsy." She starts wagging her tail when she hears her name. I reach over to pet her and she seems pleased by the affection. Now Russ turns to me with questions. "When did you get here?"

"Wednesday. Is that all your stuff in the backroom?"

"Yes. I didn't bring much. Just what I could fit on the back of my bike."

"Is that your bike over there?"

"Uh, huh. I rode it all the way from L.A."

"No kidding? I was wondering who that piece of machinery belonged to. I didn't think we were going to have a biker on the crew this year."

"I'm not a hard-core biker. I just prefer them to cars. Cars get to be a pain in the ass at times."

"I know what you mean. Well I've got to take off. I just came down to see what was going on and to meet you new guys. I guess we're supposed to get more hands up here next week."

"Do you know who's coming?" Asks Darryl.

"No. I ran into Bob in town and he told me he still had to hire some more men."

Drifty speaks up, "How much longer do you have to be in that school?"

"'Til next week Wednesday," Russ replies. "Bob will be back the week after next."

"Why so long?"

"He's in school and it don't let out 'til the seventeenth."

"What school are you in?" Marty asks.

Russ answers, "It's a Forest Service school they made me go to. It's mostly bullshit, but they make us sit through it. We get tested so I guess it means something. Besides, I'm getting paid for it." He switches the conversation abruptly. "It's almost time for P.T. Have you guys been doing any?"

"No," Darryl replies. "Today is supposed to be our first day. We've been planting trees for the last couple of weeks."

"God, I'm glad I'm not doing that shit," Russ says vehemently. "It gets monotonous."

"You're telling me! We planted over fifty thousand trees."

"No, Darryl," Drifty corrects. "You're full of shit, it was about ten thousand."

Russ, it seems, has had enough. He calls his dog to the truck and she finds her seat, riding shotgun up front. Russ closes the doors, shouts a final greeting to us, revs the truck's motor and pulls away. Now it's time for us to get back to work.

Darryl speaks first. "Lets take five more minutes then get ready for P.T. Today we're just going to run, so if you have running shoes, wear them."

The social circles break up, everyone getting ready for Physical Training. When we get to the obstacle course we find Darryl waiting for us. "You guys ready to run?" he asks.

"Yeah."

"Then let's go! Petretti, you can run with me."

We start out at a slow jog. "Breathe slow and steady," Darryl advises, but I'm huffing and puffing already and we've only gone a few hundred yards.

"How far are we running?" I manage to pant.

"Not far. About three or four miles."

"I'm never going to make it," I protest. "I never ran that far before."

"Yes you will," Darryl encourages. "Just keep up with me."

I look around. Guys are passing us by not even breathing hard. "Hey, you want to go the short cut or the scenic route?" Darryl asks.

Hell, it doesn't matter to me. I'm not going to last anyway. And since no one seems to care Darryl makes the decision on his own. "Turn left here," he calls, pointing at a side trail that leads off to the left from the dirt road we're on.

"Which way is this?" I ask, praying for the right answer.

"The short cut and the scenic route. It'll take us through the aspen grove."

"I can't do it," I pant. "My side is starting to hurt."

"Don't stop, keep running. We've still got a way to go."

"No use," I call back, "I gotta walk."

"See you later then," Darryl says, trotting off into the aspens.

"Wait!" I call with labored breath. "Where do you run to?"

He turns around, running backwards so as not to break his jog. "To the campground and back." He takes off without losing a step. I'm breathing my hardest and my side really aches. But I have gained a clear understanding of one thing: I'm going to get in shape whether I want to or not.

I am the last one back from running, and feel more than a little foolish as I walk back to the trailers. Darryl is sitting in his chair with a can of beer in his hand. He shoots me a friendly smile. "You took long enough getting back here." He says it like he's already feeling the buzz from his beer. I'm sure it's not his first one.

"I walked most of the way back. I guess I got to get used to the thin air up here." Not much of an excuse, but the best I could manage.

"Don't sweat it. You just need to get in shape and lose that winter flab," he says with a knowing look at my midsection. "Most guys are out of shape when they get up here. The best thing to do is to work out a couple a months before you get here." He takes a big gulp from his beer. "I've been running since February," he says with a self-satisfied belch.

Mortified, I answer. "I guess I'll have to try harder."

"You will if you want to keep up." Scolding over, his tone softens. "There's a beer in the refrigerator if you want one."

"Thanks. I could use a cool one."

"You going into town tonight?"

"Yeah. Greg is coming along with me."

"On your motorcycle."

"Yep, it's the only way to fly." I continue up the stairs. My calves are already tightening up and I know they'll hurt for the next few days.

I don't forget Greg's promise to hook me up with some good weed.

During our ride to town he's got plenty to say, but none of it's very interesting. He tells me his older sister went to school, but didn't finish the semester because some guy knocked her up. He wants to get hold of the guy, who is still living in the dorm on campus. The friend we're going to see knew him and could tell Greg his whereabouts. We get to the dorm where his friend is supposed to live, but he was out partying. We never did get the dope we wanted. But it isn't a total bum-out. The guy's neighbor tells us about a party being given in the girls' dorm where Greg's friend will show up later. We had to find a female escort before we were allowed in, but that was no problem. A real cutie led us through the girls' dorm to the door.

"Are you sure this is where the party is?" I question.

Greg doesn't seem very sure of it. "I don't know. It sounds too quiet," he says.

"What the heck," I say. "Let's knock." But before I can rap, a girl's voice calls from inside and invites us in. When we step through the doorway we see only three people in the small dorm room. "Excuse me," I mutter. "I thought there was supposed to be a party here." I'm saying this while I'm staring at a beer keg in front of me.

"This is it." A guy stands up to greet us. "It's Diane here's birthday and you're the first ones to show up. My name is David and this is Ralph. And you just met Diane, the birthday girl."

I hastily introduce myself and Greg. David senses my discomfort. "It's cool, man," he says. "There'll be more people coming later on. Meantime we've been here all day baby-sitting this keg. Here's the glasses. Fill 'em up and let's get acquainted."

The party starts out slow and we decide to go check on Greg's friend in the men's dorm. He isn't anywhere to be found, so Greg goes back to the party and I stay around the men's dorm to score some mushrooms from a stranger. The guy and I smoke a couple of joints together. I have a good buzz on by then and head back to the party alone.

A lot of new people have joined the fun and everyone seems to be having a good time. It's clear to me that Greg had put quite a dent in the keg. He's stumbling and boisterous, still talking about how this guy, who was supposed to be at the party, was the one who got his sister pregnant. His drunken ranting is getting on my nerves, especially since he tells me this stuff with his face about two inches away from mine. His features are even more accentuated.

The radio is playing country tunes, not my kind of music. Diane cozies up to me, and I ask her to teach me some country swing dancing. The lesson doesn't go too well in the narrow dorm hallway. I suggest we walk outside, where it's less crowded and quieter. We manage to exchange a lot of personal information, and at one point I lean over and give her a birthday kiss. She seems to like it. At least she's right there with some tongue action and some feigned passion. What the hell. I grab her and catch up on all the kisses from her previous birthdays. Now we are kissing passionately.

The outside patio is chilly, but I'm not feeling it. In fact, I'm warming up when I get a look at the hardened nipples of her large breast that are now showing through her sweater. I reach over and gently fondle and rub her excited, swollen boob. She starts to push forward toward me as we continue kissing, but suddenly backs off and mutters, "Let's go back inside and be sociable. After all, it is my party." I can't believe my lousy luck. Just when I think I'm getting somewhere it comes to a screeching halt.

Things take a turn for the better when we get back to the party. Greg is gone. Now I can enjoy myself without worrying about him. I hope he'll be OK. It sure didn't look that way earlier in the evening. All the things he said that were supposed to happen never did. Pretty soon I start worrying about my own ability to manage. I'm bombed and not functioning well. My motorcycle is still too new to trash. When I'd get like this in L.A. I could count on my built-in homing device. But I don't know this place well enough to chance it. Greg isn't here, either, so I need to find somewhere to spend the night. Diane walks me out and we exchange warm, embracing kisses. She pushes off the last one to return to the party.

It takes me awhile to find my bike because someone had knocked it over. Both handlebars are bent... one at a right angle I let out a **"God damn it!"** loud enough to wake the whole campus. I look around for some evidence. Down on the wet grass, half hidden in the brushes is Greg... crashed out, sleeping off a definitive hangover, beyond waking. He must have knocked my bike over in his stupor. My bike is still drivable so I leave Greg behind, asleep in the bushes, and I take off for the nearest Travel Lodge where I sleep off my frustrations of this night.

May 5 and 6

First order of business after my mind is ready to function is to get my handlebars fixed. I track down a bike shop and install the new bars myself. Then I head down to Phoenix to see an old pen pal I met while I was camping at Campland Mission Bay. Her name is Annie Beaubeck. I called her the other night when I was fighting off June bugs and made arrangements to meet with her tonight. I get to her place with high hopes of some fun and to my chagrin find another letdown. First, she confesses her true age. She's a lot younger than I originally thought of. She lied about her age all those years of writing to her. But that was OK, I like young girls. But what turned out even more disappointing... she's living with her boyfriend, and he's not keen on letting her go out to show me the town, even when she makes it clear that it's not a date kind of thing. In the end she gets his permission and we take a quick tour of Phoenix driving around in her car. No hugs or kisses en route, and no chance of laying her tonight or ever. Screwed again, I get a room for the night.

After breakfast at Denny's I pull into a local mall and buy a camera. If nothing else I can document my misery with it. So far my weekend social life sucks. But hey, it's my first one. I take a different route home, going through Payson, and stop there to pick up some food to take home to Blue Ridge. On the way back, I pull off the road several times to gawk at the scenery and play with my new camera. Winding up Highway 78 towards the mountains, I catch views of the desert in my rearview mirror. Cactus flowers spot the shoulders of the road, and I notice some of those cartoony looking Saguaro cacti in the background. God, I love this motorcycle! I feel at one with it leaning through the subtle curves of the highway. New territory, new asphalt, new smells, new views. Even the sound of the exhaust headers bounces new echoes from the canyon walls. My ride back home is the best part of the weekend. Home, that sounds funny to me. Home, the Blue Ridge Ranger Station, Coconino National Forest, Northern Arizona. WOW!

May 7

The music comes on, announcing the start of another day. We are actually going to do something exciting today. It'll be the start of fire school for us new guys. With still more men to be hired, the S.O. advised that Blue Ridge should get moving on the lessons.

To be fully certified and Red Carded for firefighting, each firefighter has to go through forty hours of classroom and field experience. Of course, P.T. is also on the daily agenda. I'm ready and willing to learn all that I possibly can. The thought of actually working on the fire line scares me beyond belief. The only exposure I've had to a major fire was when the hills behind my parents' house were on fire many years ago. That experience was enough to make me realize the tremendous force a raging fire can demonstrate. I was still a little kid when we were told to vacate the neighborhood, but I can still feel the fear and the adrenaline from those chaotic moments.

The classroom is set up in the shop. The Hotshots have already arranged the seating and visual aids. Lynn Neff, the district ranger, is the first speaker. Before he starts his little welcoming speech he has everyone introduce himself and tell what he does. When it's my turn, I keep it simple. "I'm Steve Petretti, I'm from L.A. and I'm on the Hotshot crew."

I get some stares when I mention where I'm from. Apparently, no one else from L.A. has ever worked up here. The shop is filled with people of all ages who work at Blue Ridge. When the introductions are over it's clear that all the old-timers are in recreation and on the fire prevention team patrols. The tanker people, the Hotshots, and most of the timber staff are younger.

The next speaker, Tom Nations, is from the safety office. He used to be a Coca-Cola distributor before he came to work for the Forest Service. His thing is safety precautions, and he lays heavy stress on them. The type of work we are going to do involves many hazards. Tom mostly talks about those around the Ranger Station. He leaves for later lectures a description of specific hazards pertaining to the individual jobs, and "other duties as assigned" as were stated in the fine print on some sheet we signed.

The veterans are already getting bored. They go through this every year. James Bedlion is about to start his talk on fire organization when the dispatcher reads out the morning weather report. In Forest Service talk, it's the morning "10-13". The winds are expected to pick up today with clear skies forecast. A cold front is expected to move in by tomorrow afternoon. Things change. No sooner does the dispatcher complete delivering his readout and 'roll calls' the towers in order, when two lookout towers report increased winds with gusts up to thirty-five to forty miles per hour.

Bedlion jokes that this might be a better day to study weather instead of fire organization. "Back to the fire boss," he continues with a bored sigh. "Under him you have the finance boss, air attack boss, division boss." He points out the various categories on a chart that looks like it's been used for years. The veterans' attention is starting to wander, and so is mine. I'm still wondering what I got myself into. I call back my wandering mind in time to hear, "...and finally you have the crew boss with two squad bosses and the labor force following them." That's me. That's what I am... the labor force, the lowest position on the organization chart.

We're still sitting there when two more lookout towers call in an increase of steady wind velocity and occasional gusts up to fifty miles an hour. The dispatcher alerts all districts to be ready for red flag conditions. Maybe it's something to be concerned about, but my stomach is growling and I'm concerned about lunch. Before we're dismissed, the dispatcher officially confirms red flag conditions for the Coconino National Forest. We break for lunch and confirm fire readiness.

The shop empties out quickly, everyone must be starving. We start walking down to the trailer area.

"Pretty boring, huh?" Remarks Drift.

"It wasn't too bad," I respond. "It's all new to me."

"This is the third time I've been through this," Drift continues. "I had a hard time keeping awake."

"Me, too. This is my fifth time," Darryl says.

"So this is supposed to be a red flag day. What does that mean?" I ask.

"Hopefully, no more school for today," Drift says.

"Why's that?"

"Because we're supposed to be fire ready," Darryl remarks sternly.

"What does that involve?"

"Getting your nomax on and making sure everything is ready to go. We can get called just like that to a fire," Darryl says, snapping his fingers for emphasis.

"You mean a real fire?" I'm starting to worry. "I don't know how to fight a fire. We haven't finished fire school yet."

Drift sees the look on my face. "Ha, Ha, ye ah a weal won," he pronounces with his slight lisp impediment. "Don't get all upset. Probably nothing will happen today. People just like to get excited around here. Especially Dennis, he gets real hyped up, like a madman."

I quickly turn to Darryl. "Darryl, is everything I need in the pack you fixed for me yesterday?"

"Yeah, you better make sure while you are on your lunch and go ahead and put your fire clothes on."

"It's on the bus."

"Well do what you have to do and get back on the bus," he says in a scolding tone. I think he enjoys bossing me around.

I'm not convinced. "If there is a fire, will we still go even without a full crew?"

Darryl chimes in. "Sure, if it's a district fire."

I jump in, "What's a district fire?"

"One that's around here. We won't go off forest or nothing."

"You get fires around here?" Drift and Darryl laugh at my naivete. "Hey, I'm not that dumb, I grew up in the country part of L.A."

"Didn't know L.A. had any country," quips Drift.

"Sure. There's a lot of cowboy country in the outskirts."

Whatever it means to be 'fire ready', I guess I am. I eat a big lunch to make up for not eating breakfast. Our trailer, with the TV and stereo is, as usual, the center of attraction. In truth, there isn't much else to amuse you up here.

We're sitting around, still eating and shooting the shit when Bill Krushak, the Tanker Boss at Blue Ridge, walks in the trailer nonchalantly and says "Hey, did you guys know you were just dispatched?"

Someone in the crowd yells back, "What? A dispatch? Where?"

"Somewhere on the Sitgraves."

Before he finishes his last statement, people are running out the door. They shove whatever food they have in hand, into their mouth. I'm still sitting there observing and feeling the excitement charge the room. I can feel my own adrenaline pumping. How can that be? This is exactly what I DID NOT want to do today, go to a fire. A FIRE! My God, a fire! By now the room is half-cleared and it dawns on me to get my ass in gear and follow the rest.

"Let's move it," Bill shouts. "You'll just have to take what you got. Darryl, how many guys do you have? The dispatcher wants to know."

"About ten or twelve," Darryl shoots back. "Are your tankers going?"

"No, it's your fire. It's on the Sitgraves near Chevelon Lake."

Now Dennis comes racing down in his Dodge Charger and skids over the gravel leaving two bare patches in the dirt. "Come on! Let's go! Let's go! Load up on the bus," he screams. By now you can hear the thump, thump, thump of heavy boots as the men run through the three trailers. It's a madhouse with everyone grabbing things at the last minute. I'm OK. I had put my fire clothes on already, and the rest of my stuff is on the bus. I grab the remains of my sandwich and run to the bus. Dennis is already in it, warming up the motor.

"Who's not here? Leveque. Koval. Who else?"

"The crew boss," I yell.

Dennis looks back at me with disdain. "He won't be going on this trip." He beeps the horn and yells out the window, "Leveque, Koval, let's go!" The bus begins to move slowly, and it has the desired effect on the laggards. They hurry toward it, Koval jumping on while it's in forward motion. Greg runs and jumps in behind him, his shoelaces still untied. Koval stalls at the door mischievously to impede Greg's entry.

"What's the matter?" he asks.

"We got a fire, asshole. Sit down."

"How big a fire?"

"Don't know, but if we don't hurry up, it'll be a great big one. Going to take us a while to get there."

I'm sitting still in my seat, quiet and suddenly chilled, while flashes of newsreels on TV, and Smokey the Bear commercials play in my head. I watch a few people get their fire clothes on as the bus moves down the highway towards Winslow. Packs are checked and some veterans get their vests ready. Jake and Darryl look pretty cool. I hope I look cool, too, but I'm plenty scared inside.

Darryl, who is sitting in front of me, turns around and asks, "Are you excited? It's your first fire." I nod my head, not trusting myself to speak. "Are you scared?" I nod again with wide-open eyes.

"Don't worry, just think of it as OJT."

"What's that?"

"On the job training."

I gulp. "Yeah, but I'd rather know a little of what I'm doing first."

"Just do what we do and you'll be fine. Are all of your things ready?"

"I think so. I hope so."

"Check it out and be sure I issued you everything you should need, even though you may not need all of it when we get there. You've got plenty of time. We won't arrive for another hour. We've got to turn south right before Winslow and it's forty miles down a dirt road."

Good. That gives me time to psych myself into it. I check out my smoke chaser pack and double check something, I'm not sure of what I'm checking. Everyone is settled down, just riding along until we get there. I try to relax back in my seat while biting my fingernails. I manage to get down to the skin and cuticles on a few. My right shoulder blade is tightening up from nervousness. I can feel it pop as I move my right shoulder. Reaching around with my left hand to massage it is no help. I tell myself that all I need to remember is to follow the others and do what they do. They don't look worried. If they are, they're not showing it.

As we travel farther down the dirt road the vegetation gets thicker than it is around the Winslow area. We're getting back up to high country, similar to the Blue Ridge area. I see flagging set out to direct us to the fire. No smoke or flames visible yet. There are still a couple of hours of daylight left.

"We should be there in a few minutes," Darryl reports. "Doesn't look like much. It's going to be a small one."

I'm relieved to hear it. I've always been a quick learner but I didn't want to start playing with fire so soon. The bus makes its way through the trees, creating its own path. The ones who put the flagging up obviously had a smaller vehicle than ours. Some Forest Service trucks are up ahead, their personnel standing around. There must not be anything too devastating or they wouldn't be so calm. Dennis parks the bus and we all hop out. I grab my smoke chaser, and everyone else makes his own preparations. Dennis goes over to talk to a Forest Service man. I'd guess he's the fire boss. I realize I've learned something already from fire school. Dennis writes a few things down and returns to the small circle of Hotshots now gathered outside of the bus. Michael Cord makes his presence known to me. He must have showed up this morning. Hadn't noticed him before in all the excitement. "Dennis, where's the fire at?"

"Here's the scoop," Dennis says. "The fire is about five chains, and over that hill to the west. Two crews and three tankers already took care of the initial attack. They managed to contain the fire to about twenty acres."

"Twenty... is that all?" Darryl asks. "Sounds like an overkill."

"We're just here to mop up. They already have a fire line around it."

"What other crews are here?" Cord asks.

"Pleasant Valley and Heber. We are relieving Heber. Pleasant Valley will stay with us tonight. Chevelon Lake is down there. The fire began at the lake because some fishermen didn't bother to put it out completely. A few chains of the line are along the lake, they stopped the fire here at the top."

"Did they catch the guys who started the fire?" Greg asks.

"Don't know, didn't ask."

I have to butt in. "What do they do to someone who starts a fire?"

"They make them pay for the suppression cost," Darryl explains.

Dennis has had enough of standing around. "Let's go. Squad up!" He barks.

Darryl laughs. "We can't do that. We haven't broken up into squads yet."

Dennis fails to find this amusing. "Well then, get them in single file and make sure everyone gets a tool."

Paul Wakeford jumps in the back of the bus and hands the tools out. Pulaskis to some and shovels to others. Dennis watches his progress. "Marty, Drifty," he calls, "get piss pumps over at that tanker and fill them up at the Porta Tank. The rest of you start hiking down."

Darryl turns to me. "Take everything you were issued," he instructs, "including your bushmaster jacket and headlamp. The jacket ain't worth a shit, but it looks like we'll be spending the night here."

We march only a few yards closer to the fire damage when the smell of burnt timber grows more pungent. We cross a blackened area blanketed in ashes that are now being stirred up by the people ahead of us. The front of the line stops to avoid a sharp drop-off. As we edge our way downward, we can see the lake through the trees. The fire stayed along the ground and never reached the tree tops. I'm feeling a lot better about this fire and almost ashamed of my earlier fears. I make what I think is an interesting discovery. "Hey, look at this trail were on," I call to Darryl.

"That's no trail," he re-emphasizes. It's the line! What do you think stopped the fire?"

I can't believe it. "This trail here is what stopped the fire? But it's only a couple of feet wide."

"That's right... and it works! You'll get your chance to dig line on another fire."

Dennis is yelling from up front, "The last two guys at the rear stay there, the rest of you spread out down the line to the lake and start mopping up, get the hot spots first."

Cord grabs me by the arm. "C'mon," he says. "I'll show you what to do." He walks over to a log still burning with small flames. He gets his pulaski, which is half axe, half hoe, and digs up some dirt. "Now get you a shovel full of dirt and throw it on the flames to knock them down," he tells me.

Easy enough. I scoop up a shovel full and pour dirt on the flames. It knocks them out for a few seconds, then they flare right back up again.

Cord shakes his head. "Here, let me show you. This is called hotspotting... when your target is still too hot to get close to the snag." He holds the shovel in an overhand position and throws the dirt hard onto the flame. "See, like that. Now, one more and we'll be able to get in there."

I follow through with similar motions but miss my target. "I guess I need some practice," I mumble.

"Yeah. All you did was blow out the flame." He gets his pulaski and starts chopping the glowing embers. "You've got to get this hot stuff off by chopping and scraping it away." He goes through the motions. "Now get some more dirt and pour it in here on the snag. Get those embers mixed in with the dirt in there and cool them down."

"OK, gotcha."

I watch while he chops and scrapes on the smoky log. The coals have changed from red to black. "Put some more dirt on this, and it should do it." We do, and it does. Finished with this we move to another. "Here," Cord instructs, "trade tools with me. You scrape on this one." We exchange and he immediately throws dirt at a glowing log, "Scrape it off now."

I do it and say, "Hey, this isn't bad at all. Is this what firefighting is all about?"

"Hell, no. This is going to be a piece of cake."

The basics are down on this so-called "mopping up" action. I wander about on my own, crushing out embers, breaking up logs and stumps. There are hot places in the ground where a whole log had been incinerated to powder. Fresh, cool dirt had to be mixed and stirred in to cool the hot earth down. If a piss pump is close by, the operator assists you with water to cool down the mess of vegetation that once was alive and growing in this forest.

Cord, Darryl, and Koval are working on a standing snag. It's hollowed out, burning inside, forming a chimney that sends smoke up the center and out the broken-off top circle with a glowing cap of embers. Cord sticks his shovel into a burnt – through opening that's about waist high. As he pokes around, knocking loose the embers inside, a gust of wind from above inverts the chimney effect. In a split-second a burst of flame, with the intensity of Godzilla's breath, spits out the opening where he is probing. The flash grabs and embraces his waist. It almost hits Koval, as well, who's standing five feet behind him. It happens so fast all Cord, and everyone who's watching, can do is just stand there half-frozen in shock. It was something you'd see in a horror flick that would leave your jaw hanging. Cord lets out an ear piercing girly scream, like from a B-rated horror flick, that echoes eerily across the lake. Then he turns around and says in a trembling voice, "Hey, did you guys catch that?"

"It almost got me, too," Koval says. "I felt the heat from that one. If I was bending down it would have singed my whole head."

"Cord, are you alright?" Darryl asks.

"Sure, I didn't get burned, didn't feel a thing. A little warm maybe. That's the first time I've ever been attacked by a dragon tree. It was trippy."

Dennis isn't far from our position. He's making a radio report, and when he's finished he calls Marty and me over to where he's standing. "They got sack lunches up there for us," he says with a smile. "Since you got your smokechaser, you can put them into that. Empty it out here. Marty, go with him and help."

"We got to go way on top?" Marty complains.

"Yes."

Marty gives me a look. "You're a new guy, huh?"

"Yes, sir." I can tell he likes that "sir" shit.

"This'll be good exercise for you," Dennis says.

Marty's not happy. "I'm not an F.N.G.," he says.

"Well, you can use the exercise, too. Hurry up before it gets dark." As Marty and I start up the hill Dennis shouts after us, "Get eighteen. It might be all we get to eat 'til they take us off in the morning."

It seems like a long way up. The sun sets quickly and it's dark by the time we reach the top. I take half of the sack lunches and Marty carries the other half in a cardboard container. I wonder how we're supposed to find our way down when Marty says, "Just follow the line down. Everyone is spread out, so just pass out a lunch sack when you see someone. I'll follow the hose lay down."

It's amazing how different the woods look at night. I find a couple of people to give sack lunches to. They help distribute them among the crew. My main concern is to find my stuff that I emptied out before I left to get the lunches. I spot my headlamp lying in the dark, but nothing else. I'm lost! I retrace my steps, covering every inch of ground up and down the hillside. My legs are tired but I don't want to eat until I find my things.

Dennis comes up to me, holding something in his hands. "Hey Petretti," he asks, "is this your fire gear?"

"I hope so. I'm getting hungry."

"Don't get down on yourself. It's confusing when you're not used to being up here."

"That's for sure," I respond gratefully. "I must have lost my sense of direction."

"You'll get better oriented with time. For now, eat your meal. We'll be here all night and there ain't much more to do. We've just got the south side. Pleasant Valley should be over there, but I haven't seen any of them yet. They're probably hiding somewhere."

It's a relief to follow his instructions. I take my time over my lunch break, sitting in deep thought. Couldn't begin to tell you what occupied my mind. Probably examining that gourmet meal up here in the middle of nowhere. Lunch consisted of two sandwiches, chips, fruit, fruit juice, and Starburst candies. Mustard and ketchup, salt and pepper were all supplied in little packets. I finally finish eating and walk over to talk with the other guys.

By 1 A.M. every hot spot appears to be put out. I keep moving just to stay awake. Conversation helps. The wind is picking up again and it's getting colder. Above us I see a small flame flare skyward. There are already a few people around it so Drift and I stay where we are, picking at a stump that's been out for awhile. "That fire up there is getting bigger," I say with concern. "You think they need help?"

"No, they're making it bigger," Drift says.

"Why would they do that?"

"It's a warming fire. They're probably cold. Aren't you cold?"

"Real cold. I just didn't want to complain. Is a fire like that legal?"

"When you're freezing your ass off, it is," he says with a laugh about the legality of it. "Come on, let's go up. There's nothing happening down here."

We get there and see Darryl, Greg, Aaron, Koval, and Dennis around a small fire. They invite us to stay. Dennis says, "Come on and get warmed up. It's going to be a long night."

I'm glad for the chance. "Yeah, these jackets aren't too warm are they?" I say with a shudder.

"I told you they were good for nothing," Darryl confirms.

Aaron jumps in and demands, "Turn off your headlamp," as it shines in his eyes. Then adds in a nicer tone, "You don't need it on. Save your batteries."

Greg is already asleep, curled up near the fire. Koval snickers and asks why we didn't come up earlier. We lie a little and tell him we were busy working. I find a cozy spot near the warmth and sit down. I didn't realize how cold it was until I start to warm up. Cord appears suddenly out of the dark and says, "I was wondering where everyone went to. I'm freezing my butt off and you guys are kicking back here." He comes up behind Darryl "Move over darlin', let me in." He nudges Greg a little with the steel toe of his boot. "Look at this beast. He's flaked out already."

Dennis puts more wood on the fire to accommodate the additional cold bodies.

"Where are the rest of the guys?" Cord asks.

"Probably doing the same thing," Darryl answers.

"There's a fire going on down there," I add, pointing to the water's edge.

"Those are some P.V. guys," Aaron says. "Thought they might be Blue Ridge at first. Went all the way down there for nothing."

The warmth of the fire is making me sleepy. I sort of nod out, still sitting up, while the voices meld in a comforting hum around me. I'm vaguely aware of someone saying, "Lucky Greg, He don't need a warming fire. He's got enough baby fat on him to keep him warm."

Then a response, "We'll have to work it off him."

May 8

I must have flopped out on the ground at some point, so tired the jagged rock in my side made no difference. I wasn't asleep for long when I woke with a shiver. People are still up and talking. The wind's blowing harder. I can hear the swooshing in the tree tops and feel its Arctic breath down my back. I think about my freezing bike ride into town last week, and the contrasting warm, sunny beaches of Southern California.

When I wake again, the warming fire is almost out, and my body is stiff. The sky is getting lighter, which means it will probably get warmer. I look around and see that I am not the only one who fell asleep. There are bodies all around me. Dennis is the only one still awake. He watches me stir. I look at him groggily and ask, "How come you're still up?"

"I'm hyper. The No Doz helps some, too. Sometimes in reverse."

"How long have I been out?"

"Only about an hour." He checks his watch to confirm it. "Yeah, about an hour and fifteen minutes."

"The last thing I remember was shivering and you and Darryl talking about guns."

"Darryl just went out."

Darryl is stirring now. "What! You guys are talking about me again?" he asks, bleary- eyed.

"Ahh, go back to sleep Darryl," Dennis orders.

"What time is it anyway?" Darryl asks, ignoring the order.

"4:35 A.M. I guess you better stay awake then. We should start moving around pretty soon. We're supposed to walk out at 0700."

Darryl looks around, "Is Pleasant Valley still here? I noticed that their warming fire went out around 3."

Drift wakes up, half-hearing what we are saying, "They're probably frozen down there."

We laugh a little to stir us awake. The conversations are loud enough to rouse all the rest of the sleepers except Greg. "Time he got up, too," Darryl decides. "We got to break him in right."

Dennis walks over and gives Greg a kick. Greg moves a little and Dennis kicks him even harder. Dennis looks over at me and winks. "Everyone wake up!" he yells. "Fire!"

Greg gets up slowly, and says, "There's NO fire."

"How the hell would you know?" Dennis chides. "Get on up. We're leaving in a couple of hours and we need to make sure everything is out." He gets a canteen and pours some water over the remnants of our fire. "This has to be put out now. Some overhead might be coming down. You guys over there... Jake, Aaron, put out that fire. Walk around and cold trail."

We all slowly get on our feet and pull ourselves together as best we can, our bodies cold and stiff from sleeping on rocks and sloping terrain.

We slosh around in the ashes until walk-out hour, then gather back at the bus. People are pulling off their fire clothes and getting back into the clean, comfortable ones they had on at the station. Minutes later we're on the bus, slowly following the flagging out to the main dirt road.

"Hey, Petretti! How do you like firefighting so far?" joshes Darryl.

"I don't, if this is all it is."

"It will get better."

"I hope so. I'll let you know then." That's the last thing I remember. Before I know it I'm asleep.

Somebody is shaking me awake. It's Aaron leaning over the back of the seat in front of me, nudging my shoulder. The bus has stopped in front of the Zane Grey Steak House and Aaron tells me we're going to eat breakfast there. My eyes sting from smoke and lack of sleep. I'm about to rub them when I notice how filthy my hands are. I look out the window and I see another crew already going into the place. I look at them and they are all dirty, with black faces, red eyes, and filthy, smelly clothes. "Who are those guys?" I ask.

"The Pleasant Valley crew," someone responds.

"So that's what they look like! I never did get to see them last night." I'm having a hard time clearing the cobwebs out of my head. I don't even remember how we got here.

As I look out the bus window again, I wonder aloud, "Where did all those clouds come from?"

Darryl jumps in, quick witted. "The weather. Hey, you gonna sit there or are you coming in to eat?"

"I'm coming, I'm coming. Let me wake up first," I say in a grumpy voice.

The Pleasant Valley crew is already eating, and our guys are standing in line. The people who run the place are serving. It's a family business. They're handing out heaping plates full of eggs, hash browns, French toast, and sausage. Wakeford is passing out the juices. When he's got a few in his pockets, he quits passing out drinks and carries milks in his hand back to the tables. I find a seat at a table with our crew members and dig right into the food. When I stop a moment for breath I look around at all the other dirty faces, their jaws chewing away, the only clean spot... their eyeballs. Then something else catches my eyes. I call to Darryl with a mumbled mouthful, "Look... over there... a Hotshot girl!"

"Not one girl. There's three of 'em over there. They're part of the Pleasant Valley crew."

"Wow! They must be tough."

"Not really, I bet the guys have to pull their work load. Probably took them on because of the Equal Rights laws."

"So how come we don't have any?"

"Because we already have a good crew." He stops to swallow. "Shut up and let me eat."

I should have known better than to ask questions while everyone was eating like animals. I guess in 'Hotshots' they follow the animal rule. Don't disturb a dog while he is eating. I shut up and devote my attention to my meal. Several of the guys get up and go for seconds. I finish what I'm eating and do the same. When we trip back to the bus, warm and sated with food, I hunker down into my seat and fall asleep. I wake up once at a sudden stop and look outside. It's snowing. Then the rhythmic tempo of the wipers puts me back to sleep again.

We pull into Blue Ridge at 1:30 P.M. and stop at the office. Dennis jumps out to do some paper work. Most of us wake up. A soft snow is falling. Refreshed and reinvigorated by our three or four hour nap we begin a lively banter. Relieved to have yesterday's events behind us, we kid around about the fire and everything else we can think of.

We're off the clock at 1:45. We have already put in our thirteen hours for the day. Some guys hit the sack as soon as we reach the trailers. Darryl and Cord talk me into staying up and getting drunk and high with them to celebrate our first fire. We add up the hours and the money we made on our overnight adventure. We stay up until right after nightfall. By then we're so loaded we pass out until morning. That government supplied metal bunk bed never felt so gooooooooooooood!

May 9 to 11

I got twelve good hours of motionless sleep, and it doesn't feel like enough. I don't know how Darryl does it, but the morning music is always on time. I lay there until I hear the sound of Cord's flip-flops, scratching on the dirty floors. He goes into the bathroom and pisses like a race horse. Must have been last night's beer. Twelve hours is a long time to hold your piss after drinking all that beer. I know if I tried it during the day I couldn't go that long. Not with a six-pack in me. I am still used to the second shift hours and don't want to move. It's going to take a while to reprogram the alarm clock in my head that gets me up and moving with no problem.

Thanks to all the on-the-job training we got at the Lake fire, we need only two more days in fire school. We spend them learning first aid, cardiopulmonary resuscitation (CPR), tanker hydraulics, weather behavior, safety, and knot tying; this latter because we're supposed to be a certified rock climbing crew. We also see films, including a Disney film on firefighting. On the last day of the week we review and then take a comprehensive test. Test scores have to be on record in order to be red carded for firefighting. Previous red card holders don't have to be tested again, but are still required to sit through fire school. When we aren't at school, the crew keeps busy by working on the bus, installing a stereo and improving the back caged section to accommodate the tools and supplies for more efficient fire readiness.

Before we go off-duty we're told that our regular days off will be Wednesdays and Thursdays. At the end of the day, we play a few vigorous games of volleyball. Blue Ridge has some real good company players, playing Blue Ridge rules. These rules are a slight modification of jungle ball. We have our last Saturday off, so it's off to a quick shower and then... town time. We are going to check out this Shakey Drakes joint.

May 12

Saturday I spend waiting for my bike to get tuned up and wondering if I did the right thing by accepting an invitation from Laura and Doug to attend their tennis social tonight. I only agreed because I am so new in town, and itching to get out to another party. Last night I went to Shakey

Drakes and had a great time. It's the only place with live Rock 'n Roll in this predominately Country 'n Western town. I met a nice sociology major there who had just gotten her bachelor's degree. We exchanged phone numbers. I would have happily canceled my plans for the tennis social if I could only have gotten a date with her, but she was never home when I called.

Food service was buffet style at the social. The guests consist almost entirely of wealthy married couples, the affluent social set Laura and Doug ran with. To my surprise, there is one single girl here tonight, and I, the only single male, am conversing with her before I finish my plate. Her name is Melinda. She's easy to talk to, so the conversation doesn't lag. Pretty, too. I dig her look. She explains that she's alone tonight because she has just recently gotten divorced. I'm surprised to hear it. She seems unusually prim and proper for a divorcee. I am on my best behavior. I know my sister and Melinda's parents are watching me.

As we chat, I catch a whiff of a familiar odor about her. I'm trying to figure out if it's something she ate at the buffet like onions or pickled herring, and then it hits me, it's the smell of a wet female crotch! I remember with pleasure and excitement an evening last summer, talking with a divorcee who really dug me. There was the same kind of smell about her. I must have turned her on like crazy because she got wet enough to stain right through her clothes.

But back to the moment. Melinda's scent is making me hornier by the minute. I'm trying to figure out if I'm right, but she's sitting down and keeps her legs crossed and her hands between them, as though they were cold. I'm thinking maybe I can figure out a way to hold her and rub some of that off on my fingers. Then I could sneak a sniff. Or maybe I could just ask her if I can smell her fingers. OK, I know that's crazy. I wonder, can a girl smell the same scent or do you have to have some sort of testosterone-powered sense to pick up on it? I mean, it's not the pungent smell you'd get at a go-go dance place or a Tijuana titty bar. It has a natural assertiveness about it. That sort of scent, I suppose, is what makes dogs go around sniffing each other. In a way, I was acting like a dog. I was sitting on the floor in front of her. Every once in a while, I'd try to "accidentally" bump or brush her leg. I could tell that her bowels were quivering. But she's a cool one, at least on the surface. Not a goose-bump on her.

Even though I haven't been laid for almost a month, I know there's nothing I can do about it tonight. For one thing, Melinda is here with her parents, the hosts of this event. My only hope is to get her phone number. I ask and she says to look her up in the phone book and give her a call. She also extends an offer to come to a barbecue next Saturday night but, worse luck, I have to work. I try to get her to agree to next Tuesday night as I have Tuesdays and Wednesdays off, but she won't commit.

Before leaving she tells me she's going to take a trip to Europe, and asks me if what she had heard about Italian men was true. I tell her maybe I'll let her find out before she leaves. It's time for us to go, so manage some kind of gracious farewell, all the time thinking of how nice it would have been to have gotten my fingers wet, at least one, on her juicy pussy.

May 13 to 15

This is the first week of regular schedule for our crew. Our RDO (regular days off) will be changed to Wednesdays and Thursdays. There are four Hotshot crews in the Coconino National Forest. Each have different work schedules, the rotation designed to ensure maximum coverage for the Coconino forest. We'd be on from 9 A.M. to 6 P.M., Friday through Tuesday. Starting at nine in the morning gave most guys time to drive back from Flagstaff before work, but limited what could be done after work before dusk.

I ride back that morning thinking about Melinda and her hot crotch. It's the only thing that keeps me warm. I hope I don't develop a boner thinking about her because that will leave less blood to circulate in my brain where my warm thoughts are.

Not to worry. The cold has already taken care of that.

When we start work on Sunday they throw a lot of new stuff at us, like project work. That's the work we'll be doing when we're not on fires. Someone has volunteered us to do tree thinning on 900 acres of land. This will be the Hotshots' busy work. To help us in this endeavor we get lectures on chainsaw safety and orientation for the F.N.G.s (fuckin' new guys). We practice on giant logs set up on sawhorses using Homelite chainsaws in two sizes, the XL and the 925 models. The macho guys grabbed the 925's, a beefier version of the XL. I lean towards the XL. It's a lot lighter. They take us out to a patch of pine trees near the station where we are to start thinning. Thinning clears out the underbrush and small trees allowing the larger trees to grow taller and healthier, and yield more board feet of lumber. Michael Reamer is with us and we'll be doing this work to his specifications.

Bob Smith, the crew boss, and Russ Copp, the other squad boss, have joined us for physical training. After the project work we do an hour of P.T... first calisthenics then a four mile run. Smith, who's short and stocky, does not accept complaints. There is no resting between exercises. We go from jumping jacks right to the ground for push-ups, then up for side-twisters. He makes everyone finish the routine. After the workout and run we loosen up our tight muscles with a few games of volleyball. I'll say one thing for Smith, after all the hard work he puts you through, you're glad to go to bed early, and you sleep well.

On our first real weekend I ride up to Flagstaff after volleyball, but I'm too sore to go out when I arrive. Instead I crash early at my sister's. Sleeping on a real bed is a treat. Doug gets a kick out of talking to me about the crew, asking a lot of questions about our duties, and about the other crew members. Everything I say sounds positive because I am so jazzed about working there. I know Doug feels responsible. It was his influence that drove me to come up here, and I can see he's pleased by the way things are going. I don't forget he's also head of Personnel in the Forest Service supervisor's office. It puts a burden on me to perform.

Score one for me! Melinda and I are going out tomorrow night. She has dance lessons and isn't free 'til 9, which gives me time to meet some of the boys at the Widowmaker, where a lot of Forest Service people go for happy hour.

May 16

By the time I leave the Widowmaker, I'm feeling pretty good. I met other Hotshots there from the Mormon Lake crew. We went through many pitchers of beer. I had my fair share, but not enough to where I couldn't maintain for Melinda later on.

When I arrive at her house, we agree it's too late to do anything, so we decide to go to Bob's Big Boy for dessert. Actually, it's going to be my dinner. Melinda doesn't seem to mind riding on by bike, lucky for me, because it's the only thing I have. We drink enough coffee to put us into a talkative mood. You can't get too romantic in Bob's, so we leave to find a more secluded area. We ride to the county fairground which is deserted, but still has the park-like surroundings. What I have in mind is some good ol' time necking under the stars, and the atmosphere at the fairgrounds is perfect. Still on the bike, I turn around and give her a big kiss. She seems to enjoy it. We hold each other close and don't want to stop kissing. The kissing gets very enthusiastic. So enthusiastic I suggest to Melinda that we get off the bike and settle ourselves somewhere more comfortable. She agrees. I lay my leather motorcycle jacket down with a chivalrous flourish, so she can sit on it and not get her clothes dirty. "How's this, Mel?" I ask.

"Fine, thanks," she says and follows with a cute curtsy.

"You don't mind if I call you Mel, do you?"

"I don't like it, but I'm used to it. People have been calling me that all my life. You can call me Mel if you like."

We sit down and continue where we left off, kissing and holding each other close. Her hand travels over my back and I respond with a hand on her back and one on her leg. I can hear her breath come faster and my boner wants to rip, jump, and leap out of my pants with every deep breath she takes.

"Do you ever think about going to bed with me?" I whisper in her ear while I'm kissing her neck.

"It has crossed my mind," she replies primly.

"Did it cross your mind the other night at the tennis party?"

"Wellllll, yeah, I guess I did think of it once."

"Just once? Not any other time."

"No, just once," she replies, hesitant to admit any more.

"And you thought about it tonight, too?"

"Yes!"

"A lot?"

"Somewhat." I see her face turn serious. "Why are you asking?"

"I'm curious, that's all. Did you have fantasies about me?"

"Some. OK?"

"You bet. Have as many as you want."

I was losing my hard on, so I get back to business... kissing her lips, then her neck and her ears. I can't believe it when she says, "Stop that!"

"Stop what?"

"What you're doing. You're giving me goose bumps."

"Well don't think of it that way. Try to distribute those goose bumps inward. Put them into feeling instead of wasting them."

"How am I suppose to do that?" she asks.

"I don't know, you can figure it out. Here try it this time." I try to maintain eye contact in a sexy way until my field of vision was blocked by her cheekbone. I lick her ear a couple of times and gently nibble on her neck.

"I can't help it. There they are again."

"Yeah, they're there alright. Look at those little guys."

"I guess I'll have to work on it."

I think I'm going to have to work on her. I decide to go for it. "Would you like to go to bed with me tonight?" I venture.

"We can't. I wouldn't feel right."

"You want to, though, don't you?"

"Yes, but it's too early. It's too early for us and it's too early after my separation."

"Yes, but if you truly want to, if you have a will, want, or desire, you should execute it. Don't play around with the idea in your head, you'll just get frustrated. Do it! Besides, it's unhealthy. What do you think your body is for? It's to execute the mind's will. Body, go occupy that space over there, and tah-dah, you take three steps and you're there. It's simple."

"You're making it sound simpler than it is."

"You need to develop that direct-line mind-body connection. The more direct it is, the easier things are to accomplish. You ever heard of 'The Talking Heads,' the new wave group?"

"No."

"There's a line in one of their songs that goes, 'There's a straight line that exists between you and the good thing. Economy and efficiency are multiplied when you reach the good thing.' Mel, you've got to set your goal, let it be fantasy if you want, but kept it reachable and obtain it."

I could tell she was thinking about something. It could have been about what I just said or about fucking the daylights out of me.

"You think you have the answers for everything."

"There are answers for everything. That's why I like philosophy. It helps you find those answers to everything."

"I never took a philosophy class. If this is what it's like, it's interesting."

"You ought to take some philosophy classes, you'd probably like them. They'll get you thinking about a lot of things... things you never thought of before. You know if you can't find a direct answer about something, you think of something related and form new ideas that eventually lead you to a reasonable answer. There are so many alternatives to choose from. Jesus, I could go into a whole new thing on choice and free will."

"Not now, we better start back home."

"Oh, yeah. I'm going home with you, and make passionate love to you."

"No, you're going to drop me off and I'm going to bed by myself."

"I can be your teddy bear and you can hold me all night."

"I already have one that I sleep with, he'll get jealous if I bring you home."

"Oh, we can't let that happen."

We make out some more and she hugs me like she appreciated what I had told her.

"We better go," she finally sighs. "I have to work tomorrow."

"Okay, we'll leave now."

We make time for one more kiss, a long one. I take her home and she thanks me for the nice evening. She gives me a quick kiss, and blurts out, "Oh, I almost forgot. Can you come to a barbecue dinner with me Saturday night?"

"I probably can. I'll call you Saturday when I get off work."

She thanks me and gives me another kiss and hug. I go home through the back roads of Flagstaff, thinking about Melinda and appreciating the stretched out section in my pants where my hard-on left an impression.

May 17

Today I follow Laura and Adam to Sedona to visit our other sister. We go to her dress shop, have lunch, and laze around the Sedona Racket Club's pool. I was introduced to a flying bug called a Cider Gnat, commonly called "can't see em's." They leave bigger bites than mosquitoes, and you can't see them. You don't know they're there 'til they bite you, and then it's too late. I return to Blue Ridge that evening while it is cold, but not freezing. Sedona has a warmer climate, and it's not as high as Flagstaff. The temperature drops fast when I climb up the mountain back into the forest.

May 18

Starting work at nine o'clock agrees with my system. We pile on the bus and drive by Bob's residence at the station. He's standing there waiting for us with his big cup of coffee. He jumps on the bus and stays at the bottom of the steps.

"Stop at the office," he says to the driver in a monotone.

"Okay," Dennis responds from behind the wheel. Bob jumps out at the office. Dennis quickly turns off the motor and follows him in.

"What are they going in there for?" Koval asks sourly. "We know what we're going to do for the next three years."

"Bob has to refill his coffee cup back up," Darryl replies.

"And what does Dennis go in for?"

"Brown nosing."

Cord calls, "Hey, Russ, put some music on the radio."

"Sure. I forgot we got the stereo in."

"You forget a lot of things," joshes Darryl. "You're getting spaced out in your old age."

Russ puts in the tape Bob made at home. It was full of Hoyt Axton. It's not for me, so I speak up. "I can't stand country western music."

"Tough. That's all they play up here," Darryl says. "So shut up, Steve, and give me five dollars. All you new guys, too. The rest of the men have paid in already."

Darryl is still collecting when Bob and Dennis jump back on the bus. "Let's go," Bob says. "Oh, I see you found my tape."

"Yeah," Cord replies. "You can leave it at home next time."

"Shut up, Cord," Bob snaps.

"What did I say wrong?" asks Cord, aggrieved.

Bob instructs Dennis to go where we had started cutting. On the way the crew indulges in their usual kidding around, but Bob doesn't say much. We can tell that he is not in the best of moods. When Dennis pulls the bus in and parks it, Bob stands right up.

"Before you start the chain saws up we need to get some things straight," he says.

We pile out and gather around the back of the bus. Wakeford, Darryl, Russ, and Marty grab for their favorite saws. Bob continues. "Timber don't like the way we've been thinning. They say we're not taking enough out. You got to cut everything under six inches in the thickest parts. Watch for crown space on the top. Leave enough room so the branches don't grow into each other like those have." He points up. Some of us wrench our necks to look. Others don't even bother. They've heard all this before.

"We also have to stack everything we cut, and I mean stack it right, in pyramid style. Make them tight with the stumps on top so the weight of the stump can compress the whole pile This will leave the needles on the bottom, so they'll light easy, and will have good consumption. Reamer doesn't like the way we stacked those piles, so we'll have to re-do them. He doesn't want things sticking out. Paul Wakeford, Steve Koval, go through and trim and buck up things like that. Now we're trying to get more saws from timber, so at least half can saw, the rest will stack 'em, and stack 'em right! I don't want to have Reamer tell us we're going to have to do it again. And, don't fight over the saws. You guys can trade off at lunch or something. Work it out amongst yourselves. Let's go!" Bob talks soft, but he makes a big impact. On his last command we hustle off and start restacking the piles.

"Stack 'em and unstack 'em! Stack 'em and unstack 'em, stack 'em and unstack 'em," Cord mutters. And he's not the only one pissed off. Each of the guys has something to say.

"He must of woken up on the wrong side of the bed."

"Lana must have not of given him any last night, or this morning."

"Maybe she made him make his own coffee."

"Naw, it sounds like Reamer read him the riot act this morning."

"Yeah, Reamer gets on the rag at times. That's probably all it is."

We work hard the rest of the day, rearranging the thinning piles. Bob must have figured that we had enough punishment for the day because at P.T. we only have to climb the rope, do pull-ups, dips, sit-ups, and run the required four miles around the campground. I still have to walk a good part of that distance. A quarter of the way my side starts aching too much to continue. What a wuss I am!

The tankers are already playing volleyball when we finish running, and I finally stumble in. We join in on the volleyball game, fitting in wherever needed to even out the teams. Enough of us show up to make a third team that rotates in to play the winners.

Bill Krushak and Buck Wickham stand on the sidelines making cracks about everyone. Reamer gets it for his white, skinny legs. Bob for killing a spike and flattening the ball. Darryl gets it for just standing there and missing the ball a few times. The best crack of all, that stuck, was Greg Leveque. He gets a new nickname, "Sluggo", from the character on the Mr. Bill sketch on the old Saturday Night Live TV show. Greg is the only one who doesn't take to his new name. It busts everyone else up because it fits him so well. At the end of the games Dennis announces a poker game at his place tonight. We scatter as we walk back to the trailers. I hasten to catch up with Darryl and Cord.

"Darryl, wait up!" I shout. "Are you going to Dennis' tonight?"

"Probably. I shouldn't, though. I've lost too much money over there. They play higher stakes than we do at the trailers."

"That sounds OK. Cord, you going?"

"Nah. I don't like to play. I might go to party, but I'm not going to play poker."

"Well, if you want to go you guys can ride with me," Darryl says.

Greg, who's been walking close behind us, listening to our conversation, walks up and calls, "Hey, Dale!"

"My name is Darryl, Sluggo. You know, Darryl, not Dale, just Darryl. D.A.R.R.Y.L."

"Yeah, and my name is Greg not Sluggo. G.R.E.G."

"No!" Cord pipes up. "You are a Sluggo! S.L.U.G.G.O."

We all laugh. Greg wants in on the party and the ride, but Darryl turns him down. "I can only take three in my car," he says. A lame explanation, but Greg seems to buy it.

Cord sidles over to Darryl. "I might not go," he says softly, "and he'll want to go with you then."

"Well, I ain't gonna take him, and that's that."

"You can take him Darryl, come on. Look how dumb he looks."

We snicker a little. Darryl thinks it over and starts to feel sorry for him. "Hey, Sluggo," he says, "if Cord doesn't go, you can go."

"Gee, thanks Darle. What time are you leaving?"

"I don't know, come over later after we eat, and we'll go."

Greg walks off and Darryl shakes his head. "He'll never get my name right," he says.

"That's why he's a Sluggo," says Cord.

A lot of people show up for the party and we have a good ol' game of poker, although only seven of us actually play cards at any one time. Cord shows up, but leaves early with Aaron and Russ, who don't play either. There's a good movie on the tube and the guys who aren't playing poker watch the flick. At the poker table when one guy goes broke, another takes his place.

We all drink... a lot! Sluggo brought over some tequila and Dennis broke open his Jack Daniels. We polish them both off plus a whole lot of beer. Sluggo gets stoned and obnoxious, talking loud, and right into your face. He says a lot of dumb stuff and doesn't notice that he's the only one laughing at it. Everyone forgets his name is Greg and calls him Sluggo. After awhile he doesn't seem to mind. Dennis and I are the big winners. He wins about $23 and I win $13.50. I learned a few good games the Hotshots play with Blue Ridge jungle rules.

We play only until one o' clock since we have to work tomorrow. Sluggo ends up going home with us, very drunk and slurring his speech. Dennis lives only three miles from the station. Greg passes out in the back seat by the time we hit the highway, it's two miles from there. When we reach the trailers Darryl pulls on the parking brake and stops with a screech on the gravel. "Get out, Sluggo," he barks.

"He can't," I tell him. "He passed out right after we left."

Darryl is in no mood for this. "Sluggo wake up," he shouts. He pulls Greg's hair to rouse him.

Sluggo comes to, struggles to get up and falls out of the car. He manages to get back on his feet and makes it to the picnic table, where he sits, slumped over. Darryl slams the car door before I can get out.

"What's going on?" I ask.

"We're going for a ride," Darryl says as puts the car in gear and pulls out of the drive.

"We are? Where?"

"You'll find out. I want to see how fast this car will go. That's why I dumped Sluggo. He'd just be dead weight."

"Well, what about me? Who says I want to get killed?"

"I need a witness."

"No, I think it's more like you need a fool. What if you crash and I get killed? There goes your witness."

"I won't crash. I know what I'm doing."

"You're crazy. You're drunk. You can't even talk straight. Well, I'm putting on my seat belt."

"Oh yeah, good idea," he laughs. "I'm glad one of us is thinking straight."

"Oh, brother, what are you getting me into?" I ask. I feel myself sobering real fast.

"A coffin. Ha, ha, ha."

"Funny. You better not."

"Don't worry. If I crash, we'll both die."

"Oh, great, a coffin for two."

He takes off down highway 87. He goes around the first curve and points to the trees.

"Two men died in a truck there last year when they went off the road. Ha, Ha."

"Great, just what I need to hear."

He continues to drive down the straightaway, right after the curve, and turns around with a certain drunken dignity. "Is your seat belt fastened?" he asks.

"Affirmative," I answer jokingly.

"Then here we go! This is a clean engine and it's fast." He floors the pedal and the car takes off. The automatic transmission whines through the gears. "How fast we going now?" Darryl asks. I take a quick look at the speedometer. I don't want him to take his eyes off the road.

"95," I answer.

"It should go faster than that," he says, pressing the pedal harder. He checks the speedometer himself. "Look," he crows, "105!"

"Darryl," I scream, "the curve! Slow down, the sign says 35 mph."

Darryl takes his foot off the pedal, but not soon enough. We hit the curve at 85 mph.

Darryl screams, "It's taking it!"

We almost complete the curve when a ripple in the road bounces the car. The car's shocks were never very strong to begin with, and it feels like the wheels have come right off the road. Darryl slams on the brakes, but by this time we're skidding sideways. I visualize us going off the shoulder and falling down the precipice, but with a screech of the tires that seems to echo in my head forever, we finally come to rest safely, facing the oncoming traffic lane and looking straight ahead at the so called "Deadman's Curve". The smoke from the tires fills the car with the smell of burned rubber. We sit there for awhile, stunned. I finally find my voice and breathe a shaky "Wow!"

Darryl's able to talk now, too. "I can't believe we stayed on the road," he says, "Look at those skid marks!" He points straight ahead.

Anger starts filling the place where my fear was. "You're a fool, Darryl, a God damn fool, but I'm the bigger fool for riding with you," I say vehemently.

"What are you talking about?" Darryl retorts. "I handled this car great. It's a great handling car."

That's bullshit and he knows it. "You're full of shit," I tell him. "You almost got us fucking killed. Now let's get back before my heart attack catches up with me. I'm giong to be a nervous wreck for days because of you."

"No sense in being nervous. Be glad we're still alive," he cackles gleefully.

"You got a point there. The only reason you're still alive is because I'm with you."

"What did you have to do with it? You just told me the curve was coming up!"

"I was the one who saw it coming, not you. You were too busy looking at the speedometer to pay attention to whether we were going off the road." I bring my anger down to a simmer and say more quietly, "Someone must want me to live, and that's why we're both still here. I want to hurry back to the trailer and get some sleep so I can wake up and pretend it was all a dream. I'll settle on a nightmare."

Darryl faces the car back to camp. The car starts bouncing and shaking, and Darryl gets all upset. "Something must of happened to the car," he says, and you can hear the concern in his voice. That's Darryl for you. His biggest concern is his car. He stops the car and we jump out to inspect the damage. There are four flattened spots on the tires, worn down right to the cords. The rubber is on the road. We just look at each other and shake our heads. We ride back, wobbling and bouncing down the highway still in a state of disbelief. We pull in and see Sluggo still laying on the table, passed out. We left him there.

May 19 to 22

"Petretti,........ Petretti wake up. Are you still alive?"

I stir around under the covers and poke my head out. Darryl's face is eye level with my top bunk, inches from my face. The stench of stale booze from his breath is melting the hair on my face. It's a chore to open my eyes. "Leave me alone," I groan. "What time is it?"

"8:45. You remember what happened last night?"

"Yeah. I'm glad I was so drunk I didn't have any nightmares about it. No, wait! I did have a nightmare. I dreamt that I was lying in a coffin shaped like a Mach I Ford Mustang."

Darryl thinks this is funny and snickers in a dull monotone.

I realize I didn't hear the music this morning. I roll over and sit up, semi-alert. "Where's Russ?" I ask.

"He's about ready to start the bus."

"Shit! I guess I'd better get up."

"I bet we'll see those skid marks on our way to thinning. Don't tell anybody what happened. If anyone says anything, we'll tell them we almost hit a deer."

I jump out of bed with wobbly legs and find my way to the bathroom. Darryl follows me in. He tells me again to make sure we get our story straight.

"Alright, so that's what we'll say," I agree, peeing like a racehorse.

"For now, anyway. You should see my tires. There's no way I can drive on them."

"I know. I felt them last night."

"It was a costly experience."

"Costly isn't the world for it. Try death defying!"

"I ruined about $300 dollars worth of tires."

"It's your own damn fault. Shit! Is that the bus starting up?"

"Sounds like it."

"Don't leave without me. Go on, let me alone so I can piss in peace."

Darryl goes out to the bus and grabs a front seat so he can have a better view of the scabs in the asphalt. I get on after him and take my regular seat. As we drive by the 75 foot long skid marks, we stand up to check them out. We look at each other with our eyes wide open and our mouths shut. Darryl breaks first. He can't keep his mouth shut and has to tell someone what happened last night. He gives his version of the "missing the deer" tale. It won't be long before he blabs the real story on how the skid marks got there. I just go along with his story. I had Melinda on my mind, and I want to forget what happened last night.

I call Melinda right after work. The guys know I don't show for volleyball because I have a hot date. Going to Flagstaff, I catch myself going 100 mph at times. Then I think of last night and slow down to 70. Even so I make it up to Flagstaff in an hour and ten minutes, my best time so far. The bugs around Lake Mary are real bad. They're all over me and the bike. Before I get to Melinda's I have to stop to comb the bugs out of my beard and mustache. That does it! It's time to break down and retire my beanie and goggles and buy a helmet!

Melinda is happy to see me. Proper as ever, she doesn't kiss me hello, I guess because there is still company at her parents' home. I come in and I see they are checking me out as they sip their wine. Melinda introduces me around and then offers me some food. The social gathering is what you'd expect of an older crowd... soft talk and a few forced laughs. They leave early, as if they had better things to do. Her parents say good night and go to their room. Fine. Now I can talk to Melinda freely. I didn't mind being polite to her folks and their company, but sweet talking her is the reason I'm there. I figure I'll earn points for good behavior that will serve me well when she's ready for me. My main objective is to get her hot and bothered for the next time I see her.

Now she lowers the lights and we sit on the couch talking like two adolescents on a porch swing, courting. Soon we're hugging, rubbing, caressing, petting, and deep tongue kissing, roofies, rollarounds, and all. Things are going great until she massages my erection. It's been nearly a month since my last release and the action comes close to filling my jeans with joy juice. Her cunt is hot and humid as my hand caresses it. But I know I have to stop it right there. I am still tired from my last night's adventure with Darryl. So just before I have an embarrassing explosion in my pants I have to call it a night.

I dread the ride back and turn in, instead, at my sister's. Rubbing Mel's clitoris tonight left a sweet odor on the back of my thumb. When I was in bed the scent of her moistness stayed with me like a faint perfume. If I were still a baby I would suck on it. Oh what the hell, who am I fooling to try to keep it fresh, to share my thumb with the crew? I insert it in my mouth to get the full effect. God! I hope I don't have a wet dream in my sister's guest bed.

When I leave Flagstaff in the morning the clouds are beginning to gather. By the time I get to Mormon Lake, there's a full-on rain. I am getting soaked, and so are about two hundred other bicyclists that I pass on Lake Mary Road. Somehow that makes me feel better. I had to make the trip, but they were crazy to have planned to ride in this weather. It isn't raining at Blue Ridge, but by now I'm so cold and wet I feel I'd be better off dead.

Two new guys, John Gustafson and Joe Rudd are standing with a small crowd of Hotshots. They look at me like I am nuts. I feel like a drenched, shivering rat. There's no time to change so I go to work with my wet clothes on. Joe picks the seat next to me on the bus as we go out for another day of thinning. There's another new guy, a wisecracking type. He has a minor limp from a motorcycle accident. His name is Jim Cruz and he's rooming with Cord in the middle room. I haven't been around the trailers the past few nights so I missed a few changes. New guys were coming in and the crew is filling out fast.

Russ doesn't like the noise and partying that goes on in our trailer every night, so Russ and Besty moved into the other trailer, to share a room with Aaron. Gus moved in with Drift, and Joe bunked with Sluggo. Joe doesn't know Sluggo very well. They make an odd pair. Joe seems too particular for Sluggo's ways. Sluggo hasn't cleaned his room or done laundry since he got here.

Joe Rudd was a quieter type. A nonsmoker, but I think I saw him dip. Reddish blond hair, freckles. About 5'10" tall with a medium build. A real normal kind of "keep to himself" guy. It'll be hard to find something about him to pick on. He seems to be too serious about things to participate in our kind of tomfoolery.

Darryl is saving his top bunk for Pat Laybe, who is still studying meteorology at a university in Madison, Wisconsin. Pat has been unofficially classified as the crew weatherman. Pat and Darryl are supposed to be "good friends." Darryl had always made it clear that his top bunk was reserved for Pat Laybe. I wonder if they're faggots, but reject that idea quickly. They're too macho for that kind of stuff. I make a little butt buddy joke to test my theory, but Darryl quickly corrects my line of thinking. Darryl wants Pat in there because Pat will go back to school early, and Darryl will have his room to himself again. Now I get it, masturbation privacy. Oh yes, masturbation. If Melinda doesn't come through soon I might have to resort to that myself. I wonder how the other guys deal with it.

Cord doesn't take to Jim Cruz's mouth and wants to move into my room. He doesn't want to see me stuck rooming with Kyle Penick, who is due to show up this coming weekend. I had heard so much about Kyle I felt that I already knew him. He was a popular personality around here. Cord was taking Tuesday off to go to Tucson to see his sweetie that he never stops taking about. Her name is Janine. We already shared some of our Janine stories. I had a Janine, myself, that I left back in the Valley. Anyway, Cord met his Janine last winter and fell in love with her. He came up to Blue Ridge with a bad attitude about work, as any guy would who is pussy whipped about being away from his lover. He is going to drive six hours in his '47 Dodge pickup just to see her over the weekend and get his rocks off. Before he leaves, Cord puts enough things on the top bunk to claim his spot in case Kyle arrives while he is gone. He assures me again that I wouldn't want to bunk with Kyle, and he's doing me a favor by taking the space. He also confides he's already thinking of leaving the crew earlier this year. Then, he says, I can have the room by myself. I like that idea, the Darryl plan, masturbation central. I can tell that the crew likes Kyle, mostly because he is different and amusing. The veterans made us all anxious about his arrival, and get a good laugh out of it.

Work goes by fast this week. We mostly stay around the station, cleaning saws and sharpening chains for awhile, then we thin and stack sticks all day, and have an exhausting workout at the day's end. Bob is really trying to get us in shape.

I have pussy on my mind all week, trying to work out a scheme to get into Mel's pants. She and I don't make any permanent plans to go out Tuesday, but I know she will be waiting for me to call when I got off work. I play two fast volleyball games to show my support and run off to get spruced up for my big date. I have a good feeling about this weekend. I suspect I'm finally going to get my way.

Just as I hoped, Mel was expecting my call. We start out at Shaky Drake's and then go to Granny's Closet, where the lights are dimmer and there are not as many people. It's a disco place, a rarity up here, and it plays a lot of slow music. We dance every slow dance real close. As I hold her tightly in my arms, my chest massages her breast. She rubs her crotch against my hard-on that nearly peeks out over my beltline. We are both plenty aroused when I suggest we go to a more secluded spot. She knows exactly where to go... where all the kids go to watch the submarine races. I have to explain that saying to her.

Our destination is Mars hill where the Lowell Observatory is perched. We hop off the bike and walk to a secluded place overlooking Flagstaff. The view of Flagstaff is spectacular from up there. We gaze down at the glimmering lights of the NAU dome and the rest of the city in the cool, crisp sky.

"It sure is beautiful. I've always liked coming up here," Mel remarks softly.

"When was the last time you came up here?"

"A long time ago."

"Back in your courting days?"

"Yeah. Before I got married."

"That was a long time ago. I'll bet you were a total fox in high school."

She must appreciate that remark because she answers with a big kiss and holds me tight. Then suddenly she stops, steps back and looks at me. "Ooooh," she exclaims.

"Did you feel that cold current, too?" I ask.

"Yeah. If we weren't kissing I would have shivered so much it would shake you off this hill."

"Ah! You're learning to control your goose-bumps."

"I've been keeping them in, alright. I've been practicing circulating them in my body."

"Have you been turning them into sexual sensations?"

"I've been working on it."

Another current hits us, a warm one this time. We both notice it and Mel asks, "Why does it do that? You know, get warm and then cold like that?"

"The cold ones are dead souls floating around."

"Wouldn't they be warm ones?"

"No, the souls are of anti-matter stuff, and heat can only survive in matter."

"No," she says, mocking me. "Where did you hear that from?"

"No one, I thought of it all by myself."

"It sounds like it."

"Well, where do you believe the soul goes? Does it go to heaven when you die?"

"Yes."

"A typical religious answer."

"Aren't you religious?"

"I used to be when I was younger."

"Don't you believe in God anymore?"

"Sure I do, but not the way most people do. God exists somewhere, but I haven't figured out where yet and maybe won't until I've thought about it for a long time."

"How long a time?"

"Probably until I'm an old man, or on my death bed. By then it will probably be too late to repent. I don't want to settle on a belief too soon. Most people do, and expect God to do all the work. People get all fanatical about God and Jesus, and tend to rely on them for all their answers, instead of trying to find the answers themselves. If everyone believed in God like they're supposed to, there would be no science. Man wouldn't have the motivation to look for an alternative way. People are going to have to learn that they have to survive on their own and learn to get along with each other. You don't need religion to be a good person. This is the way I feel. I know that I am a good person. And I plan to live what you'd call a good Christian lifestyle, practicing good things, helping mankind, and animals. I won't kill, steal, lie, or covet anyone's wife. The only difference will be that I do not believe in Jesus as the son of God."

"Now let's say that the judgment day is here and I'm resurrected in front of God. God says in his deep, spiritual voice: 'Well, Steve, I see here that you were a good person. You put out all those fires, you never killed anyone, never stole from anyone, ummm, never fucked anyone's wife, and it says here you always told the truth. Oh, but what is this? You didn't believe that Jesus was my son. You gentile fool! You are going to hell. Sorry son, that's the rule.' See, I just don't think that God will do that. If he does, he is not the God that I want to live by. He would be a very prejudiced God, the opposite of what he is supposed to be. No. I think he would let me into heaven. Maybe on probation, or something."

"This is getting too deep for me," Mel interjects.

"You're right. I'll close with this... it's just logical that we need to get along with each other, to survive on this earth. Don't get me wrong, though. I do believe in a God. There's got to be one. There are too many phenomenal coincidences that can't be explained. But to say that God had something to do with it might be a little premature. God and love are a philosopher's favorite subjects. Love is more fascinating because it deals with people directly instead of something they know little about, like God. Let's change the subject to love and lovemaking.

"Well, I do know something about love. I know it can hurt you."

"You got that right. Did you get hurt in your marriage?"

"Sure did, in more ways than one. I used to get beat up a lot by Mike. I was too blinded by love to see the damage he was doing to me, physically and emotionally."

"You must have loved him very much."

"We were high school sweethearts, and we got married soon after graduation. Other than him, you're the only person I've been with."

"You never went out with anyone before him?"

"I did a couple of times before I met him, but that was with friends. It wasn't really a date with a boyfriend. It wasn't love or anything. We didn't have sex or anything close to it."

"I've been in love a couple of times. Twice, actually."

"Did you get hurt?"

"Sure did. It scars your soul and hardens it. You become more protective about yourself."

"I know. Somehow you had a way to break through to me."

"I know. I've been trying."

Mel smiles and gives me little love punch. "How do you know?" she asks.

"I can see it, and I know that constantly feeling hurt all the time isn't the way to be. Time is the best medicine for that and you can speed things up by getting out and dealing with people again. Remember, time is a man-made idea."

"I suppose you're right."

"I know I'm right. Remember, I've been hurt before, too. What you need now is a good healthy dose of some good loving. You've been neglected for too long. Your ex-husband didn't take care of your loving needs."

"You're right. He would just fuck me. As long as I pleased him, everything was fine. That's all that mattered to him."

"You poor thing, you can love me, hold me, grasp me, and use me."

"When I'm done, then what?"

"You'll have memories, good memories of the way it's supposed to be. You'll have a good feeling inside that will be yours to keep for as long as you want. Your thoughts belong to you alone, you know. You can share them if you like, but no one can take them from you."

"And if I loved someone, I could share my deepest thoughts with him. I've told you a lot of things I never told anyone else."

"Does that mean you love me? If you do, it's probably because I'm the only person you have been with, intimately speaking and consoling wise. Not sexual wise, I mean."

"Not love, exactly. I do have a lot of feelings for you. It's too early to say that I am in love with you."

"You're right about that, but you need to be more selfish now. You need to take in all you can to mend the hurt and keep it from scarring you. What's important is your moral obligation to the person you care about. Most people just take, take, take, and it's a matter of what you do with it when you get it, and they don't care if it's at the expense of the other person. So take what you need, use it, but not at any personal sacrifice to yourself or anyone else. Except with me. You can use and take from me with no guilt. If you want to make love to me, I'll make love to you. I understand what you need, that good thing, that warmth inside of you. I want to make love to you like you've never been loved before. To give you something your soul desires, and not for the physical pleasure alone. Let me ease your craving. I'm sure it will let you think clearer."

"How do you know whether what I want and need is right or wrong?"

"When your head lets you know it isn't at someone else's expense. I care for you a lot and hate to see anyone mistreated. All this talk is getting me horny again." We hold each other then, Mel squeezing me hard like I did her a big favor. When I whisper that we should get a room she looks at me with moist eyes and agrees. We leave Mars hill and make our way to the glimmering lights below to get a room.

May 23 and 24

Mel stays home from work the next day. We spend it running errands in Flagstaff, and afterward go for a ride down Oak Creek Canyon. She says she feels fine about last night. Our pre-sex talk did a lot of good. She feels closer to me now, but that seems to bother her a little. We don't talk about it, but I can tell there's a quietness about her as if she's engaged in heavy thinking. The same heavy thinking I noticed she slipped into after her great orgasm. I hope she didn't feel guilty about our love session. We play around at Oak Creek Canyon, acting like adolescents in love, and don't talk much. This day is meant for feelings. We enjoy being together without as much emphasis on jumping into bed for another round. I'm starting to re-evaluate my own thoughts about love.

All this thinking doesn't spoil a good time. My sister Laura allowed me to use her car for the date because the weather was looking foul. We go to a movie and see "The Deer Hunter," and eat pizza afterwards at Godfathers. I would not have hesitated to make love to Mel again, but those thoughts were beginning to make me uncomfortable. Sex just for the sake of sex wasn't number one on my agenda anymore. If we did have sex it would probably move us to the next level, and we'd be on the threshold of a true, loving relationship. Maybe that's why I was starting to feel used and unsatisfied about last night. I wanted more. We end the night embracing affectionately.

Thursday is a quiet day. I look up Steve Koval and hang out at his place for a while. He offers to drive me back to Blue Ridge tomorrow morning if it is still rainy. I thank him, but I don't want to leave my bike up here. I go back to Laura's and babysit my nephew Alan so Laura and Doug can go out for the evening. I can't stop thinking about Mel. I don't feel I can call her, but it would be so nice if she came over while I sit with Alan.

May 25

Another wet ride back to Blue Ridge. The new helmet helps a lot. When I get there I see a new face in the crew. It sports a mature beard and wire framed glasses with taped-together sides. The man pushes aside the chew in his teeth and says in a slow southern drawl, "I'm James Frailsen... from Louisana. Y'all can call me James 'cause you have a Jim on the crew already. James is what they call me back home."

"From Louisiana, hey?" Sluggo says.

"Yeeaap. Lived there all my life."

"How'd you find out about this area?" Darryl asks.

"Oh, I've done some schooling at NAU before. Didn't think I'd be down yonder, though."

"Well, you ended up at the best place. This is the prettiest district in this forest."

"So I've heard."

The crowd around James breaks up when a truck pulls in at the trailers. It sounds like the truck's exhaust pipe is falling off. You could hear the racket all over the camp.

Darryl recognizes the vehicle. "It's Kyle," he shouts. "Kyle's here!"

"That's Kyle?" Wakeford asks.

"The one and only."

"Let me check this guy out."

"Who's Kyle?" James inquires.

Koval responds. "You don't know who Kyle is? Kyle Penick."

"I just got here." James says.

"He hasn't heard about Kyle yet," Russ says knowingly.

"Probably wouldn't want to if he had," adds Drift.

"Kyle go home. Go home, Kyle, we don't want you here," Dennis chants as he waves Kyle off. Undeterred, Kyle gets out of the truck, walks up to Bob with a long-drive, stiff-legged gimp, and shakes his hand.

Bob claps him on the back. "Kyle, what took you so long? You're two weeks late."

"I decided to take a vacation before I came up." Kyle looks around. "All these guys are new?"

"Yes, half the crew is new." Bob introduces us around. When he gets to Sluggo he uses his real name.

"Where's Cord?" Kyle wants to know. " Is he back this season?"

"He called in this morning for A- leave."

Kyle is 27 years old, built small and wiry. His hair is almost kinky and he wears thick, wire rimmed glasses. His clothes are clean, but patched up and wrinkled. They don't look like they've ever been hung up, just crammed any which way into a drawer. Funny thing is, the guy's wearing a pocket protector! His laugh sounds like Popeye's in those animated cartoons. Yuk, yuk, yuk. I don't know what I find funnier about him, his appearance or his laugh.

Kyle was certainly familiar with the place. This is his forth season on the crew. He has a degree in accounting and works as an accountant in the off season. By now it's almost ten o'clock and Bob decides it's too late to head into the forest for thinning. Instead he lets us work around the trailers, cleaning them up while he processes the new arrivals. It gives me a chance to get my spaghetti stuff in order for the big batch of sauce I am going to whip up. Serious spaghetti sauce takes a full day to simmer. It is my favorite thing to cook and everyone is invited. We thin during the second half of the shift in a drizzly rain so P.T. is skipped. So much for the easy day. The spaghetti dinner is great. Six of us feast. The others miss out. Oh, well, there's always next time.

May 26

When I wake up, Cord is in his bed. "Mike, Mike," I say, trying to rouse him, "when did you get back?"

"About 4:30-5:00."

"You drove all night?"

"Yeah. Marty and Sluggo just came back from somewhere, too."

"They took off to Shakey Drakes last night."

"They went all the way to that snake pit?"

"I reckon. Listen to me. I think I'm turning country. Yahoo, I'm losing my city ways."

"What time is it?"

"I don't know, but the music is on."

"Oh shit! I need to sleep about ten more hours."

"You missed a great dinner last night. Jake even made a salad!"

"You made spaghetti last night? If I'd a known, I would'a came back." He reaches down under the covers and scratches. He pulls his hand back up and sniffs it. He reconsiders. "Naw, I wouldn't."

"Did you get laid?"

"Did I? I'm sore, and Janine was walking bowed legged when I left. Her parents were gone, and we had the whole house to ourselves."

"That must of been nice. I finally got laid. Do you want to smell me?"

"You sick puppy." Then he says with congratulations, "You did, uhh? Great!"

"I didn't even hear you come in."

"You must have been out. I made enough noise. I went into my old room, I guess it's my old room now, and Kyle was snoring away."

"Cord, are you in there?" Darryl yells from behind the closed door.

"Eat me, Darryl."

Darryl opens the door, pokes his head in, "Did you get laid?" He inquires.

"Can't you tell? He's smiling with only three hours sleep."

"Yeah, he did. Hop to. It's quarter 'til."

"I know that, Darryl," Cord says as Darryl leaves. Cord turns to me. "I hope it don't rain. I hate thinning in the rain. Bob's gung-ho about this project work. He don't give a shit if it rains or not. We are not Hotshots anymore, we are Thinshots!"

"Well, I guess there's a lot to do."

"Fuck that, we're all going to get sick and die, then my dick will fall off, and I won't be able to fuck Janine anymore."

Lucky for us, Bob stays at the station to go over some applications. We're still one crew member short of the minimum required eighteen. This is counting Pat, who is due any day. You tend to lose track of the days when you thin all day.

May 27

It starts hailing on us hard, so we take an early lunch. We race back to the bus, pushing and shoving at the door in a game to see who'd be left outside the longest and get the wettest. Russ jumps in first and closes the door. That pisses a few of us off. Cord tries climbing through an open window. Paul isn't worried about getting wet, his main concern is getting the saws out of the rain. We find our seats and start to chow down. Sluggo and Jim have snuck some rations in the stored reserves to eat because they didn't wake up early enough to make lunch, and Darryl gives them a hard time about it.

"You know, Sluggo, you're not supposed to eat those just anytime you want."

"I know, but what am I supposed to do, starve?"

"Yes, it'll do you some good to lose some of that fat you've got."

"Fuck off, Darryl. I'll eat rations if I want to."

"Russell, charge Sluggo four dollars for lunch." Russ ignores him.

"I don't see how he can eat that shit," Marty remarks.

"It'll plug you up so you can't shit, you mean," Koval adds.

Sluggo ignores the comments and continues eating. I'm not really listening to the C-rations controversy, looking instead out the window at the hail falling. I jump into the verbal commotion on the bus and holler, "Why can't it be a 100 degrees outside?"

"Because you're not in Southern California anymore, Petretti!" Darryl snipes.

"Oh yes, how soon I forget."

Darryl continues, "Personally, I like the rain. It puts me in a mellow mood. I'll put some Moody Blues on after work."

"Or how about some Pink Floyd?" Cord suggests.

"OK. That, tooooo." He says with a spacey look in his face.

"Oh, Darryl, you cosmic muffin!" Cord says. Most of us hear that and laugh.

"Where did you get that saying?" Jake wants to know.

"I just made it up. Naw, not really. I heard it somewhere. Monty Python or something like that."

"Who has some T.P.?" Aaron asks.

"I do. Who needs it?"

"May I have some please?" Aaron requests, in his usual polite manner.

Marty digs in his pack and tosses it up front to Aaron. It's caught in mid-flight by someone else, and a game of "keepaway" ensues.

Koval yells, "Go for it."

Paul responds, "Gopher it? What the hell does that mean?"

By the time the game is over the toilet paper is partially unwound, and Drift surrenders it to Aaron.

"Hey, Drifty," Gus asks, "what happened to your pants? They're muddy."

"Russ pushed me down. I would have beaten him back to the bus, so he had to cheat."

Marty works his way up to the front of the bus. He opens the door and sticks his ass out and lets out a big fart.

"Alright! What a pal," says Cord.

"I think it was highly considerate of him," says Koval.

"You guys ought to be thankful," Marty says. "It was a raspy one."

"Look you can still see the cloud from the fart."

Dave has a copy of the fire school test and reads off questions. Various people shout answers. Darryl gets one right and receives a hand. Everyone is nearly through eating. Some are just kicking back reading, and not participating in the nonsense when Joe says,

"Put another log on the fire, it's cold in here."

"Get a drip torch," Paul calls.

"Put Sluggo's head in a gas can and use him as a drip torch," Cord adds.

The windows are all steamed up from the activity on the bus. Burps roll as our lunches settle. Darryl lets out a number that tops them all. Russ asks Aaron to go outside and put a rock under the bus tire so he can start it up and get the heater going. Drifty is reading from the test. Sluggo is passed out in the back seat, catching a few zzzs, still reeking of booze, and trying to sober up from last night. Steam is starting to rise from our bodies. The bus is running and the heater's turned on. Drift gives Darryl an answer to one of the test questions. Suddenly I notice that Koval is drinking beer.

"So what?" Koval says. "That's my P.B.R."

"Hey, have you ever looked on the back of Allman Brothers 'Live at the Fillmore East' album?" I ask him. "If you look closely at the picture of the road crew, they all have a tall can of P.B.R."

"Oh, really?" responds Koval. "I never noticed it."

"Ah, the official drink of the Allman Brothers Band," Cord says. "Hey! Aaron's back."

Aaron knocks on the window, but Russ won't let him in. He yells for entry, but Russ pretends he can't hear him. With all the racket inside the bus; heater blowing, guys belching and farting, talking, laughing, and the radio playing country music, it's a miracle he can hear him. Before long the din gets raised up a few more notches as the heater gets noisier and the radio gets louder. The dispatcher on the radio keeps the daily forest business going, but there's a lot of static and most of what he says is indistinguishable.

"One inch of rain so far," Russ notes.

Darryl cuts in. "Hey look at this fly walking on the glass. Look at the intricate designs his feet are making in the moist film on the steamy window."

"God, Darryl," I say, "you sounded intelligent just then."

"He learned a new word – intricate," says Cord.

"He probably doesn't even know what it means," Jake says. "It just sounds good to him."

"Darryl, you know why he's doing that?" I ask.

"Doing what?"

"Being so artful on the window?"

"No, why?"

"It's an ailment, wingfrost."

Darryl seems to believe this. Jake and Cord laugh at Darryl's gullibility. Marty finally notices what I've been doing from behind the seat. "Why are you writing?" he asks, and takes a look at what's in my hands. "Jesus! He's been writing down everything we say."

"His brother-in-law is in personnel," Cord advises. "He's a spy."

"You guys are too funny. I just might write a book or something. A spy I'm not."

The rain is slowing down and a patch of blue can be seen to the west. Looks like we'll have to go back to work soon. Our regular lunch hour is nearly over. Everyone is on the bus and quiet now. The heater is still cranked up, producing a solo monotone. Most of the crew close their eyes to get some rest. They probably all have carbon monoxide poisoning.

My cousin from New York, Larry, is going to be in Sedona. I made plans to eat dinner with him there tonight. I haven't seen him in thirteen years. He's married now and has a fourteen-month-old baby. Bob announces five minutes before the end of the shift that we have Monday off for Memorial Day. Tuesday we have to be back at work, then we get our regular weekend off. This gives me the leeway I need so I won't have to arrive back from Sedona in the morning.

May 28

It's a beautiful day. By late morning all the clouds have vanished. I play tourist with the family. We visit Montezuma's Castle and Montezuma's Well, an interesting historic part of Arizona's past. My cousin leaves in the afternoon, headed out for California. It's a good time for me to hit the road, too. I restock my grocery supply and have a beer at Oak Creek Tavern before I return to Blue Ridge. Toucan Eddie, the band that plays there, is part owner of the place. I hear they're relatives of Jane Russell, the movie star.

An interesting group of locals hangs out at the Tavern... girls with tattoos and bare-foot babies, grubby dudes and bikers, a pretty bartender, a hippie musician, and occasional tourists who don't fit the scene. A big, white, stuffed bear in a glass box is at the rear of the stage. It makes a very peculiar background. Two beers are enough for me. I ride home and arrive at nightfall.

May 29

Back at Blue Ridge, the overhead has drummed up enough work around the station to keep everyone busy all day. A few of us volunteer to get sand and rock for a seeding house. A sandy washbed down FH-211 is the source. We take our time filling up the fifth-wheeler, having fun joking around. We notice that a good size load was shoveled on during our yapping. The pickup is unable to pull it out, and the more we try the deeper it digs into wash. We have to shovel the sand back off to lighten the load enough so the truck can get out. That's our day... dig the hole then fill it up.

We've been hearing calls over the radio from Moqui lookout of disappearing smokes around Blue Ridge Reservoir. Forest Service Unit, 7-43, is finally dispatched. We hurry to get the truck unstuck and head back to the station for possible backup. Instead of going out for another load, we stay at the station and do busy work until lunch. 7-43 locates the smoke by foot and begins to lay hose to the small fire. We figure they can handle it from there, but five minutes into lunch Bob drives down in the bus honking the horn. In the time it takes to turn the bus around, we are all loaded on.

The bus is crowded with a full crew aboard. Bob's wild ride down the bumpy dirt road catches people off balance. Bodies keep landing on the floor or on someone's lap. We are in good spirits going to the fire. This was the first fire this year for a lot of people. Because it is Pat's first day at work, he takes credit for all the excitement.

When we arrive 7-43 has already put a scratch line around the two-acre fire and set up the hoses. We break up in our new squad assignments. I am a member of Squad 2. We go around the perimeter and construct a handline about two feet wide, and put in roll trenches. There are three pulaskis up front and both shovels and pulaskis behind them. Bob takes the lead pulaski position. All fuels are removed, clear down to the mineral soil, as prescribed in fire school. The smoldering duff puts out more smoke than fire. The ground is still damp to prevent rapid spreading and to hold the flames close to the ground. Roll trenches are dug diagonally across the line with downslope towards the burned portion.

This prevents hot pine cones or embers from rolling across the line and starting a spot fire. Small dirt reservoirs reinforced by rocks catch the hot coals on the low spots of the sloppy sections. These are the mechanics of a good fire line.

Darryl bucks up logs and cuts down burnt snags. The tankers hook up a Mark IV pumper at the lake. This is a big help to mop up, and makes the work a breeze on the two-acre blackened area. The fire stayed mostly on the ground and damaged only a few standing trees. The hike out of there is the hard part. Poor Sluggo has the worst climb. He is elected to haul up the Mark IV portable pumper from the bottom. We laugh at him for being a work ox. Bob quickly reminds us that any one of us could be the next to get that dirty job.

It was good experience and an excellent practice fire for the "big one" that the veterans keep praying for. The veterans guide the new guys as much as possible. They add what constructive criticism they can. It helps us understand how to handle our job better. Lives can depend on your performance on the fire line. The faster we learn the better off everyone will be. It's equally important to carry your own work load and put out maximum production. That is what this Hotshot crew is all about. Everyone does 1/18th of the work to get a handline effective enough to stop the meanest of blazes and achieve a job well done.

We gather back at the bus where we change out of our dirty clothes into the clothes we were wearing before we were dispatched. Paul likes the sweaty clothes and the lingering smell of smoke, so he stays dressed as he is. James is just lazy. We strip down to near nudity just to put on something clean. Our faces and hands are still dirty. Even a wet handkerchief cannot erase the soot that covers them. It only creates a muddy paste that feels dry to the skin, like unrinsed soap, and it cracks when you smile. Black rings outline our mouths. Front teeth have black deposits on them and bits of sand between them that crunch when you bite down. We are all in a very good mood. It was the first time we performed as a complete crew, and we did a damn good job!

Bob prowls up behind Drifty as he's balancing on one foot putting on his pants. He bumps Drifty just enough to topple him into Joe, who was in the same position. They fall like dominos and everyone has a good laugh. Bob, proud of his mischievous behavior, plays the innocent.

"Come now, this is no time to be sitting down," he says to the two he sent sprawling.

"We gotta hurry if we're going to get home before quitting time." He turns to the laughing men. "Let's go, the rest of you. Finish getting dressed on the bus."

It is all in a day's work, with an hour overtime for missing lunch. The ride is rough on the rain eroded dirt roads where tree branches stretch out and swipe the bus. The guys start swapping fishing tales. The stories and the fellowship make the ride home seem shorter and give us all a sense of family.

I've changed a lot already. Driving along I recognize the place where we planted the seedling trees on my first day. I remember how it hailed on us, and how we almost slid off the road. The roads are crusted and drier now with distinct tire grooves that lead the way back to camp. I remember the elk we saw and keep my eyes open for more. It feels like I've been here a year, but it's only been four weeks. I feel myself maturing and changing in my ideas and from my city ways. I feel refreshed and relaxed, no more an alien, but like a native of this place. I'm glad I decided to leave my home and come up here. Change shakes you up. Venturing into new situations fills the hungry soul, and the adventure and excitement that follow keeps the hunger growing.

Making decisions about small or unimportant things is fun, because it's not earthshaking how things turn out. You may have a dozen ways to go, but you can only choose one, and it's interesting to see if things come out the way you thought they would. The process also helps you become a better decision maker for the more important things in your life. Decision making is instinctual and can be life-saving. A healthy mind thrives on foreseeing the truths that lie ahead and acting on that knowledge.

Opportunities are like that. It's up to the individual to know what they entail before making a decision. Sometimes that takes a lot of soul-searching and digging, and sometimes the answers are right in front of you. Too, some opportunities are fleeting. If you don't reach out and grab them when they're there, you may never have another chance. That's where training and instinct come in, and why some people seem to be able to make their own luck.

We hit the main highway and the guys quiet down, each enveloped in his own thoughts. No volleyball after work. Time to take off for town. Our first check should be in the mail tomorrow, so most stay at the station engaging in good conversation, good highs and silly drunkenness. This is the first time I have some war stories to contribute, too.

May 30

I learn something new today. When there is a holiday in the pay week checks are due, they come a day late. I guess even postal workers observe holidays. Their service is getting bad enough with them all taking days off, too. With Darryl's promise to bring my check up tomorrow if it comes, I ride up to town. In all of the excitement I almost forgot about Melinda. We had a date, but I couldn't get there on time because of the fire. I hope she doesn't think I'm mad at her. When I get to her place and explain, she understands. Her natural sweetness allows her to make light of it and put me at ease. With a few bucks my sister loaned me, I arrange a midnight picnic with red wine and cheese. We ride up to Buffalo Park and walk into the woods towards the Peaks. A lone tree in an opening makes a suitable place for a midnight supper. We sit under the tree and kiss.

"Mmmmm," Mel murmurs. "I missed that."

"Me, too. I missed you, too."

"You did?"

"Yeah."

"I missed you, too. I thought about you all week."

"Good thoughts or bad ones?"

"Mostly good."

"You mean there were some bad ones?"

"No, it was all good. How could I think badly of you? What did you think about me?"

"A lot of good things; like how nice you are, how it's been a pleasure to know you." That earns a kiss from her. "And what a good kisser you are, and making love to you the other night."

"You're not so bad yourself."

"I try."

"It doesn't seem like you're trying."

"You're right. It just comes naturally for me." She softly punches me. I love her love taps.

"There are a lot of things that come naturally to you, and they have all been enjoyable. I'm glad I met you. You may not realize it, but you have influenced my life."

"I have? That's good to know. In a good way, I hope."

"Yes, in a very good way."

We kiss some more. I pull out her tucked-in blouse and put my hand under it. As she starts to breath harder, her breasts seem to be getting fuller. I want to make love to her again intensely. I want to get what I missed out on before. Maybe to go down on her and show her the sensuality of oral stimulation. She rubs my erection. When I assure myself that her nipples are hard, I unsnap her pants and get my fingers wet. She squirms a little, I'm not sure why. I take my hand out of her opened up pants and ease on top of her. I start to dry fuck her, but she isn't participating. I put my thumb in her belt loop and start to work her pants off.

"Please don't," she says softly, but urgently.

"Not here, huh?"

"No, not here."

"You're right, not here. I have more class than that."

"I thought so, too."

"I got carried away. I think about us making love again all the time."

"Please don't think like that."

"Why? Don't you think we'll go to bed again?"

"No."

"Why?" I answer, puzzled.

I roll off her and she zips her pants back up. I can tell there is going to be some serious talk. She looks right into my eyes.

"I used you. I had never been made love to like that before. I went for it for selfish reasons. I hadn't felt good like that for a long time."

"I know. That's why we did it in the first place."

"I just wanted to be caressed. I wanted the enjoyment in sex, and didn't care about satisfying someone else."

"I kind'a sensed that. I could feel that you were getting off but weren't putting out. Turning you on, though, turned me on. Maybe you figured I didn't need any loving last week. I did tell you it was OK to use me and be selfish with me."

I tell her this, but it's what I miss the most, that loving feeling I used to get from Castleberry.

"Steve, it would be too easy for me to fall in love with you. That's my nature I guess, to get too involved emotionally. You gave me a way out. Steve, I have such strong feelings for you, but I just can't let myself, because I'm still dealing with the breakup of my marriage. It's hard for a heart to dismiss a love it has been so involved with. Especially when breaking up was at his request."

"He wanted the separation?" I exclaim in surprise.

"Yes. Even though I did everything he asked. I played slave to him, tended to all his needs in bed and out. He used to mistreat me badly. He'd knock me down in front of our friends... beat me up."

"Oh, babe, I'm sorry," I say with heart-felt sympathy as I wipe a tear from her eye.

"No, I'm sorry. Last week in bed with you I took matters into my own hands. I soaked up everything I dished out before with Mike. So I'd feel guilty continuing sex with you. I couldn't give everything in my heart to someone who's just come into my life. Sex is still sacred to me. Even the bad times I experienced before."

"Time with yourself and your own thoughts can heal your scars."

"Loving means giving a lot. I'm not ready to give to anybody what was taken for granted for so many years."

"I understand. After all, I put the idea in your head."

"You had a lot to do with it, that's one of the good ways you've influenced me. I felt good about our sex and enjoyed it more than I ever had. It's something I'll always remember."

"I'm a nice guy, the kind of person who's easy to take advantage of, and a lot of people have done it. You're different, Melinda. The kind of person you are... well, I don't mind at all."

"Oh, Steve, there's more to you than I'll ever get to know."

"Yeah, a lot, and it's not going to get used up. I can give sympathy and love to someone who's hurting."

"Thank you so much, I love you for that."

"You see, there is some love in you for me."

"There is, but not what you want. I have to live my own life now. I'm not ready to commit to anyone. I need to make up my mind for myself. My parents are still trying to be parents to me. It will all be changing soon. I'm going to Europe with a clear head. I'll enjoy myself no matter what. When I get back, I'm thinking of moving down to Sierra Vista with my sister."

I hold her real close in the cool, soft breeze. I'm sure we both want to cry, but we keep back the tears and sit silently, holding in our feelings. Our departure is considerably less vivacious than our arrival. Melinda will be leaving for Europe in four more weeks, and when she gets back she'll have her own life to live.

I miss my Castleberry.

June 1

We expected to go thinning today and are pleased to hear that we won't have to. Bob arranged for the Payson helicopter and helitack crew to meet us at the Long Valley Work Center to acquaint the new guys on helicopter safety. With time to kill we sharpen and retool the bus. Everyone is busy, and a couple of hours go by fast. We're hoping to get a ride in the copter, but we're out of luck. No rides are going to be given today in order to cut unnecessary costs from a tight operating budget.

The copter selected for our orientation is the versatile Bell 206B. Its main use in our forest will be to transport men to lightning fires in areas inaccessible by truck or foot. A whole crew can put out a dozen such fires in one day. Helicopters are the main transportation for shuttling crews to a fire line in an emergency. The helitack crews are also valuable on the initial attack on a fire. Additionally, they can create a clearing called a helispot, for a suitable place to land and unload crews and supplies. In the latter stages of an ongoing fire the helispots may transform into helibases. These are small remote staging areas within the fire perimeter used for many functions.

The helitack crew leader is doing most of the talking, stressing the dangers of the rotating helicopter blades and of the exhaust port that can literally blow a person right into the tail rotor. We are instructed to wear the appropriate gear: a hardhat with chinstrap to keep it from being sucked up by the main rotors, gloves to protect your face in case of a fire or crash in the copter, goggles to protect from flying debris and dust. Earplugs are optional but important protection from the high-pitched whine of the jet fueled turbo. Sleeves are to be rolled down and collars up. The roll prevents hot embers and debris from going down the back of your neck.

Entering the ship is to be done in a low, crouched position from the downhill side, and always from the front in the pilots view. Disembarking follows the same procedures, only in reverse order. Any gear that is personally carried on board is to be placed between your legs during flight. All loose apparel has to be tucked in. The main rotors of the helicopter are so strong they can suck things right out of the inside of the copter. There are no doors on this ship to facilitate disembarking and to lighten the craft's weight in order to increase its payload. Seat belts are double checked by the helitack crewmembers. They are triple checked in an empty seat. A loose belt buckle can flop around outside of the ship in flight and cause severe damage. Gas in the chainsaws has to be emptied and purged before bringing the saws aboard. Dolmars are double check for leaks. (Dolmars are a gas and gear oil plastic container). Tools are taped up in groups of three. A manifest listing the flying weights of each person and his gear is always kept in the Hotshot briefcase. This aids the helitack crew in calculating appropriate flying weights.

The casual part of our day ends. After lunch, we gather around for a fire critique on the Houston fire. Bob decides our crew needs some line digging practice, so we leave the work center and find a hill near our thinning area and proceed to construct hand line for several hours.

Constructing hand line is the key to fire suppression and fire containment. One or two squads of eighteen to twenty guys pass over a given area with digging and scraping tools. The Pulaski is a combination tool with an ax head on one end and a 4" wide hoe-digging tool on the other. The scraping tool is your ordinary shovel. The two-headed McLeod has an 8" hoe blade on one side and a rake on the other. There is only one McLeod per squad. The rest of the squad alternates between using Pulaskis and shovels. Tool assignments are often determined according to the type of ground cover we will be working with. Files are used to hand sharpen the tools to an edge sharp enough to shave with, so gloves have to be worn because one slip could slice a hand wide open. Care must also be taken not to taper the edge too thin or it will pit. After sharpening, fiber tape is placed on the edge to protect it against dulling or accidental injury to the user. Some veterans carry their own files in their packs in order to fine-tune their tools. It's like watching Jed Clampett pull out his whittling knife and whittle away. Each tool is color-coded with painted stripes where the wood handle meets the metal head. The first one-inch stripe is red, designating the tool as exclusive for fire use. Better not get caught using it to dig a hole! The second colored stripe designates the forest, black for the Coconino N.F. The third one-inch stripe is blue for the Blue Ridge District. Then the handles are "boned and oiled." The wood handle is smoothed out with the shaft of a screwdriver, (boning), then well oiled with linseed oil to preserve the wood. Boning and oiling helps reduce blisters, splintering, and warping.

Properly done line construction allows enough room for a truck to pass once the crew is finished and has completely removed all fuels from the ground, as well as all roots, debris, duff and consumable organic matter. The line should be twice the width of the surrounding vegetation. Each man takes 1/20th of the debris away from the line, so by the time the last man finishes the fire line is wide enough to stop a fire from advancing. The tool line up is two Pulaskis up front, then a shovel, followed by two Pulaskis and two more shovels, and then alternates until the last tool, a McLeod, is used for final raking and sweeping action.

In high timber country, a sawyer or two will fell trees ten to twenty feet wide, while their swampers behind them clear out the fallen and bucked up trees and larger brush. Swampers are also responsible for carrying the extra support pack for the sawyer. It will include extra chains, gas, oil, files, gloves, chaps, and a few tools.

By now we have been digging lines for hours and are thoroughly tired, but still in our heavy boots we struggle through a full hour of non-stop physical training in the open field. We go from sit-ups to push-up to squats, etc., without a breather. We all thought we were going to get out of P.T. today, but Bob surprised us. What a workhorse! Jokes about Bob being a bionic bear are humorously passed around.

After work we are too sore to play volleyball, so we "loadies" get out our stashes and drive to the nearby aspen grove for a pot party. Eight people in three vehicles take part. We pull the trucks in a circle, covered wagon style, and crank up the tunes. Jake has his homegrown special, Frailsen has some hash, Mike has pot that is perfume scented from his girlfriends purse, and I pull out some Colombian I scored last weekend. The joints are smoked faster than we can roll them.

"This is what we should be doing instead of playing volleyball," Koval says as he exhales a long plume of smoke.

"I hear that," I agree. "This is the best part of the day."

James chimes in, "I sure would have liked to have gone on a helicopter ride today."

"Yeah," says Cord. "It's too bad we didn't get to."

"We wouldn't have had to dig all that line if we did go for a helicopter ride," Marty adds.

"I don't know about you guys," says Jake, "but I was getting tired out there digging line."

"You weren't the only one," I say. "I'm sore, too."

"I think Bob overdid it on P.T. today," Cord remarks.

"Did you notice that he was getting slow at the end?" asks Jake.

"It looked like he wanted to quit but didn't," Drifty says.

Cord agrees. "He was getting tired all right."

"Bob doesn't know when to quit," Koval says.

Pat joins the discussion. "We would do P.T. all day if he had his way."

"Who's got another clip?" Sluggo asks. "Owww! It's burning my fingers."

"They're all used up," says James. "Here, put it in my pipe."

Drifty asks, "Who's got the matches?"

"Here," I respond. I toss the matches to him but his reactions are too slow to catch them.

"Drifty is getting fucked up," Sluggo observes.

"I know I'm getting there," I say.

"No shit, someone's got some good pot," says Koval.

"It's all good pot," Pat says. "Oh, and the hash, too."

Cord breathes a deep sigh of relief. "No shit, I needed this. I've been waiting to get high all day."

"I've been waiting all week," Sluggo asserts with great feeling.

"Yeah, we all deserved this," James says.

"You don't, James," Cord rebuts. "I saw you goofing off at the end of the line."

"Hey, I did my work. You all were doing so good up front you all didn't leave me much'n to dig."

Koval remarks, "I'll remember that on a fire. Hey, everyone leave James some work at the end so he doesn't fall asleep next time we have to dig line."

"Funny, Koval," James retorts. "You're reallllll funny."

We sit quietly for a while, waiting for our highs to develop and blend into the beautiful aspen surroundings. The aspens look real pretty, better than ever. You can't see even ten feet into the thicket. The area is rich with underbrush of ferns. Oak and pine are scattered all around the patch of aspens. The forest floor is covered with a plush carpet of clover and grass.

I breathe an appreciative sigh. "This is the best I've ever seen this place."

"I was just noticing that," James says.

"That's because you've smoked the same stuff," explains Cord.

"You don't get a chance to sight see when you're running by," Marty reflects.

"I'm surprised something this nice is so close to the station," says Jake.

Cord nods. "This is one of my favorite spots to party."

"I bet it was the Indians favorite spot, too," Jake adds.

"Just think," I say. "The Indians could have sat in this very spot smoking many a big peace pipe."

"Could very well have been," Jake agrees. "It's amazing to think what went on around here a hundred years ago, or even a thousand years ago. So many things could have taken place in this very spot."

"Too bad we don't have a televised time machine so we could look back," muses Cord.

"Yeah," I add. "The channel selector would correspond to different years. You'd just turn the knob for whatever year you wanted to peek in on."

"Who knows, maybe one of these days they'll have something like that," Cord reflects.

"They probably thought the same way we do," says Marty.

"Yeah," I continue, "I mean they could see this beauty the same way we do, through their eyes, like everyone else does today. They probably had the exact some thoughts and sensations we have right now. It's the trees and plants, colors and beauty they'd be seeing just like we are."

"I don't know," Jake pipes up. "Their attitudes were different than ours. This was the only home they knew. We come here and make a big deal over this and they were born here and accepted nature as part of them. You have to remember, this was their civilization before the white man came."

"You're right," I agree. "It's almost impossible to perceive this place like the Indians did. We fucked up white men can never think like the natives did."

"It's a shame," Jake says. "I wonder if this place will be as nice a hundred years from now, or even a thousand years from now." A few of us nod with agreement.

Cord answers, "I doubt it. It will get fucked somehow. You know man has a way to fuck up everything." We laugh at his unintentional speech blooper. Yeah, he's fucked up.

"As in raping the land," Jake says.

"It would be nice for a UFO to land in someplace like this when they finally come," I muse aloud.

"They wouldn't know what to do with it. If they landed in the city, they could at least blow it all up," says Cord.

"If they ever came across man, they would run scared back to where they came from," I add.

Pat comes butting in unannounced, moving with stiff gestures like a robot. He has two beer bottle caps covering his eyes and two bottles in his pants like a dual hard on. In a mechanical voice he repeats, "I... need... sex-u-al... gra-ti-fi-ca-tion, Beep, beep. I... need... sex-u- al... gra-ti-fi-ca-tion, Beep, beep."

Cord answers back, "Here, I'll give you some gratification."

Mike jumps up behind Pat and sticks an empty beer bottle in Pat's posterior. Pat suspends the bottle between squeezed butt cheeks. He turns in circles, makes a short-circuit firework sound, then scuffles away saying, "all-affirmative, affirmative, affirmative." He looks like one of those ancient oriental women with bound feet, taking little tiny steps, with the beer bottle still sticking out from his buttocks. The neck of the bottle looks like it's inserted in his ass. "Beep, Beep!!" echoes as he shuffles away.

The only one not laughing is Pat. When he stops and removes the beer caps, he sees us rolling around, busting up. He gives in and joins the hysterical howling. I'd be surprised if the station didn't hear us.

"That was the funniest thing I've seen in a long time," says Marty, gasping for breath.

"He totally caught me off guard," Drifty admits.

"If our space invader is as horny as that, Blue Ridge will be in a lot of trouble," Koval remarks.

The last comment wasn't that funny, but all we need is the slightest bit of humor to put us in stitches again. The tears of laughter we shed soothe our dried-out, bloodshot eyes. We finally settle down to random chuckles. Marty blurts out an exhausted sigh of relief that echoes in the forest and it starts us up again.

"Knock it off you guys," I tell them. "My jaw and sides are aching."

"No kidding, my stomach hurts more when I laugh than when I was doing the leg lifts," Drifty says.

"Mine hurts more, too," adds Sluggo.

"OK. Then let's calm down," says Jake.

James calls out, "Hey, I need a light, I dun lost the cherry in all the excitement."

"I think I had enough to smoke," Jake says.

"Me, too," says Cord.

"Yeah, I got a good buzz going," I remark, satisfied.

"You guys will probably get lost going back," Pat warns.

"I hope not," says Cord. "You're riding with me."

Marty stands up. "Well, I'm ready to go."

Cord joins him. "Yeah, let's go. I'm hungry."

"Food sounds real good right now," I say. "Let's boogie."

We all hop in a truck and caravan back to the station. We joyously pull into the trailer area. There sits Darryl in his chair in front of the trailer, just looking at our starry-eyed mob. We each have a drug induced smile on our mug.

"Ahhh, what have you guys been doing?" Darryl asks.

Pat blurts out, "You should have been with us."

"Yeah," says Cord, "you missed Pat's out-of-this-world performance."

We start to bust up again like we know something he doesn't.

"No thanks," says Darryl dryly, "I don't smoke that stuff."

"Yeah, I know Darryl, you just sit on your ass getting drunk," Cord snipes.

"I've only had two glasses of wine and three beers," Darryl retorts.

"Oh, is that all?" I quip. "I'd be more fucked up than I am now if I drank that much."

"All you guys looked fucked up," Darryl grunts.

"We are, Darryl," says Pat, getting right into his face. "Very fucked-up!"

"Darryl can take it," Cord says. "He's an alcoholic."

"Anyway," I add in a conciliatory tone, "you missed a good party. You didn't have to smoke anything if you didn't want to."

"Yeah, well, maybe next time," Darryl says.

June 5

We have had a few days of thinning and hard P.T. Could be that Bob was punishing us party heads. He must have gotten word of what we were up to in the aspens. Either that or he heard our voices up there, having a good time. Today we are going to take a crack at some mountain and cliff climbing.

I start the day feeling nervous. Even with Darryl's slide show last night of past fires and war stories to prepare us, I still wonder what the Forest Service is getting me into. Some of the cliffs we saw in the slide show looked straight up and down, and now the people in charge want us to rappel down these same cliffs. Rappelling on these cliffs doesn't look too bad. It might even be fun. I had seen rappelling a couple of times in movies, but never in person. Darryl, the self-designated RCO (Rumor Control Officer) and photographer, gave us Fucking New Guys a good scare with his stories and slides that showed thrilling moments in mountain climbing and rappelling. He had a slide show for everything the Hotshots did during the past four years at Blue Ridge. When he found out that I had never experienced anything like it, he just laid it on heavy with the scary stuff. And I, green as grass, believed it all.

After a refresher course on basic mountaineering and assorted knots, all us fucking new guys have to take some practice falls. Bob is the only one we rookies trust to belay us on the death-defying leap. Bob anchors himself to a tree and Dennis double-checks everything before we start. "OK," Dennis calls out. "Who's first?" None of us answers.

"Darryl, why don't you go first and show them how it's done," Bob suggests.

Darryl says, "Sure," steps over to the rope and puts the rope on his carabiner. He continues as if it's his class now. "You can tie in with a butterfly or a figure eight. It's best to use two carabiners."

Dennis hands him another carabiner. "Here Darryl, here's another one," he says.

Darryl takes it and continues. "Make sure the gates open in different directions. If you don't want your hands fucked up wear your gloves. Now ease back to the edge and kick out, with your butt way out. You want to try to keep your hands and feet in front of you."

"Yeah, it's really important to keep those hands and feet in front. It keeps you from crashing into the rock," Bob says.

Darryl picks up the narrative. "Yeah, they stop you from hurting yourself, like hitting your head or you knees against the face of the cliff. Now, take a loop of rope in this hand."

"Take a bigger bite!" Bob instructs.

"OK, then. Take a bigger loop, and throw yourself out and let go of the rope," Darryl continues. As soon as he finishes his sentence, he leaps backwards, throws his hands up and disappears over the edge of the cliff. We run up to the edge as the rope jerks and tightens around Bob. There's Darryl, about fifteen feet over the edge in a scaling position. Bob pulls him back up.

"OK. Who, who's next?" Darryl asks, his voice cracking as if to reflect the frightening difficulty of the feat.

"I'll go," Gus volunteers.

"OK. Gus, tie in. Have you ever done this before?"

"Yes, I took a mountaineering class in college."

Russ remarks, "No wonder he's so brave to try it."

"You don't have to go if you don't want to," Bob tells him.

"No, I'll go. I need to get back into the mood again." With that, Gus jumps and climbs back like it was no big deal.

"Bob, you better get the communication down," Dennis reminds him.

"I guess we better. Who's next? James, you go. Now before you go, the proper communication with your belayer is, 'Prepare to fall,' and your belayer will answer back, 'Prepare to fall.' This will let the climber know that he heard the command and is ready to brake or at least have his brake on. Now when you fall, you yell, 'Falling.'"

"Yeah," says Dennis. "If you hit the ground, it should be the last thing we all should hear."

"Thanks, Dennis," James says. "I needed to know that."

"Go, James. Jump!" Bob calls.

"Push him," Russ suggests.

"No, none of that now," James says. "You all let me go on my own."

"Well, come on, James. We haven't got all day," Bob urges.

Sluggo pipes up. "Come on, James, jump. You chicken shit."

"You're next, Sluggo," Bob remarks pointedly. That draws a round of laughs from the peanut gallery.

James takes a deep breath. "OK. Here goes."

"Not 'here goes.' 'Prepare to fall.'"

"Oh, yeah, prepare to fawl."

"Prepare to fall," Bob enunciates.

James repeats, "Fawlling." He stands there for a few seconds, and then jumps over, his head still visible over the ledge. He gets back up, shaking a little.

"Now take a bigger bite this time," Bob instructs.

"You better not let me fall."

"Don't worry, I won't. Keep your feet in front of you more."

James does it again, this time showing some improvement.

Bob calls out, "Sluggo, it's your turn now."

Sluggo ties in and jumps. Tiny beads of sweat on his forehead give him away. He's plenty nervous.

"You know what you're doing, Leveque," Bob remarks.

"I hope so." Sluggo looks around at us to see who's paying attention to him. He takes a deep breath and holds it as he tries to express the proper command. "Prepare to fall."

"Prepare to fall," Bob echoes.

"Falling." Sluggo jumps, flapping his arms like an overgrown turkey. The rope around Bob's waist jerks hard from Sluggo's weight, and his face clenches in pain.

"How was that, Bob?" the unseen Sluggo's voice asks from over the ledge.

"Fine, but I think you ruptured my back."

After watching a few more jumps, I am psyched up enough to take my turn.

"Who hasn't gone yet?" Bob asks.

"Petretti hasn't," Darryl says.

Bob and Dennis call out in unison, "Petretti, you're next."

I get ready, not saying a word, afraid that I'll lose my psychic energy for it. Before the leap, I poke my head over the edge to the others that are standing there, amused. Then I execute my verbal commands, take a deep breath and jump. What a rush! For those few seconds I swear my heart stopped. I make a mistake by looking down to the ground 80 feet below me. But when the rope jerks tight my hands and feet are out in front of me to cushion by body from smashing against the rock face wall, I know I've made it. I offer a short prayer of thanks to the almighty one above, my trustworthy belayer.

The point of this exercise is to acquaint you with the feeling of falling, and to learn to trust the man who is your belayer. The adrenaline rush that accompanies the fall leaves you feeling good when it's all over. Hopefully, as my sure footedness grows, I'll never experience that fear of falling again.

Our next pursuit is rappelling. Rappelling is the quickest way to descend a 90-degree cliff. One carabiner is used. It's looped through the Swiss-seat with the gate up and out. You can use from one to three wraps around the carabiner for friction to help regulate the speed of descent. One hand is used as a brake, and this hand is normally at back pocket level. To stop, you just squeeze the rope, or wrap it around your back. To descend you let it slide through a relaxed grip. The other hand is placed in front at eye level. This hand is used only for balance. I keep wanting to grab the rope with it, because it gives me a feeling of security, but it really isn't necessary. The old guys all go down first. They make it look easy, like a lot of fun, the type of stuff I wouldn't mind doing. Gus and James are familiar enough with the process to be the next ones down the rope. What was becoming a familiar chant was heard over and over:

"On rappel."

"On belay," from a voice down below just before the jumper disappears.

Next guy up. "On rappel."

Voice from below, "On belay" and the next guy flies off.

"Wakeford, how come you didn't go yet?" I ask.

Paul answers nervously, "I've never done this before."

That got some laughs, even from him. Ahh. The big lug has a soft spot. "And here I've been thinking you're a real pro at this."

"No, I just fight fires. I've never done this before."

"Paul, you mean you never rappelled before?" Asks Dennis.

Paul shakes his head "no" and laughs nervously.

Dennis continues, "And we even let you get by from doing a practice fall."

"Sure looks that way," Paul mumbles.

"It's your turn to go down, now!"

"Sure. It looks easy enough. I think I got the hang of it." Paul backs up to the ledge. "It's a long way down there."

"Don't look down!" Dennis calls. "Get on the very edge and walk down a bit to get the feel of it."

Paul goes down waist high. "Yeah, Fuck'n A, no problem."

"Kick off then and let some rope slide through your brake hand."

Paul pushes off with his feet and short hops it with no problem all the way to the bottom.

"Let me go now," I volunteer.

"OK. How many loops are you going to use?" Dennis asks.

"I'll try two."

"You better use three. Now take the anchor end and loop it so your anchor end comes out here if you're using your right hand for braking."

"OK. How's that?"

"Looks good," Dennis says. "Remember, don't ever let go of your brake. You got a belayer at the bottom to stop you, but even so don't let go of your brake."

I step back on my toes with heels overhanging.

"Walk out and kick off," Dennis commands.

The kicking off part doesn't sound good right now, so I end up walking down halfway, sliding the rope through my brake real slowly, my left hand gripping hard on the rope.

Someone yells from below, "Petretti, kick off! Lean your ass out. Go on, lean back!"

"Like this?" Now I look like a stinkbug scaling a wall.

"More." Dennis yells. "Get your legs parallel to the ground. That's right, now kick off."

With a little kick, I let the rope slide through and descend a quick ten feet.

"That's it," a voice calls from above.

"Here I come." I make it to the ground in short hops.

"That wasn't too bad, was it?" Pat asks.

"Nope, piece of cake."

Wow! I actually did it. I am so jazzed! My ear-to-ear grin says it all. That initial adrenaline rush made me nervous for nothing. I feel a surge of joy and a strong desire to do it again. Practical considerations bring me back. "How do you get out of here?" I ask.

Pat answers, "There's a trail over there. Going down again?"

"Yeah. That was great, not bad at all."

I hurry back up to the top. Now there's a line of people waiting to go down.

"Hey, Dennis," I call. "That was alright. Downright bitchin'."

"Going down again?"

"Sure am."

"This time, kick off more."

"Yeah, I'll have to do that."

I go over to the ledge to watch the others do little tricks on their way down. Darryl stops halfway and ties up to take some pictures of everyone looking down at him. Russ stops himself and runs along laterally, parallel to the ground, as far as the rope will let him. Bob Smith goes down in two leaps and stops right before he hits the ground. He looks up and yells, "Next time it will be in one jump."

Drifty says, "Last year, he did do it in one leap, but he didn't stop. He fell over the cliff."

"He fell all the way?" I ask, astonished.

"Yeah, but not here, over at Dane Canyon."

"It's a longer way down," Drifty adds.

"Did he get hurt?" I ask.

Darryl answers. "Nope, he just got up and brushed himself off."

"How did he manage that?"

"He went to grab the rope with his brake hand and missed, but he was already on his way over the edge."

"Yeah, you could see him all the way down trying to find the rope," Drifty says.

"It's higher over there, than here?" I wonder.

"Yeah, a little higher."

"That's incredible that he didn't even get hurt."

"That's why they call him the Bionic Bear." Darryl explains. "He used to be a S.E.A.L., you know."

"A seal? Is that with the Navy or with Sea World?"

"Funny. Yeah, they say one S.E.A.L. is equivalent to 10 Green Berets."

"No, Darryl," Drifty corrects. He looks at me. "Don't believe him."

Darryl backs off a bit. "OK. Well at least five."

"Well, maybe that. They are pretty tough," Drifty allows.

"You should listen to some of his war stories. Dennis has some war stories you won't believe," Darryl adds.

"Was he a S.E.A.L., too?"

"No, he was in Special Forces. They are the Army's elite forces. Don't let Dennis hear you say that SEALS are tougher."

I look at Dennis and he looks at me with a modest smirk.

"Hey, Petretti, are you next?" Aaron calls.

"Yeah, let me up there."

Darryl hastily adds, "Hey, I'll have to tell you about them later. Remind me."

"I sure will." I got all ready to go. "On rappel."

"On belay," Pat responds.

"Kick off," Dennis says.

"Wait, let me get out there a little." I get a couple of good pushes off descending the face and stop.

"Let go of your left hand," Dennis advises. "You'll stay there. You're holding on too tight with your left hand."

I let go very gradually.

"See, you're going nowhere," Dennis says.

My foot slips and in a panic I quickly grab the rope with my left hand, then my right, and hang there with both hands above my head.

Darryl yells down to me, "What are you doing letting go of your brake hand? Get that right hand back on your ass. Don't ever let go of your brake!"

I get my brake hand and rope back into position.

Climbing at Rock Crossing

"If it wasn't for Pat, you would have ended up on the bottom real fast," Darryl continues.

"Yeah, he just saved your life," Dennis says. "I think you should owe him a six-pack. That's why you got your belay man down there."

"My foot slipped," I protest.

"You're not leaning back enough," Darryl says. "Just sit back."

"You mean Pat stopped me?"

"Yeah, you wouldn't have held yourself. You were on your way down."

"Pat, are you on the rope?" Dennis asks from behind the ledge.

"10-4," Pat responds.

"Petretti, let go now with both hands. Pat's got you, so you won't go anywhere. All he has to do is pull the rope tight and he can suspend you. This prevents the rope from slipping through the carabiner."

"Are you sure?" I ask.

"Yes," says Darryl, "let go."

I release my hands nervously and they were right. I just hang there. I look at them. "Hey look, no hands." A reluctant chuckle follows.

"Yeah, right. You big pussy," Drifty scoffs.

"You got to learn to trust your belay man," Dennis says. "That is what he's there for."

I work my way down thinking of the mess I could have made down there... my blood and guts all over the rocks. I get to the bottom and Pat laughs at me sarcastically, "Here. You belay for a while."

I agree, hoping that it will give me a chance to collect myself. That is the end of my rappelling for the day.

Our weekend is here already and Bob has to remind everyone of the two hour call back. All of us have to leave phone numbers, or where we could be found, on the chalkboard. Everyone except for Cord's contact number is posted. He took off Tuesday for Tucson to see Janine again. It's a six-hour drive for him and no way do we expect him to return in time. People are also warned about going to Phoenix, as it would be cutting it too close for the required two hour call back, since average drive time is two and a half hours. Of course, if you happened to be in Phoenix and there was an off-forest fire, you could just go to the airport. There you'd probably catch up with the others. This has happened before on a few occasions. So you'd actually luck out if it did turn out that way.

It's hard to keep us down when our weekend comes. When you live and work with the same people day in and day out, one of them is liable to get under your skin, sometimes enough to bring you to the verge of a fight. Even a day or two away from the station and into civilization is the best cure for cooling down. Living in close quarters with the crew, you eventually learn all about their virtues and vices. That kind of closeness makes getting to know them worthwhile. You can't help but get involved in everyone's life. The guys in the crew, and even more importantly, the men who share the same trailer, can harp enough on a person to make him want to quit a bad habit that might annoy only a few of us.

Cigarette smoking is our biggest gripe. It is forbidden, for example, to smoke on the bus or in trailers where no one else smokes, so the smokers bunk together in the same trailer. Unfortunately Wakeford, the biggest anti-smoker, has to live in the same trailer with all the smokers. He makes them smoke only in their rooms, and keeps a can of Ozium around for whenever the smoke starts to bother him. He's always bitching at people to quit smoking, and as a crew we all hound people to stop the habit. But heaven forbid if anyone or anything tried to influence the chewers and pot smokers. There are more cannabis smokers than tobacco smokers on the crew. But because of the strict state and federal laws relating to marijuana possession, particularly on federal land, we try our best not to annoy anyone with the telltale fragrance. We either go for a drive or a long walk when we want to light up. I think it's a shame that we have to hide when smoking weed. From the crew's standpoint, marijuana is more acceptable than cigarettes. And as it should be in our modern society.

The chewers have their own problem... like how to dispose of their spit, and their problems also become your own. You let them have the window seat so they don't have to lean over you to spit out the window and drool on your lap. Even worse is when they leave their spit bottles around and the bottles get knocked over. The stink is worse than dead cigarette butts in an ashtray. Cleanup is their duty. These guys often don't use good discretion when they deposit their spit, so it's always a good idea to check out the content of a bottle or glass before taking a gulp from it. When you're getting drunk and sipping on a beer, someone's spit bottle could be inches away. Imagine what it would be like to grab the wrong bottle! Instead of a cool refreshing brew you get a mouthful of dark warm chew and saliva guaranteed to make you puke.

A favorite pastime for the crew is picking on someone, getting on his case for a day. It's all done in jest. It becomes a kind of group therapy valve when the crew points out an undesirable quality about someone. Bringing it out in the open with constructive bantering allows the person to become aware of a particular problem.

If you have a phobia, beware letting it become publicly known. Everyone will do his best to expose you to the very thing you're afraid of. Somehow I let out I hated spiders and snakes. Ever since, every kind of bug that could be found has been thrown at me. Threats of snakes in my bed make me cautious enough to check my bed nightly before turning in. In time that kind of treatment does wonders for you. Either you go crazy with paranoia, always on the alert, or you outgrow your fear. No matter what, the crew will not allow itself to be un-amused or un-entertained, and will find something wrong with someone in order to drive them to distraction.

June 6 and 7

We are first on the list to go off-forest, so I make my weekly trip to Flagstaff an overnighter. I have to motivate myself to go, as it is so pleasant and peaceful around the station with most everyone away. I briefly visit Laura and Doug, who are temporarily staying in a hotel. The escrow closed on their house and the contractor building their new home is behind schedule. Since I am in town by myself, I decide to check out the bar scene. I go first to Shakey Drakes where the rock and rollers hang out. Across the street is the Mad Italian, a sociable pizza place, and I eat dinner there. Then I go to the Museum Club for some lively country western music. The club is located on the East side of town in what looks like a huge log cabin. It's one of the oldest buildings in Flagstaff. The interior is very rustic. In the middle of the dance floor there is a standing tree around which the structure was built. The club features good times and sells tee shirts that read, "Disco sucks, the Museum Club."

I have often wanted to call Melinda, but I knew it would be best if I didn't. I knew she would understand if we just let things end with the good feelings we had, rather than start again and stir up all those mixed emotions. I am feeling down, and miss my old girlfriends. Castleberry never wrote me back after the two letters I sent her. I don't even know if she got them. She was planning to move back to San Diego, so it's possible she's just too busy to write at the moment. My heart still longs for her good loving. For tonight, though, I just want to find someone to share my lost dreams with. Instead, I drink too much in lieu of self-pity.

Someone is knocking, real early, on my door at the cheap hotel where I crashed last night.

"Maid service," and again, "Maid service" a voice announces.

"Wait a minute!" I call as I jump out of bed to turn off the TV that I had left on all night. I hear the keys jingle, and the door opens. Standing there is an old, heavyset Indian woman. She catches me stark naked and with a morning hard-on.

"You want clean room now?" she inquires.

"No man, come back later. Can't you see I just got out of bed?"

"I sorry," she says without a hint of the shock or surprise I felt. "I clean later."

"Yeah, please do."

She slowly closes the door, staring all the while at my crotch. The nerve of that woman! Probably just wanted a cheap thrill. Well, I hope she got it. If she were any better looking I would have invited her in to clean up and make the bed. Maybe even join me in some foreplay in the shower. Crazy lady. Where was she last night when I could have used some oral gratification?

It's 8 A.M. and I can't get back to sleep. I get high and munch out at Sambo's before I make my way back to Blue Ridge. It is one of the few times I rode home in the warmth of daylight.

Back at the station, Jim and James are almost ready to go fishing. They have waited for me to join them. I think it'll probably do me some good to get out and explore some of the opportunities for recreation that the forest offers. Everything around here is beautiful and there's a lot to see. It's a good idea to get completely away from civilization and people, and enjoy the beauty of the area as the Indians did long time ago. I can just kick back, get high, and enjoy the peacefulness and solitude.

June 8 to 10

The thinning 'shots are back on the job again. We still have hundreds of acres to go. I haven't run a saw for a while, and the routine drag and stack isn't what I fancy today. Time seems to pass better when you're running a saw. I look on the map for the area we are cutting today, and take off in my own direction. I whiz through a couple of small dog-hair thickets. The earplugs I'm wearing are great for blocking out the roar of the chain saw. Without them my ears would be ringing for days. Wearing them allows me to enter my own domain of deep thought.

It's a real shame we have to murder all these little helpless trees. They'll never get the chance to mature and seed. Our civilization requires management and cultivation of these life forms. It is too bad that we try to civilize nature for our own needs. The trees have just as much right to life as any other creature. I don't know where man gets off destroying the essences that give him life, forcing his imperialistic raids on other life forms. First, he massacres the Indians on this land, now he strips the tall Ponderosa pines to give him shelter and security from his fellow beings.

"Buzz, buzz," the chains go as they rip another growing tree. The trees lie on the ground motionless, silent victims of the massacre that just took place. These pines could have been Indians lying here at this very location. The remains will all be stacked up and set afire in a timber Holocaust. The bow bar cuts into another tree. You can hear the pain as the tree cries for mercy. Life giving sap oozes from the fresh wound. The screech of death follows as it crashes to the ground. The limbs brush against neighboring trees for help, reaching out for a hand to break its fall, but the standing pines render no assistance. Roaring, the saw teeth gnaw into another. I look down and watch its life's blood squirt from the small trunk. I'm the executioner and the trees are the victims, destined to die by an outside source. I cut into another, and another. Blood pumps out with a rhythmic heartbeat.

It must be time to break for lunch. My imagination is running away with me. After lunch, my thoughts settle down some. I am tired of running the saw and want to let someone else cut, but I am still in an active thinking mood.

Thoughts of the city and old friends fill my head. One that I can't shake is the memory of Richie Johnson. I have known Richie Johnson for as long as I can remember. He lived down the street from me, but we didn't become real friends until the seventh grade. Before that, he and his brother, Ken, were just kids we knew casually from playing with the Lockwood boys next door. We got to be friends as we walked and talked from the school bus drop-off to our home up the street. Early in our friendship we got into a fight, an unimportant little scuffle common among young boys in puberty who are just beginning to test their manhood. It didn't matter much, and was, in fact, the beginning of a good friendship. As we entered the next grade, we took more classes together. He was smarter than I was. I had a lot of respect for him for that.

My family life was very difficult during my teens. School was the happiest part of my day because I hated to go home to that fatso bitch my dad married. After school when Richie walked into his yard, I would walk alone up the street trying to see through the trees and bushes if her car was in the driveway. I'd run back to Richie's house after school every day. I had to be back home by five o'clock, or I would get grounded.

Richie hated my stepmother. They never did get along. She used to call him Ichabod Crane because she said he looked like him. I never met the person, so I can't tell if that was so. Richie was always feeding me facts and trivia. He was into things that most kids our age didn't care about. He liked astronomy, science fiction, and any kind of information he could acquire to get the advantage over the next guy. I learned a lot from him. He started working on his pilot's license in Junior High. By the time he turned sixteen he passed his test and satisfied his flying hours.

We went to the same high school, but he skipped a half grade and I repeated a half grade when the Los Angeles School District went from the A and B mid-year graduation grade system to a yearly one. We were in different classes and made new friends, but we always had snacks and lunch together. My social thing in high school was the Law Enforcement Explorer Post. It was my ticket out of the house, and the only thing my fatso bitch stepmother allowed me to do. I was on the swim team for a couple of weeks with Richie. She made me quit for fear I would get involved in after school mischief and drugs. In fact, I was forbidden to do just about everything to prevent me from getting involved in drugs. I still went down to Richie's every time I could. Richie's parents had a cabin cruiser and invited me to go to Catalina with them one summer. Everyone was shocked when I was allowed to go. It was there he told me about his first love affair that happened the last time he was at Catalina. I think he made up most of it, but I didn't refute the story at all. It was entertaining, and added to my sexually deficient education. I'll always remember that trip to Catalina. We even saw Buddy Ebsen who was there for a yacht convention. Those after school and vacation escapes allowed time for a certain amount of experimentation with drinking beer and trying out cigarettes. In these and other pursuits Richie was ahead of me when it came to experiencing new highs.

In Richie's senior year at high school he attended junior college classes. He was taking a lot of science courses to enable him to graduate high school at sixteen. He had a good start in life and achieving his goals. It wasn't until I was in my first semester in college that I started to smoke pot with my friend Allen. Richie thought my friends were immature and never got along with any of them. Richie liked Allen's sister, Linda, though. She was very intelligent and they had a lot of classes together. Richie showed me my first bong and taught me how to use it. By then he had tried several drugs and told me about his head-trips and adventures. His experiences with drugs fascinated me, because he was very analytical about them.

Richie had his pilot's license only two days when he took me for a ride. I was the very first person he asked. I didn't bother to get permission from fatso bitch. He let me handle the controls, and let me feel some G-force. We flew out to the desert so he could practice his dirt landings. Even though that was my first time in the air I had full trust in him.

His parents had bought land in Big Bear, and he went up there a lot to work on the cabin. He fell in love with the mountains and soon he moved up there, leaving all his schoolwork behind. He had only one semester left to go to complete his B.S. It seemed like such a shame. While he lived up there we kept in contact, but didn't see each other much. Still he was my greatest influence. Best friends aren't necessarily the ones you see on a daily basis. He never even let me know he made the move up to the mountains. His parents told me where he was whenever I inquired about his whereabouts.

He invited me up to check out his gorgeous surroundings, and I fell in love with the mountains and the woods the first time up there. Summer was my favorite time to go. As he put it, the "Touristas" were not around. He worked at the ski lodge making snow in the winter, but I never took up his offer to go there for skiing. In the summer he was a seasonal worker with the Forest Service in trail maintenance.

Richie turned me on to philosophical thinking. The talks we had were very meaningful. I'd go visit him to get away from the city, take some drugs, listen to music, and talk about philosophy. The best time I ever had there was when he put some acid in his homemade wine without my knowledge. He put on a five-hour tape of his favorite artist, Neil Young, whom he resembled physically. After the peak we went for a 2-1/2 hour walk in the dark. He taught me to walk through the forest at night. We climbed higher and saw the dome of light and a low-pitched roar from the city. The "city" for people in Big Bear was the big city of Los Angeles. We talked for hours about society and its many problems, and how much better it is to live away from it all. I fully understood why he chose this lifestyle over his promising one in the city. Being up here in Blue Ridge helps me realize what he loved about the mountains.

On other occasions, we talked about religion and Jesus. Richie developed a good theory about him. I contributed my ideas on the subject and accepted his. It's a simple way of looking at life and reality. That's how Jesus did it. We had some excellent talks, all of them enlightening. We even talked about co-writing a philosophy book together.

When I had something that I needed to share with a good mind, I'd pack up and head for the hills. I even spent a New Year's Eve up there because the "city syndrome" was getting to me. A quiet weekend of thought was the best way I could have spent my time to relieve the stress brought on by the maddening, irritating city, and working under those fluorescent lights at Litton Industries.

I was choosy about who I brought up to his place at Big Bear. Kathy Castleberry went with me once. She liked Richie a lot for his kindness and hospitality. She's one of the few people that I can share memories of Richie with.

Well, I hadn't been up to see Richie for the longest time, and I was aching to go. The fluorescent lights at Litton Industries were really getting to me, so I tried calling from Litton to see if it was OK for me to go up that weekend. I tried two nights in a row. The line was always busy. I tried again a couple of weeks later, but his number had been disconnected and there was no new number on file. When I finally reached his parents his mother told me that he had passed away two weeks earlier. They found him sitting on the floor propped up against the door, with the phone off the hook. The coroner said he died of undetermined causes. He had a bleeding ulcer a couple of months before, but there were no indications that the ulcer caused his death. I vaguely remember the first time I called up there I didn't get through. I figured it was the ancient telephone system at Big Bear. To this day I wonder if it was my phone call that caused his death. He may have jumped up to answer it, causing that piece of carpet by the phone to slip out from under his feet. While falling his head would have hit the doorknob and rendered him unconsciousness. The mixture of an ulcer and alcohol in his stomach was said to have created a toxin that killed him. This was his parent's theory.

A year later I ran into Richie's parents in my parents' neighborhood. They let me read the autopsy report, and gave me their own theories on the circumstances of his death. They were trying to sue the Riverside County Coroner for malpractice. They also said, at the time of his death his appointment from the Forest Service was sitting in his mailbox. He had gotten a permanent job in timber. It was only seven weeks after I found out about Richie's death, that Reamer called me to work for the Forest Service.

Richie seemed very simple on the outside, but he had a very complex mind. He considered me his best friend and told me so. I believe in my heart that I was. Every time I left him he'd shake my hand. It said a lot about him because he didn't do it with anybody else. Outside of my family members he was the person I knew the longest. He may be dead now at twenty two, but it's up to me to keep his spirit and all his good qualities alive. The good parts of all the deceased should live forever, for mankind's sake. This is the essence of everlasting life; for the goodness of each individual who has passed on to live in the souls of those of us who must exist in this fucked-up society, the society Richie didn't want any part of. This is the same belief in God I have.

Here the wind whispers through the treetops as I heard it do many times in Big Bear. It must have been that subconscious, hypnotic whisper that put me into the trance I was in, remembering back to the Big Bear days, with the forest's musical score of rustling leaves and whistling needles in the treetops.

The saws have shut down and no one is around me. I put my last stick on the pile and find my way back to the bus. Solemn tears redden my eyes. The pine trees, greenery and mountain atmosphere fill my heart with their grace and an occasional sad memory. I carry their quietness back with me to the station.

We just ran for P.T. I am still feeling depressed. The rest of the week will be spent on thinning, hard P.T. workouts, and, of course, after work jungle volleyball.

June 12

It is Friday, (our Friday), and the promise of a weekend of freedom is exciting. We quit thinning somewhat earlier today than usual, and head back for the station to detail; clean the saws, sharpen chains, fix problem saws, and await P.T. We all hang around the obstacle course until Bob shows up to lead us in another difficult P.T. workout session. Before he gets there we climb the rope once and sit and wait for the rest of the guys who are still changing their clothes, lagging behind, and straggling out.

"There's Bob already. I wonder where everyone else is," Russ remarks.

"He doesn't have his P.T. clothes on," says Paul.

Cord speaks up hopefully. "Yeah, maybe we are going to skip P.T. today."

Bob stops halfway out and yells to us, "Hey, come on, we got a dispatch. Let's go!"

Darryl yells back, "Do we really?"

"Yes, we do," Bob snaps. "Get your ass in gear!"

While Darryl is still confirming the report we all start running back to get our regular fire clothes on.

"All right!" Kyle says. "We finally got a dispatch."

You could tell dollar signs were dancing in his head. I could have sworn that there were dollars signs in his eyes, as well.

"About time. I was getting tired of waiting," Marty says.

Koval grumbles, "I wanted to go into town tonight. All day I was thinking of getting laid. Michelle will never forgive me."

"Yeah, you got that sweet thing waiting for you up there. She's going out to find some other action," I say with a smirk.

Koval responds testily, "I don't know if she's going to be so sweet to me. She was a real bitch when I left her last week. I wouldn't put it past her. She's done it before."

"Why was she such a bitch?"

"She doesn't like me to leave and come down here to work. She would rather see me commute every day. Besides, she misses my big wanger."

"That's your fault," I tell him. "You should satisfy her and get her sore enough so she'll want to see you go."

"Not Michelle, she's a horny girl."

"Oh, yeah? Well, it looks like she'll have to stay horny. You aren't going anywhere."

Within 15 minutes we are all on the bus. Bob stops at the office to get the details on the fire and then we're on our way. Some of the lucky ones grab some dinner to eat on the way to our destination. We are all happy to be going to a fire. The excitement generated by the others gets me feeling jazzed and worked up.

On the road the bus is moving at top speed trying to pass slower cars. The music is playing and we're jamming to Pink Floyd and Elton John. It's a great change from the overplayed Waylon Jennings tape we are usually forced to endure on these trips. When I came up here I didn't like country western music much, but I'm starting to enjoy the stuff. Tanya Tucker has been catching my ear, and my eyes. Her hot looking outfits on her TNT album are a sight to see.

The Tonto dispatcher has us report to the Sunflower work center for further directions. This will require more driving. The ride will take a couple of hours, so we take our time putting on our final fire clothes and getting our gear ready.

The air gets warmer as we drive off the majestic Mogollon Rim. The sun is behind some cloud layers. Orange effluence fills the horizon and the sun's illuminating rays reach out of sight into the eastern darkness. We hurry all the way to Sunflower just to find out we are 10-6, on standby. What a letdown! Our desire for fire is deflated like a popped balloon. Wakeford and Russ started their firefighting careers here six years ago and still know some people stationed here. They go to get more information about what's happening. It seems there were some lightning fires in the area, and the manpower already on duty was sufficient to handle them. They want us to stick around until after dark "just in case."

While we wait, Paul and Russ bring us back some bags of potato chips and show us where the ice cold drinks are stashed. There are three trash cans full of them. Restless, we try occupying ourselves as best as we can without getting into trouble. A couple of guys check the oil and perform a short maintenance check on the bus. The ones who know someone keep busy by talking about old times.

One guy plays with a yo-yo and a few others throw a Frisbee. A stickball game starts up with the help of a broken Pulaski handle and a ball taken from a local hound dog.

The game is interrupted when a Sunflower worker brings out a volleyball and net. He is probably the dog's owner and wants his dog to have his ball back. Volleyball is more to our liking so we give the ball back to the hound. During our third game, the dispatcher comes on the air with an announcement. "7-20, (our call numbers), Phoenix dispatch."

"Bob, did you hear that?" I ask.

"Hear what?" Just as Bob finishes his question everyone hears from the dispatcher.

"7-20, Phoenix dispatch."

"Time out, you guys," Bob says as he goes over to the handset and speaks into it. "Dispatcher, 7-20."

The dispatcher responds, "10-20."

"The Sunflower work center," Bob tells him.

"Uh, 10-19 (forget it)," the voice instructs.

"10-4," Bob acknowledges, then turns to the crew. "Let's go, they don't want us hanging around anymore."

"Great, let's get the hell out of here," Russ says.

"You guys lost the last game so wrap the net and put it in the office. Wakeford, show 'em where it goes," Bob says.

Quickly we wrap up the stuff and join the others on the bus. The tape is pushed in. "Ladies and Gentlemen... Mr. Waylon Jennings," and as the audience cheers and applauds on the live tape, so do we in the great green sardine can, drawing peculiar looks from the people at Sunflower watching us depart. We ride off singing, "on a Hotshot bus... headed for the highway." Wakeford has his shirt stuffed with fruit and candy bars and passes some out to the others. That's where he was when we were playing volleyball, raiding lunch sacks for the goodies. This should tide us over until we get home.

I don't know why, but we seem happier because we did not go to a fire. The veterans are quiet at first, disappointed at not getting their feet warm at a fire, but it doesn't take them long to join in the horseplay. Cord is lying in his seat with his head overhanging a wastebasket and his feet in the racks above.

Pat gets up and sits on Cord's chest. "Thay," he lisps, "you want to meth around?"

"Oh, no thank you. I'm not your type."

Cord gets up and starts singing in a high-pitched voice to a Loretta Lynn song that is playing. He's mocking her, standing up in the aisle, "Boop, boop, de booping," like Betty Boop. He grabs the handrails on the ceiling and acts like a monkey. Drifty is behind him and tickles him hard. Others throw candy wrappers, apple cores, and orange peels at him. Soon everyone gets into the throwing act. We had gotten ourselves all worked up on the way to the fires, and now we have all this energy to release. Wakeford gets real pissed when an orange peel hits him from behind. No one claims to be the culprit. We stop after Wakeford gets totally pissed because he's so strong he could kill someone accidentally just horsing around. We stop in Strawberry to change drivers, Aaron goes to buy some Skoal and Drifty has to take a leak. Russ stands at the door and yells out, "Come on Driftwood. We're leaving."

"Pinch it off," Jim calls to Drifty.

"You're going to be left behind," Russ warns.

Drifty runs out from behind a parked truck and as soon as Bob sees him he slowly pulls away, making him run for it.

"I remember when Drifty got left behind," Darryl recollects.

"Yeah, I remember that. It was hilarious. Real funny," Pat says.

Drifty is in no mood for this. "I didn't think it was so funny."

Cord speaks up, "That's because you were the one left behind."

Darryl turns to me. "Did you ever hear the story about leaving Drift?"

"No. Darryl, tell me the story about leaving Drift, this one I haven't heard yet."

"We were on this fire all night, we worked a double shift."

"Dave," I call, "what was the name of the fire?"

"I don't remember," Drifty mumbles. "I was out of it."

"Oh, well. It doesn't matter," I say.

Darryl continues, "Anyhow, we were sitting around waiting to go back to fire camp to bed down and Drifty fell asleep. So did some others but we woke them up when we proceeded back to the bus. Everyone got up quietly and left Dave sleeping there."

"Yeah, I was in ozone land," Drifty admits. "I didn't get to sleep like most of you did that night."

"We got on the bus and started honking the horn yelling, 'Fire! Fire!' to play a joke on him. He didn't even budge. We had to send someone back to wake him up."

"You could have left me there all day and I would have never known."

"I went back to wake him up," Pat relates, "and I had to kick him hard to get him up."

"Hey, I told you I was out of it. And when we got back to fire camp the fuckers wouldn't let me get any sleep."

"Oh, you poor thing," Paul chimes in. "What were you doing sleeping on government time anyway?"

"Poor thing is right! I was zonked."

"We got to keep our eye on Drifty," Darryl concludes. "He likes to fall asleep whenever it's convenient."

A full moon is coming up over the skyline. The passing trees strobe the moonlight as the wolves inside the bus howl along the eerie highway. An elk darts out and the driver has to apply the brakes. The howling stops and hunting takes over as the main topic of conversation. The trip home seems shorter than the trip out.

When we arrive at the station Russ tells Bob, "Bob, you need to go into the office."

"Naw, I'll take care of the paperwork in the morning."

"On your day off?" queries Dennis.

"Sure, why not? Just drop me off at my house."

Before he jumps off, Bob gets his pack and turns to us and continues, "I hope everyone still knows we are still first on the list to go, even though we got 10-19, we still keep our order in line."

"You mean we didn't lose our turn?" Sluggo asks.

"That's what I just said, and I don't want anybody going far away. That means you Cord, no Tucson."

"Hey, did I say I was going down there?"

"You never do. I always find out after the fact. Dennis, you make sure everyone leaves you a number where they are going to be."

"What about going to Phoenix?" Kyle inquires.

"If that means you can't be back in the required two hour call back, no. I don't want anyone fucking up our chance to go because we couldn't get a hold of you," Bob answers, and walks away.

"Bye, Bob. So long, Boss," the crew calls to his disappearing back.

"Yeah, right," Cord mutters. "How can we have a nice weekend if we can't go anywhere?"

"I can make it back from Phoenix in two hours," Kyle says. "Besides, he didn't say I couldn't go."

"Koval," I call.

"What?"

"Are you going up to Flagstaff tonight?"

"What do you think?"

"Yes, I should have known better."

"Well, hey, give me a call tomorrow and we'll get together and party or play tennis."

"Yeah, I can get into playing tennis."

"OK. Then give me a call when you get up."

"Sure, I'm going to wait for my check and then I'll be right up."

"When will that be?"

"Oh, about one or so."

"OK, I even have an extra racket you can use."

"Great, I'll need one."

Darryl interjects, "Steve, what are you having for dinner?"

"I don't know. First I am going to have a couple of ice cold beers and a joint then I'll worry about dinner."

"That sounds like a great idea," Cord says.

"Pat," I say, "You want to join us? We're going for a walk when we get back."

Pat answers in his Mr. Rodgers Neighborhood voice, "Sure, sure I will. I like that very much."

"There goes the loadies again," Darryl says snidely.

"Well, Darryl," Cord says, "why don't you see how much you can guzzle while we're gone, you fucking alcoholic hypocrite."

"Hey, I'm not an alcoholic," Darryl retorts.

"Like hell. You are so. Then don't call us loadies!"

"Well, you are."

"You're full of shit." You could tell Cord had Tucson on his mind. He wasn't in the greatest mood.

When we come back from getting high, Jake and Darryl are talking about something serious. Good, just where I wanted to go with my high. Darryl looks like he's already drunk a six-pack, but it turns out it was just a couple of homemade daiquiris. I grab a cold beer from the freezer and join in on the symposium.

"Jake, you want another beer?" I ask. "It's ice cold."

"Sure, it will save me from getting one from my trailer."

I turn to Darryl. "So what are we arguing about?"

"Killing people."

"I should have known that's what you're talking about, your favorite subject."

Darryl goes on and on about how he despises rapists and child molesters. I listen for a while until he starts repeating himself after each drink. Good night, all.

June 13

After a few good sets of tennis on a beautiful day, I start to make my way down to Sedona, where my sister lives. My appetite is set on a home-cooked meal and Silvia is a great cook. The contact number that I left Bob was my sister's number in Sedona. Because our unit is first on the firefighting list I feel jumpy, knowing that at any time the Hotshots and I could get a phone call, so before I leave the Flagstaff area, I phone her to make sure nobody is looking for me.

I briefly interrupt my ride to Sedona for a quick natural high by Oak Creek. The softly flowing creek fills my ears with blessed sounds of nature. The red hills and green trees uplift and gratify my senses. Good thoughts flow naturally in such surroundings. The colors are deeper, brighter, and more abundant here, the perspective so deep I could almost imagine it contained a fourth dimension.

That night I decide to check out the local pub action in this well-to-do town. The sleazy El Coyote Inn is my first stop. I find it unimpressive, just a local hangout for dart throwers, pool players, and bikers. Everyone knows everyone in here and I feel out of place. A grill in the back seems to be a gathering spot for separated and unwed mothers to flaunt themselves.

The Oak Creek Tavern is on the main drag in town. The tourists aren't out this late, but a diverse crowd occupies the place. My ears are ready for some live musical entertainment, but the Toucan Eddie Band is off for the night. The flirty bartender keeps me around longer than I intend to stay.

My next stop, and only suggestion from my sister, is Paco Diablo's. This is a classy country club/time share/hotel with huge weeping willow trees on the golf course. My nephew works here as a bus boy. The brother and sister combo who play here sound like the Carpenters and look like the Captain and Tennille. The tuxedo clothed bartender shoots a scornful look at my Levis, but I don't care. My Levis sink into the plush swivel chairs just like any fancy outfit would. The ladies seated in there are heavily made up and perfumed, elegant in their high society attire. I didn't care much for their stuck-up attitudes and leave quickly.

The rest of my drinking time I spend at the Rainbow Lounge getting totally shit-faced. Only a few people are in here. The Rainbow Lounge is less than a quarter of a mile from my sister's, on the outskirts of town. I find Laura, the bartender, a "muy simpatico person". She keeps everyone in good spirits with her great personality. She gives me a free beer as a salute to the Old Country and sweet Napoli. When my head starts spinning with infatuation, or maybe because of the booze, I make my way home.

When I get to the house, I discover that my niece forgot to leave the garage door unlocked for me. I decide to play with the lock to get the door open. At some point I must have given up because I awaken on the garage floor hours later. The family cat is snoozing right next to me keeping warm, my warmth being more agreeable than that of the nearby water heater.

A day of sobriety and leisure is number one on my agenda before I return to work. I kick back at the slide rocks, entertaining my voyeuristic side by leering at the excitable teenyboppers. After the cuties slide down the natural rockslide, the coldness of the water and cool breeze through the canyon covers their young bodies with goose bumps. The sensual nipples of their firm, virgin breasts showing through their bathing suit tops and wet tee shirts are an obvious visual delight, as are views of firm buttock cheeks that peer out of last year's outgrown swimsuits. Cautious and protective mothers wrap towels around the exposed signs of burgeoning feminine maturity. It's fun watching mothers keep an eye out for men who get off on excited young girls. Shame, shame, shame on me!

I spend the latter part of the afternoon in a Jacuzzi and at the community poolside in my sister's Sedona Racquet Club. A relaxing family home evening, in front of the boob tube, makes me drowsy enough to turn in early and get rested up for the ride back to Blue Ridge in the morning. There have been no phone calls for me all day.

June 14 and 15

Back at work I feel like doing some firefighting, not thinning. The dispatcher is busy this morning. There are smokes popping up all over the forest. Two of them are in our district, but not big enough to call a whole Hotshot crew. They are suppressible by tanker crews. The dispatcher declares a Red Flag day for the Coconino N.F., therefore all chainsaw operations have to cease. We break for lunch twenty minutes early and stick close to the bus so we can keep an ear on the radio in hopes of a dispatch. The radio air traffic is heavy and the winds are increasing. Everyone is itchy for a fire. Some even put their fire clothes on in case of an expected attack.

Suddenly a voice on the radio alerts us. "Moqui."

"Hey, quiet everyone, listen up," Dennis says.

"Moqui," the tower answers back to dispatch.

"Moqui: Dispatcher," from the radio.

"All right," Dennis says. "Here's our dispatch."

The throaty, female voice from Moqui continues, "Yeah, uh, I got a small white smoke at 250 degrees about 8 miles."

The dispatcher, Baker Butte, responds. "Go ahead."

"I have a cross reference on Moqui's smoke at 35 degrees."

"10-4 Baker Butte."

"It sounds like ours," Darryl says, an edge of excitement in his voice.

"Yeah, we'll go, too, because General Spring is out by the rim," Marty notes.

"Fuckin' A," says Wakeford. "About time!"

"7-20: Dispatcher."

Russ snaps, "Let's go! On the bus!"

Bob gets on the microphone and answers back, "Dispatcher: 7-20."

"10-20."

"Little Springs draw."

"10-49. Go to Range 10 Township 14 southwest, southeast corner."

"10-4."

Within seconds, Russ has the bus started up. We have the saws loaded up and are all aboard. Everyone lets out a big cheer.

"Bitchin', about time. I didn't want to thin today anyway. Yahoo!!!" Cord exalts.

Sluggo is practically jumping up and down. "Stevie, Stevie," he sing-songs, "We're going to a fire! We're going to a fire!"

James chimes in, teacher-like, "Settle down, y'all."

"Really," Koval concurs. "You're all acting like kids on your first field trip to the zoo."

"Come on Koval, get excited," James says, relenting somewhat.

"Hey, I've been to enough fires."

"Sure, Koval," Darryl says sarcastically.

"Oh, excuse me, Darryl. I'm not a seasoned veteran like you."

"Don't get cocky."

Paul claps his hands. "Fuckin' A. Let's go." But before we can get out of the draw the dispatcher comes on the radio again.

"7-20: dispatcher."

"Hey, quiet down," Bob yells at us. "7-20, click."

"10-19."

Everybody groans. "Shit! Fuck! God-damn-it! God damn, what the fuck he do that for? What did they 10-19 us for?"

"4-42: Dispatcher."

"Shit. They're sending fucking Happy Jack."

"Dispatcher: 4-42"

"10-49 to Range 10 T 14 Southwest of Southwest 1/4."

"10-4. We are on our way."

"Oh, man, what they do that for?" Gus wonders aloud.

"We cost too much money," says Darryl.

"4-42 always gets our fires," Aaron gripes.

"It's probably not big enough for us," Cord says.

"Yeah," Jake agrees. "They only said a 'small white smoke.'"

"That's probably why," says Wakeford.

Dennis notices the look on Paul's face. "Paul looks like he wants to kill someone."

"Yeah," Paul acknowledges. "Maybe I'll take it out on Kyle. Them fuckers got me all worked up for nothing."

"No shit. How do you think I feel?" Marty says, aggrieved.

Bob shakes his head. "That's the way it goes."

"7-20: 7-4."

"7-20."

"Yeah, Bob, why don't you come back to the station"?

"10-4. Did you hear what happened?"

"TEN FOUR."

When we get back to the station, Reamer makes us work until 7:00 P.M. Our disappointment puts us in a bad mood for working. We just keep busy, though, making sure not to exert ourselves in case we got called again. Now, in the last hour, we get a game of volleyball going. Reamer comes jogging by, takes Bob aside and asks, "What are you doing playing volleyball?"

"I didn't want everyone out of his fire clothes and running around."

"You're supposed to be doing P.T. only, not playing games. If you don't want them out of their fire clothes have them do P.T. in their boots, but no volleyball."

Bob walks back to the game looking disgusted. "Let's go!" he barks. "Reamer wants us off the court and doing P.T."

"What the fuck is his problem?" Cord asks irritably.

"I don't know. He's on the rag or something."

Aaron pipes up, "Yeah, his fucking tankers don't do a fucking thing all day, and we play a little V-ball for P.T. and he jumps all over our asses."

"Aaron," says Bob, "quit your bitching, or I'll jump all over you."

"Can we just run?"

"I don't care what you do, just get your tennis shoes on and get out of here, and stay out of the weight room. Wakeford!"

"What a fucked day," James mutters.

Sluggo agrees. "Yeah, it wasn't even worth the hour overtime."

Everyone takes off, running in different directions. I run for a while then pull off to meditate. I never do see Sluggo running. He is most likely hiding out in the trailers.

June 16 and 17

It's a hang around the station day. The wind is blowing, but not enough for a red flag day. Darryl, Cord, Pat, and I get the brilliant idea to build a porch out the back door to give us that 'lounging on the Riviera' feeling. Cord and I have a better use for the porch. We can use it instead of taking those long walks.

We have our work cut out for us the second half of the day so we drink a beer and take out our bongs, skipping eating altogether. By the time lunch is over, we have a good buzz going. Right after lunch, we stand around the partially built porch shooting the shit and staying out of sight.

"Where's Darryl?" I ask.

"He didn't want to work with us loadies," Pat says.

"He's on that trip again."

"Yeah," Cord says. "He's up kissing ass right now."

I think I hear something. "Hey listen!" We all freeze and stare at each other.

Pat speaks first. "It's the busses' horn. Our fire call."

"All right," Cord shouts, "we got a fire!"

"Bitchin'," I say, "Let's jam."

"All right, I got a good high for traveling." Pat says.

The bus comes down to the trailer area and we jump on. Russ is in the driver seat.

"Where's the fire, Russ?" I ask.

"In the units, units 4 & 5."

"Isn't that where Marty lives?" Cord asks.

"Yeap," Marty says.

"Hey, Marty, your house is on fire," Russ says.

"It better not be."

"Shirley is home, isn't she?"

"Yeap."

Dennis cries, "Oh, no!" I know what he meant. Marty doesn't like us kidding about that. It's too close to home.

"Where's Bob?" Sluggo asks.

"We're picking him up at the office," Dennis replies.

When we pull up to the office, Bob is standing outside ready to jump on without stopping the bus. He commands, "Get your asses in gear. We'll be there in less than five minutes."

"Five minutes?" I say.

"Yeah, five minutes," Darryl responds.

Everyone is jamming, trying to get dressed. Dennis is driving like a madman. People are falling all over the aisle and misplacing things. We're still not ready by the time we get there. Only half the crew gets off the bus and grabs tools. 7-41 is already there with a hose lay, red lights on, and the radio over the P.A. Bob yells through the window from the outside, "Leveque, Petretti, Frailsen, Cord, Let's go!"

"Aye, aye, Captain," says James.

"Squad up and split up. Get a scratch line around first."

Bill Krushak comes up to Bob and tells him, "We got a wet line around most of it. Get your guys to finish up with a hand line."

Bob nods and calls to us, "Move it in there!"

Residents are out with their hoses helping us. Others are just out there to catch the excitement. The duff burning on the forest floor puts out a lot of smoke. I forgot my goggles on the bus. A cloud of steam and smoke drifts by and stings my eyes and makes me grimace with pain.

We hustle like pros and contain the fire to a quarter of an acre. If we had arrived even five minutes later a nearby structure would have burned.

We lost our high in the excitement and are starting to get very hungry. Now we slow down and mop up. The residents were a big help throughout... bringing us water, encouraging us, and sticking around to help in the mop up. One guy brags about how sweet tasting his well water is, so we just have to sample it. It is, in fact, very good... cooling and refreshing my cottonmouth. Wow! Pure well water. That's something different for a city boy. I take another gulp and pass it along.

"You guys are alright," one of the homeowners comments. "You got here fast."

"We've been praying for fire all week. You're just a blessing for us," Dennis replies modestly.

"I tell you what, you boys sure earn your money."

"It's all in a day's work," I say.

"We're lucky to live so close to the Ranger station," another resident comments.

"That you are," says Dennis. "I live in unit six, and it's at least ten more minutes to get out there."

"I would have hated to see what ten more minutes without you boys would have done."

Marty says, "Me, too, I just live over there."

"Oh, yes, you're Lankford's boy. I thought you looked familiar."

"Thanks for the drink," Dennis says, and Marty and I chime in, "Yeah, thanks."

Dennis turns to us and says, "Let's get this mopped so we can get off on time. I'm barbecuing a big elk steak tonight."

"Ahh," I can feel my stomach rumble. "You're making me hungry."

"We'll have this mopped up in no time with all this water," Cord observes.

"We still have to retool when we get back," Dennis warns.

We have everything finished in an hour, and head back to the station. There's enough time to re-sharpen the tools we used. We take our time, and boast about our thrill and great performance. By ten to six we are all done, just hanging around the shop. Our relaxation is interrupted by a signal from the dispatcher. "4-20."

"Dennis, dispatcher is calling you," Sluggo prompts. Dennis runs to the radio.

"No, Dennis," Aaron says. "He called for 4-20."

"4-20 is off. They were off at four o'clock," Dennis tells him. The voice of the dispatcher is heard again. "4-20." No contact is heard and the dispatcher tries again. "7-20."

Dennis answers quickly, "7-20."

"10-20."

"Blue Ridge Ranger Station."

"Is your crew mobile?"

"10-4."

"We got another dispatch for you. Report to the Fire Boss at the Cornville-Cottonwood interchange, southwest Sedona."

"10-4. We're on our way. 7-20." Dennis turns to Darryl, "We got another hot one. Darryl, did you gas up the bus?"

"Sure I did."

We are on the road again and no one minds at all. Finally, fire season officially starts for us today. No more waiting around being bored. We can feel the money jingle in our pockets. We book down the road with Waylon Jennings blasting the airways. It's at least a two-hour bus ride and all of us still have our fire clothes on. We just sit back with good attitudes, feeling like professionals, on a mental high enjoying the ride.

As we get closer we see a lot more Forest Service vehicles. The Cornville Volunteer Fire Department house has its doors open and its bay areas are empty. Private vehicles line the blackened areas beside the road. We even see a chromed-out Harley Davidson with a special "Volunteer F.D." plate.

The fire boss is right where the dispatcher said he would be. He was the one who radioed in our 10-97 at the Presbyterian fire. He leads us around, starting on the church grounds to the far end of the fire away from the road. The fire burned itself out at about 100 acres and looks easy to handle. The fire boss instructs Bob to construct line around the perimeter and not to worry about mopping up. The fire looks like it's completely out anyway. We assemble in our respective squads. Bob falls in with squad one. Squad two, my squad, will deploy in the other direction. Before we take off, Bob has a personal talk with Dennis. Dennis comes over to us and tells us the news. We are going to have fun tonight. We will start here and punch line to the road. Squad one will do the same from their direction, and hopefully we will meet up at the same place.

"No problem," Pat says.

"This is going to be easy," Marty agrees.

"Looks like a cake shift," Joe says.

"You mean easy money?" I ask no one in particular.

Darryl speaks up. "Kyle, I want an hourly report on how much money we're making."

"You got it."

Pat turns to me and explains, "He's our crew accountant."

"Oh, I see."

"He gives us an hourly report on how much money we are making." Bob hears Pat's comment and just shakes his head.

"Bob, see you later," Dennis says.

"See yaw in the morning," Bob responds.

Dennis turns to our squad. "Let's hit it guys, just take it nice and steady."

"Don't worry, we will," Sluggo says cheerfully.

"I said steady, Sluggo, not slow."

"I heard you."

We proceed to dig, all of us in a jovial mood, without a worry in the world. Each one takes a turn reciting a joke or just cutting, putting down someone in a non-serious manner. A slow hour passes and we're still excavating away. It's been quiet for a bit, and my stomach reminds me that it's been awhile since the last time I ate. I wish I had taken time out from smoking to eat some breakfast or lunch. Pat and Mike must be pretty hungry, too, I figure. I guess we're all pretty hungry.

It's been mostly quiet the past hour or so. We've run out of things to say. I'm getting really hungry. Kyle opens a can of crackers from a ration pack without holding up the line. This makes us all even hungrier. For some reason I remember a lunch special jingle on the KROQ Mike Raphone Show lunchtime request hour. I decide to let the others in on a little hunger humor. I call out, "Who's hungry?" and quickly turn to Pat for his participation. "Say that you're hungry," I instruct in a low voice.

"I'm hungry."

"Me, too," says Sluggo.

I jump in with an orchestrated script. "Sluggo, wait 'til your turn. After Pat says 'I'm hungry,' you can say 'I'm hungry,' then everyone else says, 'We're all hungry!'"

"Ain't that the truth," James comments, rolling his eyes.

"From the top now. Whooooo's hungry?"

"I'm hungry," Pat responds.

Sluggo is right on his key. "I'm hungry." He looks at me like a dog that's just done a trick on command, awaiting a treat.

"Now everyone."

The squad shouts, "We're all hungry!"

"Well then, let's eat. Yeaaaaa!! OK, once more from the top. Whooooooo's hungry?" And like a bunch of trained stage pros they perform wonderfully. "One more time! Who's hungry?" I shout. The chorus responds like a finely tuned orchestra.

"Shit, Petretti, we could have done without that," Jim remarks when it's over.

"Oh, well, I thought someone would have liked it."

"We all know we're hungry and don't need to be reminded," Dennis rebukes.

"No shit!" Aaron says. "I didn't know it was such a touchy subject." Pat adjusts his speed to get closer to me. I can tell he wants to share something.

Darryl notices the change of pace and tries to eavesdrop. Pat says in a low voice, "I wished I hadn't gotten high at lunch."

"You, too, uh?"

"Yeap."

"See what you get?" taunts Darryl who's heard most of this.

Pat snaps, "Mind your own fucking business."

"You guys should know better by now to be prepared," Darryl says.

"Hey, we're still learning," I protest. "What did you bring to eat, Darryl?"

"Uh, nothing."

"You fool," comments Jim.

Darryl continues. "Kyle's the only one that probably brought something to eat."

"Kyle is always eating," Aaron says.

Kyle rushes to his own defense. "I need food. I always carry at least two rations with me everywhere we go."

"Come on, Kyle, give us some," Jim says ingratiatingly.

"No way! I carry it, I eat it."

Aaron sniffs. "Kyle misers his food like he does his money."

I agree. "Yeah, miser and miserable come from the same root word."

"Ha! Ha! I may be the miser but you all are the miserable," Kyle says with obvious satisfaction, drawing a laugh from all listeners.

All the while we pound away at the ground, building the hand line. Strike the ground with your tool and move along.

"You stuck your foot in that one," Aaron says to me.

"You got that right."

Three and a half, four hours have gone by, and we are still ching, chinging away, striking the ground, separating the fuels from the mineral soil, making a path between the blackened area and the unburned area, when Sluggo speaks up. "Hey, Dennis, how about a break?"

"Yeah," Jim echoes. "How 'bout one?"

Dennis is adamant. "Bob said no breaks."

"Well, how about a nice juicy steak?" I say, hoping to add a little levity.

"Ooo yeah, with a baked potato, too."

"With sour cream and chives, and a side plate of Maine lobster."

"Knock it off, you guys," Jim says gruffly.

"What's the matter?" Dennis asks sarcastically. "Getting hungry?"

Joe answers, "We all are."

"Kyle's not," Darryl points out.

"I'm even running out of food. I don't know if can last until morning," Kyle says, full of self-pity.

"Dennis, what time is it?" Sluggo wants to know.

"12:45. We got a long way to go."

Three or four of us mumble, "Ohhhh noooooo."

"God damn, I'm getting tired," Jim declares.

I add in my two cents worth. "Me, too."

"Me, three," says Sluggo.

"Well, change the pattern a little," Dennis suggests. "The front man bump back to the end and we'll all take turns with the McLeod up front."

"That ain't going to stop my arms from dropping off," I complain.

Darryl shoots back, "Just think of what good shape you'll be in."

"Thanks, Darryl, that's just what I needed. It don't solve the problem."

"How about some ice cream?" Darryl asks sweetly.

"That I could go for. That would be an immediate solution. But my arms are so tired that I probably wouldn't be able to feed myself."

"How 'bout some strawberry cheesecake?" Dennis inquires.

"Oh, yeah," says Darryl. "That sounds better."

Jim chimes in. "How 'bout chocolate cake?"

"A big chef's salad with avocado dressing." That's Aaron.

"No," I say. "I need something spicy like a pizza with everything on it."

That strikes a chord with Darryl. "Wow, I could go for some more of your spaghetti right now."

"Me, too," Aaron says.

Dennis lets loose a yell at the top of his lungs. "Strawberry cheeeeeesecake..."

Everyone goes "Ummmmmm." I bellow out, "Pizza," Darryl follows with "Steak with mushrooms and onions." Everyone goes "Ummmmm" again.

"Beef enchiladas," Joe sings out.

In a chorus everyone says, "Ummmmmmmmm."

"A banana split," says Sluggo.

"Ummmmmm."

I feel a need to throw a twist into this. "Liver and onions."

"Icky, I hate liver," Aaron says.

Sluggo is back with savory suggestions. "Chocolate chip pancakes."

"Oh, yeah, ummmmmmmmm."

Darryl screams, "Knock it off, you guys. It's getting unbearable."

Aaron calls sharply, "Hey, Dennis. Dennis come here! Pat's getting sick."

Dennis calls, "Next guy bump back and keep on digging." He runs to the back where Pat has just finished throwing up. "Are you all right?"

Aaron answers instead. "I think all that food talk got him sick."

"Or the lack of it," says Pat spitting out drools of bile. All of a sudden Aaron let's out a chorus of dry heaves.

"Oh shit," Dennis says. "Just what I needed."

"You mean I got to work by him and smell it?" Aaron asks.

I put in my two cents worth. "I think it was the liver and onions."

"OK. You can take five. Pat rest up a little," Dennis says. Everyone drops in his tracks. Dennis turns to Pat again. "Are you going to be alright?" Pat nods. "When was the last time you ate?"

Pat heaves again. "This morning at breakfast."

"Well," Dennis says, "I guess it wouldn't hurt to take a break. Drink some water, Laybe."

When we stop I can feel how sore my muscles are. My back aches, my legs are weak and my arms feel ready to drop off. In what seems like only a few seconds, we get the order to get back up and continue digging line.

Everyone is quiet now, feeling his own pain and discomfort. What we thought would be a piece of cake shift turned out to be the hardest work we have encountered so far.

Finally Darryl speaks up. "Kyle, how much have we made so far?"

"I don't know. I lost track a long time ago. I can't add on an empty stomach."

"Dennis, what time is it?" Sluggo asks.

"You don't want to know."

"Yes, I do."

"We don't, Sluggo," Aaron says.

Darryl says through gritted teeth, "Just keep working."

"Next guy bump down," Dennis instructs.

Chink, chink, ching chink, hit and move, hit and move. Hours have passed and the pain turns to numbness.

"Let's take another five," Dennis says.

Without a word we drop to the ground. Dennis checks up on Pat to see how he's doing. He's holding his own.

"Listen," Steve says. "Everyone be still. You can hear the guys on the other side." Quietly we listen as their tools hit the rocks beneath them, the clanging and chinking never once ceasing.

Sluggo looks up. "I wonder if they took any breaks."

Aaron says, "Knowing Bob, they worked straight through."

"I bet James is flaking out," Darryl says.

Dennis breaks the quiet. "Back up, let's go."

We get up unwillingly. Our chinking and clinking, punctuated with grunts and groans harmonizes with the others across the blackened area. Hopefully we are getting closer. We continue on like zombies on a chain gang. Then, the keying of a radio squelch is heard, the first break we have had all night.

"Savage, Smith," Bob reports.

"Go ahead," Dennis says.

"Can you see the road?" Bob asks.

"10-4."

"We're about 4 chains from it," Bob reckons.

"Uh, yeah. We are just a few hundred yards from the main road. I didn't realize that we were so close to it. How about if I go bring the bus down, and the rest of my squad will start working towards you guys?" Dennis asks.

"Sounds good." The radio crackles. "How are your guys holding out?"

Dennis responds, "Pat got a little sick but he seems to be doing all right now."

"We almost lost Frailsen. He tried to pass out on us."

"Yeah. We're all pretty tired."

"We're getting there. Smith. Out."

"Savage out." Dennis leaves the rest of the digging for us to complete, and starts hiking to the bus.

What a relief, we're almost done. The sun is starting to peek above the horizon and light up the sky. Now the other squad is easily visible. We work faster on the longest yard, just to get done.

Without even stopping to rest, we hike back to the bus where James and Bob are waiting. Everyone grabs a ration and devours it. Some don't even finish their food. They pass out with an open can in one hand and a plastic spoon falling from the other.

We drive the long way home through Flagstaff to make sure we hit an open gas station. It's amazing the different positions you can sleep in when you're tired. We get back at the station at 7 A.M. We still have to work for an hour to get our eight hours in for the day. The short recuperation on the bus gives us enough strength to re-sharpen the same tools we had sharpened just fourteen hours ago. When eight o'clock comes around I am wide awake again, but feeling very spacey.

Darryl talks me into going to Winslow with him for grocery shopping. We eat at Kentucky Fried Chicken before we hit the market. We buy just about everything we were teasing ourselves with last night, cook up a feast and drown ourselves in expensive imported beer.

We crash before darkness, falling asleep immediately and not stirring until morning. No one mentions that we worked right into Father's Day. I wonder what my Dad is doing today. I feel bad that I haven't called him. It's easy to forget the family when your own existence is the only thing that matters. The crew becomes your substitute family. Bob is our dad. Dennis and Russ are our big brothers. We all intervene and look out for each other, and work as a unit. We take up the slack of the weakest until the weakest can take care of himself. Group pressure and spirit is the best motivating force for the weakening will. It's group therapy for stress.

June 18 to 20

For the rest of our work week we do busy work around the station. We modify the bus some, finish our porch, and clean almost everything around the station that needs cleaning... bathrooms, laundry room, shops, and the office. Bob counters this relatively easy work with vigorous P.T. sessions. Our muscles still hurt from all the line digging. He makes sure they are still hurting by the time our days off come around.

On Monday night Cord leaves with Jim to go down to Tucson. We lost our first place spot on the Presbyterian fire. Now, we are fourth on the list to go off-forest. This offers us a little more flexibility on the two hour call back on weekends. By Tuesday night, we are back up to second behind the Happy Jack Hotshots. Mormon Lake and Flagstaff crews must have gone somewhere.

Darryl and I boogie up to town after work Tuesday. We take separate vehicles and race to the Widowmaker, our first stop. Darryl runs into an old friend who lets us stay at his place that night, but not until we got down to some serious drinking at Daddy Morebucks and the Mad Italian. Joe is telling us that Morebucks had Rock & Roll Night on Tuesdays, but we find it's still disc spinning on the turntable. I don't mind as much as Darryl because Daddy Morebucks is the closest thing there is to L.A. nightlife.

We agree that tomorrow I'll get my Arizona license and we'll go bike riding down Oak Creek canyon and go swimming for a short, but different, kind of workout. In the morning, Darryl is anxious to take me to breakfast at this cheap place he knows about in downtown Flagstaff.

Turns out to be just what I was hoping to wake up to... a hot cup of real coffee, and a friendly old lady for our waitress. Too bad we couldn't get it served in bed. The food is inexpensive, greasy, and delicious. Our waitress is a picture in her soiled white dress and white shoes. Her gray hair is confined in a net. Warts and a noticeable mustache embellish her face. The Ace bandage around her swollen wrist probably contributes to her sloppy handwriting on the check. We flirt a lot with her and it makes her day. We leave a tip as generous as the service and helpings were.

It's a beautiful day, not a cloud in the sky or even a whistle of wind, but it doesn't take a weatherman to know that the nicest of conditions can take a 180-degree turn in northern Arizona. Anyhow, this morning is perfect bike riding weather. It can only get better as we get closer to Sedona with its warmer, high desert climate. Sedona is only 27 miles from Flagstaff, and the ride is extremely scenic, but it seems a lot longer because of the many hairy switchbacks. Before we hit the departure off the rim to Sedona, I turn around and yell, "Darryl, how do you like it so far?"

"Nice, real nice," he screams back.

"OK, I can hear you. You don't have to scream in my ear. You say you've never been on a bike before?"

"Once, maybe twice. My brother used to have one. He took me for a ride."

"Yeah? What kind was it?"

"I don't know. It was a big one."

"Like this one, or bigger?"

"Oh, it was about this size. This one seems nicer."

"I know. That's because it's mine."

"How do you know?"

"Because I know. It's a great bike."

He notices me looking at him in the mirror, makes a face and sticks out his tongue.

"Don't do that," I say. "You'll be sorry if you catch a bug. A couple weeks ago riding along here a bee got caught down my shirt and stung the shit out of me."

"Oh, yeah?"

"Hey are you still in charge of getting the keg for the party?"

"Yeah, I already ordered it."

"Where at?"

"State Liquor Mart... I got Michelob."

"Good choice."

"Look, what's that up there?"

"I don't know. A road crew or something."

"Maybe an accident."

"Naw, there's no police around."

A few cars are stopped ahead and I make my downshifts loud as the header-pipe pops through the gears. We slow down and pass the waiting cars and proceed to the front of the line. A road worker is standing there with a stop sign.

Darryl addresses me with a twinkle in his eye and a crack in his voice. "It's a girl."

"No shit, Sherlock, I can see."

"Say something to her," he urges.

I pull right up to her, flash her a smile and comment, "So you're here stopping traffic. What a job!"

She smiles back. "It's not bad. What do you do for work?"

Darryl answers. "We're firefighters."

"For the Forest Service? I used to work for the Forest Service on the Kaibab."

"Oh, yeah," Darryl says. "Doing what?"

"Recreation. We emptied the trash cans along the forest highway."

I jump in. "Another easy job. Have you ever worked in your life?"

She laughs. "Yes, I've done some bookkeeping. Hated it."

"You look like the outdoors type," I say. "Oh, by the way, I'm Steve and that's Darryl."

"My name's Linda."

"Hi," Darryl says, his voice cracking like an adolescent asking out a girl for his first date. "You want to go to a party?"

"Yeah," I chime in. "Would you like to come to a kegger party in the woods this Saturday? No, next Saturday."

"Where's it at?"

Darryl answers, "Blue Ridge. Ever heard of it?"

"I've heard of it, but I'm not sure where it's at."

"It's on Highway 87, ten miles north from where Lake Mary Road ends."

"You ought to come," I tell her. "Who's on the other end stopping traffic?"

"My friend, Kathy."

"Another girl? Bring her, too."

"If I go, she'll come, too."

"We'll ask her as we drive by."

The cars going in the other direction have all passed and it's our turn to go. She gives us a nod. "You guys better go now, you're holding up traffic."

"Just call the station, Blue Ridge Ranger Station, for better directions," I tell her.

"O.K., Bye now."

"Bye, see you later."

"See you next Saturday," Darryl calls.

Sure enough, Kathy is at the other end as we ride by. I yell at her, "Hi, Kathy. You're invited to a party. Ask Linda." She looks at us as if we were a couple of weirdos.

"We did all right," Darryl crows.

"What do you mean we? I did all the talking," I shoot back.

"I asked first about the party."

"You didn't give me a chance to ask. I would of. Hang on, here comes the fun part." The road gets windy up ahead with hairpin switchbacks at a few of the curves. I lean the bike and scrape my crash bars.

"What was that?" Darryl asks nervously.

"Oh, nothing."

"Nothing? You scared the shit out of me!"

"I've had this bike so low I've scraped the bottom of my boot," I tell him.

"You're crazy."

"Relax," I say with easy assurance. "I know what I'm doing. Just remember, I don't want to go down or die, so you have nothing to worry about. I'll think of my safety first and you'll be alright."

Our first stop is the slide rocks. I want to show him all the cuties that hang out there. He already knows about them. I should have guessed. He suggests we go further down the road to Grasshopper Point. I've seen the sign many times, but never have been down there. We park and walk down to the water.

Three girls are nearby drinking some wine. "Darryl," I say. "Look. Let's go get friendly. Maybe we can get them to come to the party, too."

"I don't feel like getting friendly. Besides, there won't be any party," he says despairingly, his voice cracking.

"You're crazy. Why?"

"Because every time we plan a party, we get called to a fire."

"Well, I hope so."

"Come on over here. There's bigger pools downstream."

A few hundred feet down is a big pool. People are jumping down into it from adjoining cliffs forty to fifty feet high. "Look at that, I'm going off there," I say to Darryl. "See you later."

"Leave the wine here then."

I make a few jumps while Darryl drinks the wine. He looks bored so I return.

"Let's go down further," Darryl suggests. "There are too many people here.

"Why? So you can fag off with me?"

"Funny," Darryl says, but you can tell he doesn't think so.

"Do you think Pat's a fag? I mean gay. You're the one who ought to know. You sleep in the same room with him."

"No, he's not. He's been to bed with girls before."

"How do you know?"

"He's had girlfriends before and last season he picked up this Indian woman hitchhiker. He made her fuck him before he dropped her off."

"You mean he raped her?"

"No, she was willing."

I cut him off, "Or thankful for the ride. Oh, well, you're both faggots and you're covering for him." I am walking in front of Darryl while we talk and don't see him pick up a rock that he throws into the water right near me as I cross a small rock bridge.

"You cocksucker!" I call. "Oh, excuse me, you guys take that as a compliment."

He laughs it off.

I'm not about to let this go. "What's Pat doing this weekend?" I ask.

"He's probably playing with himself."

We approach another big pool. On one side is a beach area, on the other just straight up cliffs.

"Darryl, look! A real live girl."

"Wow, she's beautiful."

"So is her dog."

"The dog's swimming better than she is."

"Let's just stay here for a while," I suggest.

"Yeah, there's nothing down further."

"Have you been down there further?"

"No," Darryl responds, sounding bored.

"You asshole, you don't know nothing."

"You sure been on my case lately, you cockdick."

"I know. I like teasing you. Where did you come up with cockdick? Wow, a big word for your vocabulary."

"From you, that's what you remind me of."

"There you go again thinking about cocks an' dicks. Don't you ever think about pussys and cunts?"

"Yes, you cunt."

With that last statement Darryl pushes me in and dives in himself, but in a different direction. I'm not about to swim after him and I tell him so. "I'm not about to chase after you, you faggot!"

"Hey, cool it," he replies.

The lady and her dog leave and we are alone swimming and floating around. Then I look up on shore and notice that we are not alone after all.

"Darryl," I call, excited. "Look up there on the shore." Darryl is floating on his back and doesn't bother to look. "Darryl, look! Naked people!"

"You're full of shit," he says.

"No. Really. Look."

Up on the shore is a guy, stark naked, and two girls. I relay my findings to Darryl. "Not bad looking at all, with only their bikini bottoms on."

Darryl rouses himself to look. "Wow, they really are naked."

"You don't need to be embarrassed," I say. "They're only boobs."

"That one is beautiful. What's she doing here?"

"That what? That girl or that boob?" Darryl laughs. "They are getting it all tanned," I continue.

"I can't believe what I'm seeing."

"You never seen a naked girl before?" I say, surprised.

"Yes, I've seen 'em."

"Don't stare. They'll think something's wrong."

"I can't help it. I've never seen people naked like that here before."

"Shit, they probably do it all the time. You've never been to a nude beach?"

"No," Darryl says, "I've heard about them."

"I've been to lots of them," I say, hoping to sound worldly.

"You have?"

"You probably wouldn't last two seconds without embarrassing yourself. You would get so red from embarrassment you would look like you had sunburn. Or your li'l pecker will be erect and embarrass you that way."

"I wouldn't go to a place like that."

"Yeah, I should have known. That's why some of them Mormon Lake boys call you Decent Darryl," I taunt. We both laugh at that one. "It is more true than not, isn't it?" Darryl doesn't answer and I quickly change the subject. "Lets get out of here and go swimming in a real pool."

"Where are we going to swim in a real pool?"

"At my sisters. The Sedona Racquet Club."

"Sure," he agrees, his voice cracking again. It must have been an adolescent type reaction from watching naked girls.

"That's the second or third time today you have done that. I swear you are going from manhood to childhood. Or is it that every time your pecker gets excited it makes your voice crack?" I ask.

"Watch it," Darryl warns.

"Let's get out of here before I beat up that guy and rape those two girls," I say.

We ride over to Silvia's, and just like I suspect, they are already down at the pool. We walk right in and I assure the counter lady we aren't staying long. Across the pool Silvia spots us right away and waves her arms. We go over to where she's sitting.

"Steven, you're here!"

"Hello, Silvia." I give her a hug and a brotherly kiss. "This is Darryl. He works with me."

"Fighting fires?"

"Yeap," Darryl says.

"Glad to meet you. You remember Rita?"

"Yeah," I say. "I haven't seen her in a long time, since you lived on Liana Street in Burbank."

Rita acknowledges the introduction. "Hello, Steve. Silvia was just saying you're a firefighter now around here."

"Not real close to here, but up in the mountains. We just went to a fire around here a couple of days ago."

"I wondered if you guys were working out there. Where was it again?" Silvia asks.

Darryl answers, "Around Cornville."

"Oh, yeah," says Silvia, remembering.

Darryl does his favorite thing and tells them all about the fire. His war stories are only slightly exaggerated. I have to tone them down a little so Silvia won't make them sound too bad when she repeats them to my father, like I know she will.

While we're there, we hit on the lifeguard. She has one of the darkest tans I've ever seen this side of sunny southern California. My guess is she's from San Diego, but no, she's a Cornhusker from her hometown local university. She's a senior whose summer employment brings her to Sedona. We extend our party invitation to her and her roommate. We get a not so positive "yes" from her. If we kept asking girls there will be more girls than Hotshots at the party.

Before heading back to Flagstaff, I have to show Darryl the pretty bartenders I discovered last week. He gets off on their looks, but it doesn't take much for Darryl to get off. The few beers we have, on an empty gut, make the ride back more enjoyable. Up in Flag we scarf down a fully dressed pizza at the Mad Italian.

We're back to work tomorrow on Friday. Darryl tells everyone about our exciting adventures. He assures me that our day out was the most enjoyable he's had all year. I guess he doesn't get out and do much, because I considered it to be routine. The guys start calling me the Mad Italian, and from then on the nickname sticks.

When I go into the city, I try to make every day like the one Darryl and I had. I believe Darryl learned something by watching me laying lines on the women we met. He still calls me a slut and a whore, though. And I still think he and Pat are butt-hole buddies. I'm still surprised that there aren't any queers on the crew. Living with all those guys, some of them have to think weird stuff at one time or another.

June 21 to 23

The thinning Hotshots are back in action again and thinning is all that is on the agenda for the next several days. Cord and Jim haven't made it back from Tucson yet. However, we're sure they'll return in time for the party this Saturday night. We get everyone excited about the party when Darryl and I tell them how many girls we invited. We joke about how Darryl is going to get laid at the party, and all the asses the others are going to grab. Joe, Aaron, Marty, and Kyle all say they've invited females to attend, but no one really believes Kyle. He's all talk when it comes to girls. Besides me, he's got one of the more perverted minds on the crew. It's the only thing we have in common.

That night, we work ourselves up at a poker game. It's my lucky night, and I win fifteen dollars. I have a feeling that next Saturday is going to be a lucky night, too.

The Blondie band is going to be on the Midnight Special after Johnny Carson. I want to make sure I stay awake to watch it. Darryl informs us that NBC in Flagstaff goes off the air after Johnny. I never find out if he's correct, as I am way too drunk to stay up any longer, and go to bed shortly after Johnny's confrontation with big Ed. Darryl went to bed right after we got home. Mike Cord did his re-appearing act while we were playing poker and is sawing logs; sleeping away, when I turn in. In bed I reminisce a little about Castleberry, hoping to have sweet dreams of her. God, I wish she were with me right now. It doesn't take long before I join in a snoring duet with a fellow 'shot.

*****

The screen door slams and heavy footsteps rattle the trailer and my head. Talk over the Forest Service radio echoes loudly from the living room. The footsteps grow louder as they draw nearer to the bedroom door. It's Bob, and he yells my name.

"Petretti! Petretti!"

"What?" I mumble. "What's wrong?"

"Let's go, we got a fire. Did Cord ever come back?"

"Yes, last night."

"Get a move on, we've got to leave in twenty-five minutes!"

"Mike," I ask, "did you hear that?"

"Fuck, yes."

"What time is it? It's still dark outside."

"Twelve-twenty," Cord responds.

"Don't tell me that," I groan. "I just went to bed."

"Hey, I'm telling you that because that's what time it is." he says nastily.

"Shit, what a time to go to a fire."

"It wouldn't be the first time. Just what the fuck I needed. I hardly got any sleep the past few days."

Bob comes back. This time he opens the door and asks, "Mike, where's Jim Cruz?"

"Fuck, I don't know," Cord says. "I called him at the number he gave me several times and he was never there. What am I supposed to do, baby-sit him?"

"Great," Bob says in disgust. "Koval's not around either. Darryl said he went fishing or something."

"I don't know," I tell him. "Haven't heard."

"Let's get at it," says Bob, his last word on the subject.

By this time we are the only ones left in bed, so we jump out to get ready. Everyone is running around frantically. Darryl puts some frozen chicken in the microwave and guzzles down a beer.

"Drinking on government time. Shame on you," I chide.

"Hey, this will help me sleep in the bus on the way down there."

"Good idea, although I'm still drunk from last night, uh, from today, or this morning or whenever the hell it is."

"Ain't we in a good mood," Darryl observes.

I grump back, "I never did like getting up so abruptly on such little sleep."

"You better get used to it," Darryl says. "It happens a lot. I knew we were going to get called. It never fails when we plan a party or when we get really fucked up. We had two things against us. Just talking about the party, and getting fucked up playing poker."

Dennis comes through the door, "We got fifteen minutes, you guys. Can you believe it?"

Darryl, who is all too familiar with the Forest Service says, "Yeap."

I, on the other hand say, "I can't."

Dennis continues. "I had just closed my eyes and was on my way to 'never-never land,' and then the phone rang. I knew what it was right away."

"I thought we were second," I say.

"We were," Dennis replies. "Happy Jack is going with us."

"Where is the fire?" Darryl asks him.

"On the Tonto."

Darryl considers the implications of this. "It's going to be hot down there. It was 99 degrees in Tucson yesterday."

"I believe it," Dennis says. He turns around to head out of the room. "I'm going to see if everyone's up. Let's get loaded on the bus."

I laugh at the double entendre. "Sounds good to me."

"Jim Cruz and Steve Koval aren't here," Darryl notes.

"Yeah," Dennis says. "Bob told me. He wasn't too happy about it."

"What are we going to do? We only have sixteen people," I comment.

Darryl replies, "We'll pick up somebody."

We hear the bus start up and make a run for last second preparations along with everyone else on the crew. I manage to get a peanut butter and honey sandwich put together. Darryl brings his hot chicken. Gus, with his shoestrings dragging, has his coffee. Paul Wakeford has a whole bag of cookies. Aaron has his peach nectar. Sluggo carries the remains of a half-gallon of milk. Russ munches down on a produce bag full of plums, carrots and celery.

Dennis drives the bus up to the tanker crew's quarters and Don Reed, a timber guy, jumps in. "What took you guys so long?" he asks.

Russ groans. "Oh, no. You're not going with?"

"Wouldn't miss it for the world," says Don.

Bob jumps out and knocks on a timber man's door and runs back.

Darryl asks, "Bob, who was that?"

"Manthei, he's going with us."

We wait only a few minutes before he hops on the bus. Trying to get comfortable with two people to a seat is a pain in the ass. I let Joe have the whole seat and find some floor space where I can stretch out a little. The revving roar of the engine and the hum of the highway tires make it difficult to sleep. Most of the guys pass out in awkward positions.

We hit a dirt road and it jars me awake. Apparently I did get some shuteye, about forty winks worth. I wake Joe up to make some room for me to sit down. The Happy Jack bus is parked up ahead. They probably can't make it down the eroded road any further. Dennis drives up to it carefully to avoid running over any Happy Jack Hotshots. They are scattered around on the ground and in their bus, all sacked out.

We slowly file out and find spots to sleep. Someone makes a wise crack about being aware of possible night intruders, like tarantulas, snakes and scorpions. There was no way I could sleep on the ground after hearing that

I might be bedding down with creatures like those. The inside of the bus is filled to capacity with slumbering bodies. The solution? I decide to climb up to the roof of the bus where I find Dennis and Gus all ready to zonk out. Dennis invites me. "Come on up," he says. "There's room for one more."

"Good, I don't like the idea of sleeping with rodents on the ground," I say.

"I know what you mean."

"Dennis, what time is it?"

He checks his watch. "About three-thirty."

"Shhh," Gus says. "Sack out, Petretti."

And I do.

***** *****

The guys inside are up and walking around. The bus is shaking and it stirs me awake. Dennis is gone and Gus is sitting up with his hair a mess. Mine isn't looking any better, I'm sure. Our eyes simultaneously catch sight of each other's morning hair and we smile. We're too tired to laugh, saving our energy for the fire line.

I peer over the edge of the bus and see that the Happy Jack crew is all lined up and ready to walk out. Some of our guys are ready as well, and standing around. The morning sun is just peeking over the horizon. I climb off the bus and get my shit together. We hurry up and form a single file line behind Happy Jack. I'm no way near awake, having had only an hour and a half of sleep. The bright sunshine is burning my tired, bloodshot eyes. We march, out of step, over to some forest green vehicles where we will be given our plans for the day. Bob and Russ advance along with the Happy Jack leaders to the fire boss.

A coin is tossed in the air, and immediately everyone has something to say about it.

"Looks like we're hiking up. Happy Jack is flying up," Bob says.

Pat asks, "Did you check the coin before the toss?"

So much for my first helicopter ride.

There is a faint haze in the air from the smoke of the Cholla fire that luckily stopped at a couple hundred acres. Cholla is an appropriate name. Cholla are the prominent cacti here, along with prickly pears and saguaros. The vegetation is sparse and desert-like, though the terrain is hilly. It's only 5:15 A.M., but the warmth of the morning sun is already oppressive. I take a few gulps of water, for that's all we're having for breakfast.

We get in our respective squads and proceed to the fire. We come across a small stream wash that provides a suitable fire line. Natural fire breaks are a firefighter's most appreciated allies. We walk along the wash bed cleaning out all potential fuels and throwing them to the unburned side. Black and charred coals are tossed into the burned area. A few smoky spots are still erupting making this detail no treat. The sides of the wash keep getting steeper and eventually become a ravine that leads in a rocky, uphill direction. The fire line is still on our left. We aren't worried about clearing any more debris, but we become more preoccupied and careful climbing up the canyon over the loose rocks. Our tools will be handed up after we get there, so they don't interfere with a safe climb.

Half the crew has finished climbing over this one spot when a rattler stirs. The first squad looks back at us, laughing at the ones who still have to cross over the same area. Dennis gets a stick and keeps the snake occupied as the others pass by it. I don't care to look at it, but others want a peek. The snake rattles until we are out of sight.

The 'black line,' or edge of the fire line, is heading away from the ravine. Our line digging starts here along the cold black line up the steep, rocky, mountain. The heliport, where the Happy Jack crew were dropped off, is a few ridges over. We are to meet up with the Happy Jack crew halfway in our line building efforts.

It's heating up fast and my water supply is getting lighter. I wish I had brought more than three quarts. Some veterans were carrying as much as six to eight quarts. Make a note: *Bring more water next time.*

The line digging isn't as strenuous as it was at the Presbyterian fire. Other factors make up for it, like the heat. Only a few hours into the day, and it is already over ninety degrees. The steepness of the hillside hampers us.

Under the hard hats bandannas are getting saturated with salty sweat. The overload drips down the men's faces and beads up on beards and mustaches. Salt deposits start to accumulate on our working shirts. Sweat rolls down my back and into the crack of my ass. The unbroken-in boots I'm wearing hurt my feet, and the black steel-toed tops intensify the heat inside. I'll have to remember to wear two pairs of socks next time.

Tired of leaning over the digging line, I take a short stand-up break and finish off my second quart of water. I look at Aaron and he just rolls his eyes and shakes his head. Directly over his right shoulder, in the far distance, are two small green specks, the buses we arrived in. It didn't seem to me that we had hiked up so high and so far from the buses. We both stop to look when I notice something.

"Aaron, what's that yellow to the left of the buses?"

"Looks like they're setting up for camp. It's a good sign we'll be fed tonight."

"Great, I'm starting to get hungry now, though."

"If we're lucky they might have some lunch for us."

"Is it getting close to noon?"

"It should be."

"How's your water holding out?" I ask.

"I got enough," Aaron replies. He bends over and continues to scrape the line. Water is the most valuable thing out here. I couldn't ask for any extra from someone else unless I was dying. No one was about to give up his stash of water. I'm finding that out the hard way. Next time I'll bring more water, two pairs of socks and, my God, I still have a lot to learn about this firefighting stuff! Someone from above yells down at me to get back to work. Without looking uphill, I continue where I left off. We haven't had a break yet and I'm beginning to run on empty. Smith does not believe in breaks when there's work to be done. Darryl takes notice of my sluggish movements.

"Hey, Petretti," he calls, "how's your water holding out?"

"Oh, I got about a quart left."

"How many did you bring?"

"Only three."

"You'll learn."

Wakeford turns around and laughs at me. "I bring at least two gallons on these desert fires."

"I guess you FNG's will learn the hard way," Darryl says.

"Yeap," I respond. "I guess so. That's my style, learning the hard way."

Cord is right in front of me and I whisper to him so no one else will hear, "Hey, Mike, What's FNG?"

Cord chuckles. "It's a Fucking New Guy, like yourself."

"It must be over a hundred out here."

"People like Smith and Wakeford, the heat don't even faze them. They're all desert boys," Cord says.

"I can tell."

Chink, chink, ping, chink. These are the sounds heard as the busy Hotshots ascend the mountain. We can see the Happy Jacks at the top of the same ridge we're working on. Scorching moments later, Bob's command brings relief to our ears, "You can take a break when we tie in."

On the break the few shady spots are taken up fast. Dennis comes down and informs us that all we have to do is hike up to the top where the heliport is. Our lunches and cold water will be there at two o'clock.

When we are through eating lunch we are to improve the line on the other side of the blackened area and mop up any hot spots. Happy Jack will be doing the same on this side. We, and the 'Jack crew, are too hot and tired to socialize together. I finish off the rest of my water, which is warm by now. We work our way to the top following the hand line Happy Jack built. They did as good a job as we did. We are careful not to disturb the water bars, but use them as steps. We remove the occasional root to increase the quality of the line. Only a few stumps are smoking. Basically the fire is pretty cold.

We arrive at the top minutes before the helicopter. The helitack people drop off a couple of boxes and about a dozen canteens. We scramble for the lunches and water like starving refugees. Quickly we return to the limited shade each of us has staked claim to with his gear. The few unburned leafless shrubs have to accommodate a crowd. As a result only our heads are shaded, the rest of our bodies simmer in the blazing sun. To our surprise the lunches are completely frozen. Sandwiches feature hard chunks of butter on green turkey loaf. The juices are frozen and undrinkable, and water in the canteens is warm! We remove the fruit before it freezes. Comments are made that these are last year's lunches held over for this year's fires. The veterans say that similar cloth-like lunch sacks were used last year on other Tonto fires.

The helicopter takes off, creating a wall of dust and ash that permeates the eyes. The condition of the food doesn't stop anybody from devouring it. Some fill their canteens first to allow the food to thaw a little. The water goes fast, the lunches not so quickly, but as bad as it was, it sure was revitalizing.

The heat continues to pour down on us like the breath of a blast furnace as the familiar sound of, "Back to work," brings us to our feet again for another round of torture in the cotton fields. Still, the short rest built up our spirits. We have the rest of the day to work down to the bottom of the hill. Our orders are to improve the line and mop up a chain within. Squad one is assigned to improve line, and we get mop up duty, contouring along the line.

About three quarters of the way down, we notice a half dozen guys huddled in a bunch. We figure they're on break, but realize quickly that things are more serious then that. Someone is lying down and Jake, our EMT, is hovering over him. Turns out Marty injured himself. Dennis makes us all stay put while he goes over to see what happened. When he is only a few feet away, Bob calls the Fire Boss on the radio. Dennis stops in his tracks, takes the radio out of the holder, and holds it up to his ear.

"Go ahead Blue Ridge," he hears the Fire Boss say.

Bob responds, "We have a man with an injured knee."

"Is he able to walk?"

Bob pauses for a moment, and we see him talking to Marty and Jake. "Uh, 10-4, but we are still on a very steep section of the line. Is there a copter available for transport?"

"Negative," comes the reply. "The ship ran out of flight time. Do you have an EMT on your crew?"

"10-4, we'll have to wrap it up and assist him down the best we can."

"Sounds good, we'll have a doctor available at the fire camp. Have two of your men bring him to the road an we'll have a truck ready there for transport."

"10-4."

Jake and Mike Manthei help Marty down the hill, moving slowly on each side of him, supporting his weight.

"Well," Dennis says, "that's that. You guys be real careful with your footing. I don't want anyone else hurt. Start working your way down."

We give up on the mopping action and continue downhill at a measured pace. We meet up with the other squad a ways down and cut through the blackened area to the bottom. When we arrive, we find Jake and Manthei sitting by a natural spring that seems to flow out of nowhere.

Bob tells us, "Take five. Jake, did you get him out OK?"

"Yeah. It sounds like he might have pulled his ligaments."

"That's what I suspected. Was a doctor with the truck?"

"No. They said they were transporting him to the Payson hospital. You're supposed to talk to Plans when we get to fire camp."

"OK. Thanks, Jake."

Meanwhile, the rest of us have stripped our shirts off and stuck our heads in the stream to soak up the cool refreshment. Gus takes off his boots and lies down in the water. We pour hats full of water over our heads. It was the best thing we could have come across! Even Bob takes time out to indulge. With Bob's instigation, a water fight breaks out and we throw hats full of water at each other. We rinse out our sweaty bandannas and wash the crust off our faces. We fill all our canteens as if we were never going to see water again. The short intermission makes us momentarily forget the torture we went through earlier.

Bob puts an end to our idyll. "That's it. Back to work! Squad up and let's start walking out of here."

We get dressed again, but not without throwing a few wet bandannas around at each other. We are all pretty well soaked from the water fight. Fully recuperated we get back to our usual slaving selves again and walk away. Like the seven dwarfs in Disney's "Snow White" we start whistling a chorus of, "I owe, I owe, it's off to work we go." When we arrive in fire camp, there's a hell of a lot more going on than when we left.

Happy Jack beat us back and those guys are lounging around drinking soda pop and juices. We each get a couple of sodas ourselves. Several tarps are up and designated for certain fire organization functions. Three Indian crews have been brought in for mop up on the night shift. One is an all woman crew. A few of us giggle as we walk by. Kyle makes his usual dumb, warped remarks that no one pays any attention to. When we stop, Bob goes to Plans, and Russ and Paul go over to timekeeping to say "Hi" to some girl they know from a Tonto fire many years ago. She turns them onto a wading pool about a hundred yards behind their tent-like structure. Most of us head down without hesitating. Dinner isn't ready yet, and we have enough time to take a dip.

Wild horses are around the water. Our approach frightens them

off, but it doesn't take them long before curiosity brings them back to see us skinny dipping in their watering hole. I knew the horses were having their own private horselaugh at our hanging dongs, so puny compared to theirs. We pass around a joint to make our swim even better. Cord makes friends with one of the horses and hops on his back... Mr. Godiva at his best. What a sight! Ten naked dudes and one Darryl with a modest tee shirt on. We are skinny-dipping in the middle of the Tonto desert, with wild horses watching us from around the perimeter of the pond.

Darryl is the only exception to this optional swimsuit area. He keeps his tee shirt on. In the water, little minnows swim about and nibble on our flesh. I don't worry about them catching hold of any vitals. I figure to them it looks like one-eyed eel. Now, if salmon or sturgeon occupied these waters, we'd all have something to worry about.

We thoroughly rinse off the salty, sweaty crust we had acquired earlier, and head back for chow. The couple hits we took off a joint gives us a case of the munchies and a considerably improved attitude about the day. There's a long food line and half the people are already sitting down eating. The night shift people ate first so they could hurry out to the fire area. The Indian women are still giggling and talking about us in their Indian language. They were probably spying on us while we were skinny-dipping. That's all right by us. Cheap thrills are hard to come by out here in the middle of the desert.

Russ goes off to find Bob to see what the plans are. We grab another soda and find our place at the end of the line. Russ returns rather quickly to let us know what's happening.

"We're being released after we eat," he announces.

James looks up with a smile. "We are? Great!"

"Too bad, I was just starting to like it here," Cord says.

Jake asks, "Where's Marty at? Did they take him to the hospital?"

"He's at Payson Medical," Russ tells him. "We get to stop by there on the way home and pick him up."

"Did Bob say what was wrong with him?"

"Nope, he didn't know. All he knew was that they took him to the hospital."

"I hope he's not seriously hurt."

Russ turns to me. "Ah, Petretti, were you saving my place?"

"I didn't know I was," I remark as he cuts in front of me in line. "I guess I am now."

"Thanks. You're a real pal."

"Don't mention it," I say sarcastically.

"Looks like we're having barf bags," Russ comments.

"Is that what's in those drums?" Sluggo wants to know.

"Yeap, last year's, just like the lunches. Kyle and James are over there trying to hustle the timekeepers."

"Where are they at?"

"Over there where the Plans tent is. I was talking to Bob and saw them move right in. They sat down right next to them and started eating."

"They are already eating? How'd they manage that?" I say.

"Kyle has a way of being first in the food line. He always pigs out at fire camp. You'll see him going back for seconds and thirds."

Darryl butts in. "He doesn't eat anything at Blue Ridge but egg sandwiches, milk and cereal, and rations."

"God, how can he eat rations?" I say.

"Simple, he doesn't have to pay for it."

Russ shakes his head. "I don't see how he survives on what he eats."

Darryl says, "He starves himself all the time and then porks out at fire camps."

"He has to pay for that, too," Russ reminds him.

"You mean we got to pay for this food?" I say indignantly.

"You think you get it for nothing? Sure you have to pay for it," Darryl responds.

"Darryl, you asshole," Cord says and turns to me to clarify. "You get sixteen dollars a day for travel expenses, and they take four dollars out for every meal."

"That's only twelve dollars," I say.

Russ explains, "The rest you get in a check. It's your 'per diem' check."

"That's not bad," I say, somewhat mollified.

"Yeah," says Darryl. "On a big fire it gets up to a hundred dollars sometimes. It all adds up and you get an unexpected check at the end of the month."

Adds Russ, "It comes in handy at times."

Darryl continues, "I like to save them and cash them all at once at the end of the season. You can save a few hundred dollars up that way easily."

"That food don't look too good," I remark.

"It isn't," says Cord. "It tastes like dog shit."

The food is boiled in separate plastic bags, thrown together in a netted plastic pouch. Salisbury steak, lima beans, chunk potatoes, salad, fruit, and stale bread are on the menu tonight. It reminds me of eating a TV dinner. It definitely isn't worth the four dollars. Tonto figures to go with cheap and convenient, not quality. But hunger, as they say, is the best relish. Hungry as we are, we eat everything we get. Juices and soda pop fill up the empty spaces that the boiled gut bags don't satisfy. We have a quick dinner and head for home, re-hydrated and with full bellies.

On our way we pick up Marty at the hospital. The doctor says he will be out of work for a while due to sprained ligaments. We get off the clock at midnight, but not until we replace the dull tools with fresh ones. Not bad for a twenty-four hour shift! We were on the clock for twenty-and-a-half hours this day. On our trip back, Kyle stands up and makes a general announcement giving an up-to-the-cent figure on our earnings for the day. Looking back on the whole episode, it wasn't all that bad. The cool night mountain air made us forget the blazing hot sun we encountered earlier in the day. Extreme hot and cold are only temporary discomforts. In this time away from Los Angeles, I have experienced both the hottest and coldest temperatures of my life. We all forgot about the party we missed.

June 24

Sunday is a keep busy day around the station. Dull tools are sharpened, the bus cleaned out real good, inside and out. Dirty fire clothes are washed and mended, smoke chasers reorganized and repacked. Necessary things are added to the packs and vests, to make the next fire a little more comfortable. Items are removed to lighten the carrying load. A necessity in my cache was accommodation for more water so I wouldn't come up short and dry again.

We devote half the day to constructing a new volleyball court and manicuring the old one. Bob had accepted a challenge from the Happy Jacks Hotshots to a few games of volleyball. Reamer is excited about the contest and allows us to put in some time after work at recreation's expense. Koval, Jim, and I take off for the reservoir to go fishing. This time we bring an FS radio.

"So, I hear I didn't miss much," Koval says.

"Just a lot of heat and frustration," I answer.

"Sounds like the Tonto. I hate it down there. I'm kind of glad I didn't go."

"You supposedly went fishing. Did you ever go?"

"Yes, but only for about half an hour. I wasn't getting no bites so I took off for Flagstaff."

"I know you didn't get enough over the weekend," Jim says. "That was my problem. Cord kept on calling me, right when I was getting laid. And, like hell I was going to answer the fucking phone."

"I was going up Friday anyway," Koval explains. "I just wanted to fish a little on the way up."

"Where did you go fishing?" I ask.

"I went up to Long Lake. It's on the way to Flagstaff. Boy, sometimes I think Michelle's a nympho. She never gets enough. I mean we fucked all weekend."

"That's what I did," says Jim. "Fucked all weekend. I tell you what! I would rather be snuggled up to a warm pussy than be around all them dirty, smelly, horny guys all day. It was worth missing the fire for."

"You got that right," Koval agrees.

"This girl I was with is a registered nurse working on her Biology master's degree at U of A, and boy can she fuck your socks off."

"You guys are making me horny," I protest.

"What happened to that girl I saw you with on your bike a few weeks ago?" Koval asks me.

"Oh, I had to let her go her own way."

"That's too bad. She looked pretty from what I saw of her."

"Yeah, I know. I have been thinking about her. I'm sorry it happened, but she's on her way to Europe this weekend."

"Is she rich?" Jim inquires.

"No, she's getting some divorce allocations that's paying her way."

"You should have come down to Tucson with me and Cord."

"I know. Cord has been trying to get me to go down with him ever since I met him. He said he could fix me up with Janine's friend any time. According to Mike, she's supposed to be anxious to meet me."

"I could fix you up with lots of girls if he don't," Jim offers.

"He probably told her what a big Italian cock you have and got her all hot," Koval says.

"I wouldn't doubt it, he'd say something like that. Well, one of these days I'll have to get down there to party after fire season slows down a little. It should be picking up now, though."

"Yes, it should be getting crazy real soon," Koval agrees.

"Darryl said that Bob wrote us up for not going to the fire," Jim says.

"That's what I heard. He was pretty pissed off about you guys being gone," I report.

"I don't know why he was so pissed," Koval says. "You guys went anyway."

I explain. "We had to get two timber people. Reamer said from now on if everyone isn't here, we won't go and no more borrowing people to fill out the crew. I don't know what Bob's going to do now that Marty could be out for the rest of the season."

"That's right. Marty hurt himself. He had a bad knee last year I seem to remember. He'll have to hire another body to take his place," Koval says.

"I really don't care if he writes me up or not," Jim says. "I'm not coming back to this desolate place again. I need the city lights and action and the pussy to survive. I can do without the city lights. It's the pussy I'm finding a problem to cope without."

"I hear that," says Koval. "I still haven't been able to do without pussy my whole life." We all concur with that statement. Koval adds, "Beating off isn't my style."

"Mine either," says Jim.

"Hey, Steve, roll another joint. It's your turn."

The only thing we caught was a good buzz. The whole crew goes to bed early, still tired from the day before.

June 25 to 27

The next day we are fully reinvigorated and resume our thinning. The second half of the day is devoted to finishing up our work on the volleyball courts for the big game tomorrow. P.T. never changes, but my endurance and muscles are improving. Each day of running, I push myself further and further, walking less and less each time. My lungs are adapting nicely to the altitude. Deep breaths come more frequently and hurt less. I can feel deep pockets of my lungs open up for fresh air after many years compressed like an unused balloon. I am coughing up dark green plugs of mucus that originated from city smog. My body feels good. I am in the best shape of my life.

At times I'd remember how the smog would get in L.A. It was so bad in the sixties and seventies that by the time you got home from school, your lungs would hurt with every breath you took. You couldn't even take a full breath without feeling a sharp pain in your rib cage. Your eyes would sting and water constantly. What a crime! But the kissing of corporate big bastard asses forced people to put up with this shit in our air. When I was in the Law Enforcement Explorers, we took a tour of the county morgue. The mortician pulled out the lung of a man who smoked. His lung was all brown. Then he pulled out the lung of a person who had lived in L.A. all his life. That lung was all black! The worst part about it was that my parents used to accuse me of being on drugs, judging by the way I looked coming home from school. How can a student function in that atmosphere? But, hey, that's what my parents and most parents, and the citizens of this fine country must have wanted. They are the ones who voted into office those political bastards who allowed our air to get so poisonous. How can our own government gas their own people like that?

Exercises aren't getting easier. Bob adds on to the count a little at a time. Still, the best thing of all about P.T. is that it is on government time. The volleyball games with Happy Jack turn out to be a jock event, which leaves most of us out of it. So we put together a makeshift volley court right across the road to play the second string team. Happy Jack makes a sweep on both courts beating Blue Ridge two out of three games.

The main sporting event tonight is an all-night, get drunk, pool tournament. We play doubles for beers. Drifty is my partner and his stick is as hot as mine. We get too drunk to play, so we let someone else win a game. Sluggo and James are partners and take a lot of verbal abuse from everyone. They are the live entertainment.

Cord departs for Tucson again. This time he asks for Friday off, and once again he'll be working a Cord week. We call it that, jokingly. His plan is four days on, three days off. We are all convinced he is pussy whipped. I am awakened on my day off by heavy footsteps on the roof. I know this is not the usual way to alert the crew about a fire. It reminds me of when I was a kid and our neighbor's peacocks would get loose and fly on our rooftop. Their peculiar cries sounded like a child in distress calling, "Help! Help!" The noise on our trailer roof this morning sounds like an oversized ostrich walking around. Of course it isn't, but it comes from a breed just as dumb, the tankers. Lying in bed, I yell for the buzzards to identify themselves.

"What the hell is going on up there? Darryl get your gun, the buzzards are raiding us."

A voice wafts down from the rooftop, "Wake up in there!"

"No, let me sleep."

More voices from above, barely distinguishable. "Who was that?"

"I don't know, Couldn't tell. Sounded like Petretti."

"Hey, Petretti, is that you?"

"Yes, it is.

"Are you awake?"

"Thanks to you."

My kidneys hurt from needing to piss all night, a consequence of all those beers I drank. In pain I crawl out of bed to relieve myself, meanwhile listening closely to the voices above me, hoping to identify at least one of them.

"Darryl, what are they doing up there?" I call. Then it hits me... that awful smell. "Never mind, I just smelled the tar."

I walk out to the kitchen and see that Darryl, in an apron, has been busy cleaning house all morning. "Good morning," he says.

"Good morning, dear. Is my breakfast ready?"

Darryl chuckles. "How did you like the alarm clock?"

"What alarm clock? I thought it was an earthquake."

"There are no earthquakes up here. I'm telling you, you've been in California too long."

"Maybe I was dreaming I was in California before I woke up."

Jim Bedlion suddenly struts in, smelling like tar. Darryl addresses him. "You've been tarring the roofs." Jim ignores us and continues to walk around the trailer like he owns the place, checking things out.

"About time," Darryl continues. "You're lucky we haven't had any downpours yet."

Bedlion still ignores his comments and parks himself in front of a bow and arrow Darryl owns, regarding the weapon with a sneer. "What a piece of shit," he comments.

"Don't say that, I bought it from you two years ago."

"No shit? So that's why it looks familiar. How much did I sell it to you for?"

"Sixty dollars."

"You got a good buy."

"I know."

Bedlion turns from the bow and arrow and faces us. "Darryl, you want to work today?" he asks.

"Naw."

"I do," I say. "I'll work today."

"Let's go, then. You can help the idiots tar roofs today."

"Great, my favorite thing to do. They used to call me 'Tarbaby.'"

"You've done it before?"

"Sure, lots of times."

"Good, you can take my place and I'll go hang out in the office so someone can kiss *my* ass. Gee, maybe I'll have you idiots do my trailer, too." He departs as quickly as he entered, strutting.

"Nice way to start out the new pay period," Darryl remarks. "I would of volunteered but I don't like doing that shit. Besides, I like my days off."

"Why? You don't do anything but lay around," I say.

"Yeap, lay around without a worry in the world. Besides, I had fun last weekend. Too much fun. I have to save some of that fun for this weekend."

"That's because I made you go out and have fun."

After a cup of coffee, I join Hopkins, Wickham, Corky, and the 7-41 crew on the trailer tops. Toward the end of the day I run into Darryl again. "How was working with tankers today?" Darryl asks me.

"Not bad, I was keeping the Hotshot attitude. I just kept adding up all the money I made."

"Did Bedlion work with you all day?"

"Most of it. We even tarred his trailer over in the units."

"Is that the one he's selling to the station?"

"Yeah, I think. Wickham mentioned something to that effect."

"You want to go?"

"Go where?"

"To my favorite place to go. I'll even get stoned with you."

"Now, that's an occasion," I say with surprise.

"You can even bring your camera. There are a lot of good shots there."

"Where is this place?"

"Moqui Ranch, it's only a couple of miles away."

"Sounds good, we'll take my bike. I hope I won't be disappointed."

"You won't. I told you it was my favorite place to go."

"That ain't telling me much, I know what kind of things you get off on. Well I'm ready. You ready?"

"Yeah. Oh, let me get one more thing." Darryl goes into his room and brings out a wicked looking rifle. "This is my equalizer," he explains.

"What kind is it? Looks like something I've seen Patty Hurst carry."

"Almost. This is an M-15. I'll let you shoot it at Moqui Draw. That's our shooting range."

Darryl is right about the picturesque scenery around Moqui Ranch. A well-known rancher owns the place and a few sections of land in the vicinity. He uses the cabins when it's round-up time for his cowboys. Darryl says they've tried to get the ranger to let the Hotshots use the cabins for crew quarters. The three rustic structures are full of cobwebs and mice, as no one has lived in them since last year. The furniture inside is old and rotten. Cans of food are still in the closet, kept there for any traveler who gets stuck in the snow.

The ranch sits in a colorful meadow liberally sprinkled with a variety of flowers. It's nice to imagine waking up in such a beautiful, unspoiled place. I leave my bike in front of the handmade log cabins with their rusted, corrugated tin roofs. A spider web woven between barbed wire fences glistens

with dewdrops. Cows by a stock tank, and a cabin in the background, add to the bucolic charm. The setting sun silhouettes a leaning snag, fully dressed with widowmakers. A rutted and rarely traveled dirt road with a grass island stretches up to a deserted shack with broken stalls adjacent. It's a real treat for the senses, one that I prefer over a whole page layout of Playboy bunnies.

June 28

I awake slowly and naturally Thursday morning. The automatic alarm clock in my head gently tunes me in to greet another beautiful day. It is especially quiet this morning because Darryl left the trailer early this morning. I wake up in a pensive mood, roll a joint and go outside to find a place behind the cabins where I can sit amidst natural beauty and meditate. I find a good spot and enter into a much-needed and blissful meditation. It's wonderful coming out of a deep meditation and opening your eyes and ears to surroundings of pure nature. I smoke the joint and think about Castleberry and Richie. They were also a beautiful part of nature. Two people who were close to me, who spread goodness to others. The world needs more good people like them. Slowly, through the ages, I feel like the good people of the earth are becoming an endangered species.

I am overwhelmed, thinking of all the negative characteristics of the human race. I want to sit there and cry out loud in pain and pity for mankind, praying that one day all hatred, and every bad quality of the human race will diminish. Somehow I know it will never happen, because of the very primitive essence and low form of the human will. There are bad characteristics in all of us. Some people choose to exercise negative qualities of human will, instead of emphasizing their good qualities in harmony with nature. The bad animal instinct in humans always seems to dominate. At least it takes more of an effort to exercise the divine human qualities. It is too easy to be bad. My present involvement in the problem consists of sitting there and mourning mankind's follies. I do this as I re-enter reality from my meditation.

Darryl is back and in a better mood, playing his usual weekend tapes of Crosby, Stills, Nash and Young, and the sound track from "Tommy." Every weekend that I have been around him he has played the same music.

"The checks should be in. Are you going to town?" Darryl asks.

"I was waiting for you to ask me to go with you."

"You're not going to stay the night this time?"

"No, not this time. I'll help pay for gas."

"Did you go get stoned again?"

"What does it look like?"

"Yes. I don't know about you guys. It's going to catch up with you one of these days."

"I'm sure it will," I agree. I didn't want to tell him my main reasons for going on a walk. He wouldn't understand the mood I was in. "Darryl," I sigh, "you're so ignorant."

"What brought that on?"

"Oh, nothing. Forget I even said it."

A frown crosses Darryl's face. "I was going to have you come with me anyway to help me with the keg."

I remember why. "That's right, I almost forgot about the party Saturday night. We'll have to see how many people we can invite this time. We'll get the whole town of Flagstaff and every student at NAU down here."

"I'm not going to invite any more to come. I got a feeling we're not going to be here."

"Why are you worried about getting the keg then?"

"In case we don't go to a fire."

"Oh, I see."

We meet the all female archeology group at Bruce's and invite them to the party. They were filling up the state vehicles. We remember that 7-41 was saying something about them the other day during the volleyball games with Happy Jack. It was rumored that the girls do their digs in the buff.

We finish running errands in time to "do" a happy hour. The last stop before returning to Blue Ridge has consistently been at the Widowmaker. It's been in Darryl's routine for years, and it's becoming part of mine. Drifty and Aaron are already indulging by the time we show up. Some Mormon Lake Hotshots and a few Flagstaff Hotshots are gathered around, working on three pitchers of beer.

"Hey, Darryl," a voice yells out from across the bar.

"Who said that?" Darryl asks.

I tell him, "That guy on the Mormon Lake crew, over there. He's over by Drifty and Aaron."

"Oh, yeah, I see him."

"What was his name again?"

"Kellogg, Danny Kellogg. Come on. Meet some more 'shots."

We shove our way to the corner of the bar and are cordially greeted by Danny. "Hey, how y'all doing Darryl?" he asks.

"Fine."

"Hi, Danny," I say.

"Hey, it's the Mad Italian." I guess my reputation is getting around.

"Where did you get the 'Mad Italian' from? I want to know."

"Drifty told me to call you that."

"Drifty, did you tell him that?"

"Yes, that's because you are."

"Get some glasses, you guys," Danny says. He looks up at the bartender and waits for her to catch his eye. "Caroline, I need two glasses, please." She gets them and brings them over to the table. "Thanks, beautiful."

"Let me fill these up for yas," she offers. She pours the glasses full at the proper angle, being careful not to leave a foamy head.

"Have a beer, Steven," Danny says.

"Thanks."

"Have you met these bums I work with?" he continues.

"No, man, you're the only one I know from your crew," I reply.

"Steven, this is Rolando, the Mexican on the crew."

Rolando acknowledges the introduction with a "Si."

"Glad to meet you," I say holding out my hand. We shake.

"This is Johansen and Porkchop, (Danny Kellogg)."

"Hi, guys, glad to meet you."

"So, you're on the Blue Ridge crew. First year?" Rolando queries.

"Yeap. Have you ever worked down there?"

"No, but Porkchop has."

"Oh, yeah? When?"

"Three years ago, when that asshole Holinstadt was crew boss."

"I haven't heard anything good about him."

"There isn't anything good to say about him," says Porkchop.

"So, that's why you're working on Mormon Lake?"

"Yes, and because it's closer to town."

"I hear that," I tell him. I don't dig having to drive 70 miles every time I come to town." I raise my glass and quickly finish my first glass. I let out a big, "Ahhhhhhh. I needed that."

"Here, let me fill your glass up," says Rolando hospitably.

"Alright. Thanks."

Porkchop cautions, "David, we need to get these pitchers refilled before happy hour is over."

Dan calls to the barmaid, "Caroline, three more, please."

"You want three more?"

"They have to keep all of us happy."

"Make it four," I say. "I'll buy one."

Rolando nods. "Four it is. We got some suds to soak down."

"We got all night," says Porkchop.

"And a lot of help," I add. I see some guys still sitting there that I haven't been formally introduced to yet. "Who are these guys? Are they on your crew?"

"No," Dan says. "They are on the Flagstaff crew. This is Davy Jones and Henry."

"Davy Jones uhh, I hear you used to be a good sailor," I quip.

"Huh? I've never been to the sea."

"Oh, never mind. It was a bad joke. Hi, Hank, how are you?"

"Getting drunk."

"Yeah, that seems to be the thing to do right now."

June 29

It's a typical Monday at work with everyone moving about in slow motion as we load into the bus. Russ drives up to the office and parks. Bob stays a little longer in the office than usual. Gus gets up and heads out the door to go into the office.

"Gus, where are you going?" Cord inquires.

"To get a Coke."

"Can you get me one, too?"

"You got some money?"

Mike Cord digs in his pocket and tosses out a quarter. "Keep the change," he says.

James joins in. "Gus, get me one, too."

"You got a quarter?"

"No. Why don't you lend me one?"

"No way! I'll never see it again."

"Pat," James says. "You got a quarter you can lend me?"

"Nope."

"Come on," Gus pleads. "Someone lend him a quarter."

"I know not to even ask Kyle," James says. "Petretti, got a quarter?"

"Yeah, here."

"Just toss it to Gus."

"Anyone else before I go?" Gus asks wearily.

"Yeah," Drifty says. "Get me some coffee."

"Fuck that, this is just a coke run."

Pat speaks up now. "Gus, get me a beer."

"I wish I could, I'd get us all one."

"See what's taking Bob so long," Darryl says.

"He's probably getting a second cup," says Cord.

"Oh, but he never asks for seconds," Pat says, like they do in the coffee commercial.

"They're serving Yuban in there now." That's my contribution.

Cord adds wisely, "Yeah, that Colombian grown."

Sluggo pipes up. "I could use come Colombian grown right now."

"Sluggo, you asshole, that's not what I meant," Cord snaps.

"I know what you meant. I was just trying to be funny."

"You don't have to be funny," Darryl tells him. "You look funny twenty-four hours a day."

"James," Dennis says. "You have no room to laugh. You're always a sorry sight, too."

"That's not funny," James sulks.

"I think Bob's checking up on hiring a new guy," Russ remarks.

"That's right," Darryl says. "I forgot about Marty not being with us anymore."

"Darryl, if your head wasn't glued on you'd forget that, too.

"Cord, shut up."

"You're right, I'm running out of funny things to say."

"I'm getting out of here, you're all crazy," Paul says in disgust.

"What got into him?" says Pat.

"Old age is setting in," Darryl explains.

Joe calls out, "Russ, put some music on."

"Good idea, I'm getting sick of listening to you assholes."

"Ladies and Gentlemen, Mr. Waylon Jennings..." blares from the speaker on cue. Some cheer while others bitch, "Oh, no, not this tape again. Take it off, take it off. Rock 'n Roll, Rock n Roll."

"It's staying in!" Russ pronounces.

Bob comes out of the office walking fast. Gus is right behind him handling all the sodas. At first it looks like we've been dispatched. No such luck. Bob instructs Russ to go where we left off thinning.

The sawyers are far enough ahead of the stackers that we can hear ourselves talk now. Keeping a conversation going while you're dragging and stacking helps the time go by more bearably. An occasional pinecone fight helps break up the monotony as well as builds character and fast reactions. Of all the billions and billions of things to talk about, sex and hunting take up ninety-nine percent of the conversations.

At lunchtime we are entertained by ant lions. It is easy to spot their funnel shaped death traps. We go on an insect hunt to feed the ant lions. The insects try desperately to escape, but the trap sucks them in like quicksand. The insect struggles for a while, then rigor mortis seems to hit it and the ant lion swallows it up beneath the sand. We throw several types and sizes of insects to their death. Only a few manage to flee for their lives. We figure after feeding a particular ant lion a handful of bugs it will be too full to bury itself deep in the sand. But no matter how full it gets, or how fast we try to dig it out, we can never catch one to see what it looks like. No one in the crew has ever actually seen one, so our efforts grow more intense. We try drowning it out by pouring water in its hole. We even light the hole on fire with a fuse, but no ant lion appears. We still wonder what the varmints look like.

In our efforts we had all but forgotten Bob. Suddenly his distinctive echoing cry of, "Back to work!" rings out.

During work a couple of saws break down, so most of us are left stacking sticks. We all talk and joke about the huge party coming up tomorrow. Darryl, as usual, is warning us not to get over anxious, not to expect something that probably won't happen. He feels it's his duty as RCO, (rumor control officer), to keep reminding us of the possibility that we'll be going to a fire, our efforts to make this a great party setting Murphy's Law in action. I wonder where we are on the dispatch list.

June 30

Distantly, in my dream, I hear the tires lock up and slide over the gravel in front of our trailers. What seem like hours in dreamland are only minutes later when Pat comes in to wake us up by turning on the light. In his Mr. Rogers voice he chirps, "Good morning, boys and girls." He stands there in profile. It occurs to me that he not only talks like Mr. Rogers, but looks like him, too. "We're going to take a walk in the Tonto neighborhood today."

Cord growls at him, "Would you like to get beat up?"

"Sure. Sure I would."

"We got a fire on the Tonto?" I ask groggily.

"That's what Dennis said."

"Is he running around all hyper again?" Cord asks.

"Yes, he came in to wake us up and ran out. He said he had to get the others up."

"How much time do we have to get ready?" I ask.

"He didn't say."

"Knowing Dennis, we always have fifteen minutes," says Cord.

Dennis comes back in our trailer and yells, "How come no one is up in here? This is the first place I came to."

"You mean you were here before?" I ask, surprised.

"We're awake," Cord says.

"I better get Kyle and Jim up," Pat says.

Cord says bitterly, "Who can sleep when Dennis is running around all hyped up? I hate it when he gets that way."

"I know what you mean," I agree. "He gets me all nervous when there's no need to. Mike, what time is it?"

"Let me look. It's one-fifteen."

"At least we got a couple hours sleep this time."

"Here we go again, a repeat from last week."

"Deja vu."

Once again the trailer rocks, fast footsteps clomping on the hollow floors. Everyone is running around like chickens with their heads cut off. Darryl has his microwave and stereo cranked. Cord is bitching about everything he possibly can. Pat is bumping into people pretending he's sleepwalking, checking for morning hard-ons. Kyle's making sure the juices he nabbed at the Cholla fire are properly placed in his vest for quick recovery. Jim Cruz is being an asshole, and I'm checking everyone out. Bob comes in with a giant cup of coffee. "We're leaving in five minutes," he announces.

Darryl turns the music off and says, "Last one out shut the door," and we all scramble out the door, half-dressed, arms full of stuff.

Wakeford is standing at his doorway with a bag of cookies in his hand and a can of Pepsi and calls out, "Bob, who are we going to take along? We still only have seventeen."

"Dispatcher knows we're only taking seventeen," Bob replies. "They just want a crew right now."

"For the day shift?"

"Yes. Is everyone out of their trailers?"

"No," Wakeford replies. "That slow poke, James, is still poking around. He moves as slow as he talks." He shouts, "Get his ass in gear!"

Bob calls out, "I'm putting you in charge to get him moving."

Wakeford yells into the trailer, "James, we are leaving you behind, boy. You'd better hurry up." He lets out another cheerful scream and jumps off the stairs.

James finally comes out and walks slowly across the jagged gravel in his bare feet, his boots over his shoulder. "Coming, y' all," he drawls.

To rouse another straggler, Russ leans out of the driver's window and says, "Sluggo, we're leaving."

A few more voices scream out of the bus, "Come on, Sluggo!" "Let's go, Sluggo!" Bob wonders out loud if Sluggo even got out of bed.

Everyone loads up and we head out for the flatlands with a clear road ahead. It doesn't take long for most of the guys to pick up their dreaming where they left off. A few of us stay awake. Russ is driving, Bob is overly caffeined, Dennis is No Dozed, Paul Wakeford is on a sugar high, and I just can't sleep in crowded conditions.

"Boy, I'm so happy. I'm just tickled pink," Paul says.

"Why are you so happy?" I ask.

"Boy, I'm so happy 'cause we're going to another fire on the Tonto. Yeap, I like the Tonto. Yeap that hot Tonto." He looks at the others getting settled in their seats, falling back to sleep. "Why aren't you going back to sleep?"

"Sleep with all this excitement going on? Who can sleep with all this going on? Why aren't you sleeping?"

"I can't sleep in these conditions."

"There, you see, I can't sleep either. Besides, I got enough last night."

"You only got a couple of hours at the most."

"Hey, that's all I need. I feel good now," I say.

"Yeap, real good." Wakeford gestures with his head toward the sleeping masses. "Look at all these tired mother fuckers. They'd rather sleep, but not me. Nope, not me. Bob's still awake. Dennis is always awake. You know he takes those pills to keep him awake. Yeah, that Dennis is a real pill popper. Bob is just like me, he can't sleep either with all this shit going on."

Cord speaks up. "Yeah, and Cord can't sleep because Wakeford can't keep his big mouth shut."

Wakeford answers with obviously fake concern, "Oh, my goodness, someone is getting upset 'cause they can't sleep."

This doesn't sit too well with Cord who shows signs of getting really pissed. "Damn it, Wakeford, lighten up on the mouth."

Bob turns around and exerts his authority, requesting consideration for others. "Hey, Paul, don't eat any more cookies, and keep it down."

"Oh, OK, Bob boss." Wakeford says. "I just can't help it. I just can't wait to get out there in the heat and put them fires out. Just like old times."

"Shhhhhhh!" Aaron hisses.

"I better keep quiet before someone beats me up," Wakeford says softly, and chuckles. He nudges me from across the aisle. "Look at that Kyle, he's sleeping with his hard hat on. I bet he sleeps with it all the time."

I reply, "He does, he goes to bed with it on all the time. When I go in to tuck him in, I take it off."

Paul laughs heartily and says in an undertone, "I bet that it's glued to his head."

I have a hard time trying not to laugh out loud at that one, and just have to add one more dig. "That is why his hair is so messed up. It's full of glue."

Wakeford mimes laughing out loud. Kyle's head is leaning against the window. Wakeford reaches over the seat and slowly pushes Kyle's head forward until it bobbles freely. Without waking, Kyle resumes his previous position against the window. It amuses Wakeford so much he does it again. Then he turns to me and says, "That Kyle is really something, he sure is a particular boy. Fuckin' A. Aren't we there yet? Well shit, I guess I'll rest up." He gets a gallon of water and drinks about half of it. Then blurts out, "Ahhh, I needed that. I better save the rest, cause I'll need it later."

Everyone is ignoring him now so he proceeds to relax and keeps quiet, fiddling with his gear. I doze off, but shake awake many times from the movement of the bus. Each time I look around at the different positions the others are in. Kyle is still against the window. Wakeford looks over, smiles and nods at me. He says softly, "You are getting into this firefighting stuff, aren't ya?" I smile back in agreement.

We arrive at our destination around 0500 hours. The sign I noticed a way back indicated that we were near Superior. As soon as we stop Bob goes to find out our detail. We file out of the bus and watch the light of another day come over the eastern horizon. The Happy Jack bus is already down here and those guys are lined up, with tools in their hands, roaring to go to work. Dennis makes us get our tools and line up. Bob returns after a brief check-in and goes up to Russ.

"Get the guys on the bus," Bob says. "We're moving out right away."

"That was quick. Get your tools back on the bus. Darryl, is the bow bar on a saw?"

"Yes. How many are we taking?"

"One. And you will carry it. You can trade off with Paul," Bob says.

"Alright, alright." Wakeford says. "Let's go fight some fire."

"Come on guys," Dennis calls. "Let's hustle up. Squad two, let's go."

We load the tools back up and drive down the narrow dirt road, pulling up by a tanker at the start of a cat line. A cat line is one that a bulldozer makes wide enough to drive a truck on. One good passing of the blade on the desert floor will take all growth down to mineral soil.

"Let's squad up and everyone grab some fuses," Bob commands.

"We're going to burn out! Let's go start some fires," Wakeford cries eagerly.

"On the bus, off the bus, on the bus, off the bus," Cord bitches.

Koval echoes the complaint, "The forest circus is at it again, on the bus, off the bus."

We quickly squad up and start off down the cat line, spreading out as we go along the fuel break. Bob, up front, orders three people experienced in backfiring to begin firing off the unburned brush. Aaron, Darryl and Dennis strike up the fuses and begin torching off the hillside. They continue down the firebreak instructing us to watch out for spots that might jump across the fire line.

The tanker at the beginning of the cat line is at our disposal for anything that gets out of hand. When the backfire moves up the hill, it eliminates any danger of spotting. We bump on down the line with the front guys slightly ahead of the ones lighting off the brush. Another crew, the Globe Hotshots, follows behind us to maintain the cat line along the newly burned area. The backfire area is the new expanded black area. We come to the end of the Cat constructed fuel break. From there the terrain is too rough for us to continue.

It's time now to remove the safety tape from the freshly sharpened edges of our tools. We're going to construct a hand line that will be the new starting point for backfiring. There are about two chains, approximately fifty-two feet, of unburned brush to the edge of the black line where the fire extinguished itself. No fire is considered controlled and safe until a complete line or fuel break surrounds the perimeter of the black line. All unburned fuel islands must be torched off. At our newly constructed hand line the black burned edge was in an inconvenient and inaccessible area. Two guys are left holding fuses and the rest of us build line faster and harder than we ever have, just to keep up with the torches. The torcher lights the brush right behind the last man and we really have to hustle to keep up with the spreading head of the fire. Crew at the end got most of the heat and smoke. It's only about seven thirty and already we're working our asses off, sweat saturating our sweatbands and bandannas.

This is the kind of action we work out for during P.T. There is no slacking off today. Everyone pulls his share, striking and chopping the ground with Pulaskis and scooping out and slicing weeds with the shovels. Forward progress moves a step at a time, with each passing member putting forth a little more effort to reach the mineral earth. The last man leaves a clean line about two feet wide, just wide enough to prevent the flames from crossing over. Later, after about eight chains of work, we dig right into a mossy riverbed from a creek that is barely running. We tie into the wash and quickly return along the hand line to check for possible spotting. The Globe Hotshot crew is still holding the cat line and follows through to our hand line. This allows us to catch our breath and dry up the sweat as we watch for spots.

The day starts out hot and the water goes down fast. I drink three quarters of a quart just standing there. It takes that much irrigation to cut through the dust and smoke in my mouth and throat. The relief doesn't last long. We move out and pick up where we left off. The Globe Hotshots bump down and stretch along our hand line. We leave the fire to Globe and regroup where the hand line meets the wash.

Once again we spread out with two more guys setting the unburned brush on fire along the wash bed. The last few guys move on up the stream as soon as the fire cools down enough. The crew continues in this fashion for many chains before we tie into another cat line, where the black line of the fire edge meets up to the hand constructed lines, leaving not a trace of brush to the cleared fuel break. We quit progressing there and spread back out about half a chain apart, maintaining and holding the fire line.

When opportunity knocks you grab for it. Almost everyone dunks their heads, with hardhats still on, and drenches their clothes while drinking nature's water supply instead of consuming our own. Our bandannas are washed out, and the cool stream water soothes our overheated foreheads. We even get to sit down for fifteen minutes before voices up the stream rouse us up again and tell us to head out. When we come to the stream and cat line crossing, Dennis holds up his squad until everyone catches up. Squad one has disappeared.

Dennis asks Aaron, "Are you the last one?"

"I think so, no one passed me up."

"Did you see Globe at all?"

"No, didn't see anyone pass me."

"Let me try to get a hold of Bob." He speaks into the radio, "Smith, Savage."

Russ answers, "Savage, copy."

"Yeah, where'd you go? Where's Bob?"

"Bob just embarked on the helicopter and we should be on the ridge right above you. Are you on the cat line?"

"10-4." Dennis replies. "But I don't see anyone above us."

"We're just over the ridge."

Just then a copter flies up from behind the ridge.

"Did you see that? Did you spot that ship?" Russ asks.

"10-4, we're on our way."

In a cloud of smoke, we jam up the hill, making a race out of it. Our crew is to be flown to a hotter side of the fire. By the time we reach the ridge top, half of Squad One has already been shuttled over to our new assignment.

The tools are being taped up by the ones on deck ready to fly up. The helitack people manifest us on loads according to weight, giving the pilot some consistency on takeoffs. It is the same helicopter that we had used at orientation a few weeks ago.

I don't have a chance to psych myself up about going on my first helicopter ride. "Frailsen, Savage, Petretti — next load." That got me excited! The only other time I've been in the air was when Richie took me in his parents' small Cessna, right after he got his license. If I was able to survive that, I should be able to handle a helicopter ride. Then Dennis speaks to me, "Is this your first time in a copter?" I nod yes. "Good, we'll let you sit up front." I smile and nod again to hide my fear, and to show my appreciation for the bird's eye view. Actually I am scared to death.

The ride ends almost as quickly as it started. The pilot didn't gain much altitude and we were able to see the outline of the whole fire. He drops us off at the highest point of the fire on a ridge top covered with fresh slurry. As we disembark, the helitack warns us to watch our footing. The wet slurry is very slippery on the rocks and in the puddles. Everything is covered with pink goo that had been dumped by fixed wing aircraft to dampen the fire. The plane's spray width is about a chain wide. There's a strong odor of ammonia around. Drifty says it's due to the fertilizers and ammonium nitrate base they use in slurry. I sit there and watch the other's disembark.

The heat bores down as the morning wears on. It's only a little before 10 A.M. and the temperature must be about a hundred degrees. As soon as the last man disembarks, the crew quickly reassembles into squads. We adjust our gear, grab tools, and take a last gulp of warm water before heading out to the end of the slurry line to build more hand line. The saws take the lead in clearing the brush to expose a pathway for a hand line. Dig, dig, dig, chink, chink, ping, chink. We dig for hours, with no end in sight. You can't take a break when there's work to be done. The sweat is pouring out faster than I'm replenishing it by drinking. Sweat rolls off my head and beads upon the ground. The fine dust and soot from the blackened fire acts like an insulator/moisture proofing against the ground.

There's no word regarding when lunch is going to be available. My body feels weak, my back and arms tired, but I ignore the pain. The sun is draining all of us of our strength and of our precious body fluid levels. The sweat beads up on my heavy eyebrows and runs, like a cloudburst, down my face. The salty sting of it makes me grit my teeth in pain. My cheekbones are rubbed raw from constantly wiping the sweat off with my gloves and shirtsleeve. The stiff fire shirt irritates my skin with each passing wipe.

My last half-quart of water goes fast. It has gotten so hot from exposure to the heat of the day that it upsets my empty stomach when I drink it. We continue working, slowing slightly to prevent heat exhaustion. I can feel my stomach shrink as the last drop of moisture goes down. The acid is building up and I'm feeling nauseous, interfering with my work. I'm beginning to get dehydrated, my skin shrinking to squeeze out any moisture it can.

My only relief is to keep my mind occupied by thinking of the cool stream we may come across, or the crisp ocean breeze against my face. Better yet, the thought of standing on the bow of a ocean cabin cruiser crashing through swells, tasting the fine, salty mist. How nice it would be to catch a whiff of an ocean breeze in this dry desert air. It is so dry here that my sweat evaporates directly from my pores. My skin is drying up and becoming layered with salt that stiffens and cracks as I move. Mired in misery I am overjoyed to hear the good news that lunch is on its way.

The helicopter lands minutes later, unseen, over the ridge and disappears in a cloud of dust, a genie fulfilling my wish for food and water! We hurry and complete the hand line, and race to the treasure chest of food. Our luck... it's the same frozen shit with green turkey and darker green beef. If you try to thaw out the sandwiches first, the bread gets dried out and hard. The juices are frozen, as well, but we put them to refreshing use, melting them against our sizzling foreheads. Only seven gallon canteens were delivered, less than two quarts apiece, and the water in them was warm. The Pope couldn't have blessed the gift of food and water more than we did. As soon as I drank some water, I started to sweat again.

Our lunch rest is short. The Globe Hotshots are still burning out behind us for some reason. We wonder if they even know where we are. Small clouds of smoke appear over the ridge from where we just were. A small smoke inside the black line gusts up into some unburned, withering brush. It doesn't take much for a smoke to spark up and turn into a blaze. The crackling we heard, as we broiled over insufficient sustenance, grew a flame large enough to require our attention. What we didn't notice was another small flame head moving slowly in another direction. Bob notices what's developing and makes his famous cry, "Let's go. Back to work!"

Dennis shouts to him, "Bob, it's moving down that gully on the other side."

"Take your squad and catch it before it gets away," Bob responds.

"Squad two. Double time. Let's go."

Whoever is ready runs down to the flames and proceeds to bat down the flame head with dirt and shovels. The rest of the squad quickly forms a line. We need top speed to stay with the moving fire head. Small as it is, an all-out effort is necessary to prevent the fire from going around us before we can cut it off at the gully. On the next ridge over from the gully, we work toward an Apache Crew. They see our hot line efforts and dig feverishly to tie into us at the gully. Relief is in sight, and squad one pounds away at the ground even harder because of this.

My arms are getting weak. The food I just ate hadn't had the time to generate the energy my muscles need. The Pulaski I hold feels like it weighs ninety pounds, and is harder to handle than usual. I have to make every blow count, being careful not to waste any energy. A bush catches fire against the line and bites my ass, burning me enough to loosen every swear word I ever knew. I swing the Pulaski at it as if it was an attacking dog. People behind me throw dirt on the bush to cool it down. Squad one moves behind us, improving our scratch line.

We come to a gully and tie in. One by one we drop our tools and plop to the ground, panting like dogs and dirtier than a chimneysweep. We file off the line as each guy completes his duty. The gully bed fills up with limp, exhausted bodies. The Apache Crew just watches us as they tie into us, unhurried by any danger of fire. We are definitely more exhausted than they are. The sector boss who works with the Indian crew praises us for stopping the spread of such a small inferno. We all just look at each other, too tired to say a word. Everyone feels a certain amount of pride, and contented smiles brighten our grubby faces. We all know what could have happened if this hot area had run down the hillside.

We are still trying to catch our breaths when a black cloud, the size of the Goodyear blimp, comes out of nowhere and sprinkles us with rain. We bless with appreciation this baptism that comes at the perfect moment. Our day's work comes to an end here. While everyone is still in his spot, I set my camera up on the auto timer and take a group picture.

We have to hike several miles out to a road where transportation is waiting for us. The helicopters are busy on the other side of the fire, shuttling crews between the shift changes. There is no helicopter for us. We contour the hillside back to the roads. Gut bags are available for dinner, a reward unworthy of the effort we had put into the day's work. We shower after eating and quickly bed down on broken glass, rocks and sticks. I fall asleep at once.

July 1

The loudspeakers from Plans blare early. It's 4:30 A.M. and still dark outside. The noise doesn't move me until Bob Smith's name is aired. This stirs everyone up. The rock I slept on left a sore spot on my back. I hear Dennis ask Bob if he heard his name called. Bob just grunts in the affirmative. He gets dressed to make his way to Plans. We know this is our cue to get up for another day of hotshotting in this cursed desert.

The Apache One crew will be working along with us today. They proclaim Bob Smith Sector Boss for the day. The plan is to reassign and airlift us to the other end of the fire. We hurriedly eat our breakfast, more gut bags of pancakes or French toast. It's hard to tell which of the two it is as they are both flat, greenish, and rubbery. Other substances similar to edible food are potatoes and some stuff that tastes like apples. I could do without it, but it's better than eating combat rations.

The hurry-up-and-wait routine keeps us lounging around for three and a half hours, twenty minutes of it under a cloudburst, waiting for our turn to be airlifted to our assignment. Rain provides a break from the heat we all need, and gives us the opportunity to take a short snooze.

An oil leak is found while refueling one of the ships, and the ship is grounded. With no plane available, the two crews are bussed as fast and as far as the bus can go. We hike up the rest of the way. The poor crews on the night shift are still waiting for our arrival so they can be relieved.

We are a welcome sight for their tired eyes as we single-file up a cold hand line. A Colorado crew from Pike, and a New Mexico crew walk past us with dirty, but smiling, faces. Crews are flown in from all over the United States to assist in the many fires that are spreading throughout southern Arizona.

Jim Cruz twists his ankle on the way up and hobbles back to base camp with the out-of-state crews. It's too bad because we have an easy day of line improvement. The Apache One Indian crew mops up behind us. When we tie into another crew we will backtrack, mopping up isolated smokes. It isn't as hot today as yesterday, barely reaching one hundred degrees. Scattered clouds offer the relief of occasional shade. I brought ample water this time to make sure not to run dry. We work at a comfortable pace, entertaining ourselves with jovial conversation. We keep bumping down until a crew is in sight. When we are in sight of the Carson Crew they seem to slack off, stalling around until we start to catch up with them. For the last forty-five minutes they have been in the same place. This pisses off a few of our crewmembers. When we are a chain away they begin working toward our direction.

They would have been better off staying where they were. As they come down the steep sides, someone near the tip of the ridge knocks a big rock loose. The only warning received by those below is the falling boulder itself. Our crew yells, "Rock! Rock!" The boulder gains speed as it comes toward us and kicks off a larger rockslide. Carson Hotshots are dodging the rocks. One guy from their crew tries to hurdle the stone, but an unexpectedly high bounce catches him in the knee. Seeing this makes us more attentive to the danger descending upon us. Wakeford and Savage are in front of our crew screaming, "Rock! Rock!" as it tumbles closer and closer to them. Falling rocks move more unpredictably than a football on an on-side kick. The best protection is to take cover behind a tree or sturdy shrub.

Wakeford and Savage position themselves behind some scrub oak. The main boulder on this rockslide takes a bounce right into the shrub they used for cover. Everyone down the line laughs when Paul and Dennis grab hold of each other, fearful that the boulder will come to rest on them. They must have thought they were doomed. When they realize the danger is over they become aware of their terrified embrace, push away from one another, and laugh along with us. It was pretty funny, all right, but I guess you had to be there to appreciate it.

Jake notices that the Carson guy who got nailed by the boulders is holding his knee in pain. Jake hurries up the hill to administer any medical attention he may need. He wraps up the swollen knee, and a couple of Carson guys walk the injured man out. We decide it's a good time to take a break and eat the lunches we've been carrying around all morning.

This also gives us time to cool down a little from our rockslide excitement. Blood really gets rushing when you're faced with danger. Lunches turn out to be the same frozen crap. It tastes worse and is a darker green when it's completely thawed out. We work the rest of the day at a more relaxed pace and regroup at a ridge-top where a white flag was planted earlier by recreational hikers. We pose triumphantly for a picture, trying to re-enact the Iwo Jima marine scene, but with Hotshots as flag raisers. Although we don't have any Semper Fi's on the crew, the Army and Navy are fully represented. Our patriotic feelings surge with the flag raising. I start to whistle a well-known tune, and in moments we all are whistling Col. Bogie's March from "The Bridge Over The River Kwai" as we hike down to the waiting buses. We whistle louder as we approach the buses that brought in the relief night crew. We know the next crew will have a cake shift because we put out every smoke within two chains of the fire line. The bus drivers must think we've been on the mountain too long.

We make jokes about the other crews and the women on them. At least a third of them are girls, and half of them have heavy facial hair. The relief crews have a long night ahead of them with hardly anything to do. That's all right with them, they brought their own entertainment along.

In a way, we are eating our hearts out because we have no girls on our crew. If anything, the ladies are along for morale purposes because they don't look like they could hold up to the hardships of this job, especially the kind our crew went through yesterday. On the other hand, we're happy not to have females aboard. We are not the type to take up anyone's slack. There were some comments made to that effect, about Jim acting like a pussy with his ankle.

On the way back to fire camp we pass our own bus, full of Indians. We cheer and yell as it passes. The Indians in the bus look baffled by all the attention they get from unfamiliar faces. We are all in a good mood from an easy day of work. The gut bags for dinner are even starting to taste good, except for the lima beans. They have a rotten smell about them. After dinner and a refreshing shower, we pull out our stashes of brandy and weed and take a long walk as nightfall cools the desert. For a change, Darryl comes along on this walk, but he's interested in the booze, not the smoke. With a good buzz on, and some wind-down conversation, we rack out at about 2100 hours.

July 2

Someone nudges me as I sleep and I begin to hear people rustling around in their packs. I think I'm dreaming until Russell stirs me awake.

"Come on, Petretti. We're going to leave you behind."

"Is it morning already?" I mumble. "I don't even remember dreaming last night."

"It's not morning yet, and you probably didn't have time to dream."

"What time is it?"

Russ quickly responds, "11:30."

Cord asks, "What the fuck is everyone doing?"

"We're moving out," Dennis says.

"Where?"

"To the Prescott," Russ tells him.

"Something broke out there?" Dennis asks.

"What happened there?" I grumble irritably. "Like, I don't even know where the hell Prescott is!"

"I don't know," Dennis says. "All I know is that we're going there. Hurry up now, you can sleep on the bus."

"Be quiet so you don't wake up the other crews," Russ admonishes.

I lift my head. Everyone else is moving about quietly, packing up.

"Russ, where's our bus?"

"Darryl went to get it at Plans."

"I'm still high," Cord says.

"Good," Russ responds. "It will help you sleep on the bus. We might have to work the day shift, so I suggest you get as much sleep as you can."

"I ain't gonna wake up. I'm going to sleepwalk my things together and get on the bus asleep. I hate to have to try to sleep on that sardine can," Cord complains.

Russ concludes sternly, "I don't care what you do, just get going."

We stop a couple of times, at a gas station and a Circle K. I don't leave my seat. I just open one eye to see if we are there yet, wherever *there* is. I have no idea where we are. By 3:30 A.M. we are at a fire camp. The generators are cranking and floodlights are on. Personnel are walking around planning the day's assignments and activities. It's warm outside, and I know we are still in the stinking desert. The people in Plans weren't expecting us. They give us some paper sleeping bags and show us a spot where we can bed down for the rest of the morning. No one in the crew has much to say, and we all find a suitable spot to rest our bones. I turn over to get the flood lights out of my eyes. The whining generators hum me fast asleep.

I wake on my own, a good sign, as it means we were not put out on the line this morning. The sun has already started warming up the day. I turn over and see some of our guys walking away. Cord is standing up next to me, getting dressed. "Where's everyone going?" I ask him.

"To eat breakfast. I hear they got a catering service. No more barf bags."

"Far out! I guess that means were not working today. I don't think I can stomach those sponges they call pancakes and French toast."

"Sure looks that way."

"Is that bacon I smell?"

"Sure is."

"Yahooo! I feel better already." I jump out of the bag and put my boots on. "Mike, what time is it?"

"7:30."

"Yeah, my stomach is going to like me again."

Cord waits for me and we stroll over to the good smells of a country breakfast being cooked. Our noses have a field day as they catch the delicious odors of scrambled eggs, bacon, shredded potatoes, juices, coffee, milk, toast and sweet rolls. We stand in line as young girls dish out the food. The one scooping out the eggs looks a lot like my K.C. I stop right in front of her and stare. She has a red bandana on, just like the one Kathy was wearing when I first set eyes on her. Her face and body structure is also very similar to Kathy's. I stand there, lost in thought, with my plate still extended as she piles on the eggs.

"Do you want more than that?" she asks.

I come back to earth, look down at my plate and see there's more on it than I could ever eat.

"Oh, sorry. No, that's enough," I apologize. "You just reminded me of someone I'm in love with."

She just smiles and put some eggs on Mike's plate. He is wondering why the hell I am holding up the line. "Sure Steve," he says, "I bet they all say that to her."

"No, really. You've heard me talk about Castleberry, haven't you?"

"Yeah, more than once."

"Well, that girl looks just like her. In fact I'd swear it was if I knew she wasn't still in L.A. or San Diego."

"You've been away from it too long," Cord says. "I get that way about Janine. Every girl I look at in fire camp reminds me of her. That girl is just a Y.A.C.C. (Young Adult Conservation Corps). They all look good when you haven't had any for a while."

"I guess you're right. Besides, Castleberry is much cuter and prettier."

While I eat, I keep my eyes on the Y.A.C.C. girl. She never once looks at me like I hope she will. I get so lost in thinking about my K.C., and how much I miss her, that I don't even enjoy my great breakfast. I swallow it along with lonely, sentimental thoughts of Castleberry. Nevertheless, that big breakfast hits the spot, and my innards show satisfaction by generating some resounding belches.

We are at the Castle fire, the largest thing cooking in Arizona. Its spread has been stopped at 29,000 acres thanks to forty-five Hotshot crews from all over the country. Two hundred more people are still on their way. We don't know whether or not we'll be put on the night shift. Plans is still figuring out what to do with all the people they have. The crews out on the fire are burning out and holding the line. We are put on standby until 1400 hours, when we'll be notified what to do.

Another hot day is cooking up, so we pitch a tarp for shade and start playing a few hands of poker. Bill Krushak comes by for a few hands. He is a tanker relief boss for this fire. After a couple of hours of doing nothing, Gus, Drift, and I decide to explore nearby. We find a creek in a shaded area, a cool oasis with overhanging trees, grass, and grazing donkeys.

There's also a two-foot waterfall and a small pond to go skinny-dipping in. We take turns sitting under the waterfall, letting the water cascade over our shoulders and neck in a cool, refreshing massage. It is possible to lean back into the air pocket behind the fall and look out through the water, but the torrent crashing down on your diaphragm makes it difficult to breathe. These few moments make the past few days worthwhile.

Gus and Drift wander downstream to see if there are any better places to wade. I don't want to move for I am satisfied here. A few tanker slugs come by, pretend to ignore me, and make some comment on how some Hotshots should dig out the pond more. I feel too mellow to respond to those smart asses.

Away in my own world behind the waterfall, I hear familiar voices approach. I recognize Sluggo's big voice, then Jake's.

"Ah," Jake says. "This is real nice. Someone is sitting behind the falls. Must be an air pocket in there."

"I wonder who it is?" Sluggo says.

"Whoever it is, they are naked."

"It's a girl!" Koval says hopefully.

Without revealing my identity, I lift my leg out of the water and splash it down.

"Hey, Treddy, is that you in there?" Koval shouts. I confirm the guess with another splash. "Yeah, that's Treddy. I can tell from the ugly legs and familiar donkey dick."

I rise out of the water like the creature from the black lagoon and say, "Take a seat, you can lean back and breathe in there."

Sluggo asks, "Is the water cold?"

"Yeah, that's what makes it feel so good."

"I ain't worried about that, I just want to keep these cokes cold."

"It'll keep 'em cold. Give me one."

"Sure. Here, catch." Sluggo throws it overhand to make sure it splashes. "Uh, thanks."

"Just getting you back for splashing me."

"Oh, you baby," Koval snickers.

"I didn't want to get my clothes wet."

"Well, take them off," Jake says.

"Good idea, I'll do that," Koval says. He strips down and lays out stark naked.

"What if some girls come by?" Sluggo worries.

"Good. Then they can sit on my face, then fuck me to death."

"I thought Gus and Dave were here, too."

"They were," I tell him. "They went downstream to find a better place."

"This is nice right here," Jake observes.

"That's why I stayed," I tell him.

"Didn't expect something like this to be here. The desert is full of surprises."

Sluggo looks up. "Here comes Dave and Gus," he says. "Hey, you guys, did you find a better place down there?"

"Naw, not really," Drifty answers. "This is the best place. Just some jackasses down there."

"You must of come across the tanker slugs," I remark.

"I see there's some more up here, too," Gus says.

"Hey, don't include me in that statement," Jake says.

"Look at Koval," Drifty says. "He thinks he's a nature boy." Dave gets some water in his hands and sprinkles some on Koval.

"You cocksucker, leave me alone," Koval snaps.

"Was there any word to what we're doing?" Gus wants to know.

"Nope, none." Jake answers. "Everyone is laying around, playing cards and bullshitting."

"Sounds like real fun," Dave says.

I wash the fire sediment crud out of my nomaxes and wear them back wet. I dig out the couple dollars I have left and lose it quickly in a few hands of poker. Around 1600 hours the fire boss comes around and tells us we can go home any time, which is immediately to us. Russ goes to the stream to gather up the others and we take off for home.

The ride home is joyful. We make a piss stop at Cordes Junction, a place that bears no relationship to Mike Cord, and buy some newspapers to catch up on what's happening in the real world. The fires in Arizona are the headlines. Fifteen different fires blackened over 80,000 acres. Southern California was also busy putting out their fires. We boogie up the Mogollon Rim, jamming to Waylon and getting goofy, as the air thins out and the mountain chill fills our lungs. Most are thinking about the party tomorrow night. The party! Finally we can pop open those kegs tomorrow night.

July 3

Since our regular day off falls on the 4th of July, we were to have our vacation today. Instead we have to work. We'll probably have to work on the 4th, as well. That's all right by us. We all dream of money jingling in our pockets from holiday pay. Bob lets us keep busy around the station while the paperwork is being handled in the office.

We take care of the tools, and thoroughly clean out the bus. P.T. is waived for the day as Bob figures we had a good enough workout over the weekend.

We spend the whole day getting psyched up for the party. The rest of the people at the station saved the food for our return. They knew we'd be in the party mood. The end of the shift is coming up as we gather for the magic moment when the Lowenbrau keg will be tapped. We agree that the party starts tonight, as we never know what tomorrow will bring.

Darryl seems especially anxious, hovering over the keg when Dennis says, "Darryl, it's not time yet."

"By my clock, it's time," he replies. "I don't care what your clock says, we're going by mine."

We hear the Dispatcher's voice call, "10-4, Apache Maid. 1801 KOP437."

Sluggo reports, "Dennis, your watch is slow."

"Oh, so I'm off a few minutes."

"Precious minutes of serious beer drinking," Jim remarks.

Darryl takes matters into his own hands. "Here goes," he says, and we all cheer as he taps the keg and pumps the handle to let the foam run off.

"Hey, you all shouldn't waste all that good beer," James cautions.

"There's more where that come from," says Jim.

"Darryl, where's all those girls you and Steve invited?" Kyle asks.

"I don't know. They probably showed up Saturday and there was no one around."

Aaron informs us, "Bill and Buck said no one came by."

"They had their own party. They said all that come by were some people from Happy Jack. There were a couple of girls with them," Russ says.

Cord asks him, "Whose friends were they?"

"Theirs, probably."

"Mary called first to see if we were here," Joe adds.

"Good thing she did," says Dennis.

"Yeah, I told her to make sure we were around before driving out."

"Is she coming down tonight?" Dennis asks.

"No. She has to work tomorrow."

"I wondered if those Arches ever came by," Pat muses.

"Oh," says Dennis, "I forgot to tell you guys. They'll all be here tonight."

Kyle pulls a punch jokingly. "What? They are? Why didn't you tell us?"

"Kyle, settle down. Where's all the women you said were going to be here?" Darryl asks.

"I called them from Cordes Junction and told them it was cancelled for fire emergency."

"Sure, Kyle, they weren't coming anyway," Koval says.

"Hey, what about the Arches now?" Cord asks.

Dennis replies, "Well when I was in the office earlier they came by to see if the Hotshots were back yet. They were in Saturday afternoon and Norma told them where we were. From what I hear, they've been coming around every day waiting for us to get back. They have been planning to come for a long time."

"How many are going to come tonight?" asks Drifty with keen interest.

"Well, there are fourteen girls out there."

Koval asks, "And no guys?"

"Just girls from the sounds of it," Dennis says. "They all might come."

All in earshot enthusiastically receives his answer. "Wow! Yahoo!"

Gus ambles over. "What's all the commotion here?" he asks.

Sluggo pipes up first. "You know all those Arches?"

"Yeah, what about them?"

"They're coming to our party tonight."

"No kidding?"

"Weally!"

"Sluggo, when are you going to start talking right?" Russ asks.

"Hey, when you quit calling me Sluggo. My name is Greg."

"No, it's not. It's Sluggo, and you *are* a Sluggo."

"Looks like we might get our dicks wet tonight," I suggest.

"I hear that and I'm ready," Cord says. "I've been horny for Janine all week."

"Well, she ain't going to do you any good now," I tell him.

"I know, I'm thinking about going on another Cord Week. If we didn't have to work tomorrow, I'd be on my way down there."

"I know what you mean. I wish Castleberry was with me now."

"I got to call Janine and let her know the bad news before this party gets going."

"Give her my love," I say.

"Yeah, right, you know I will. She wants to meet you one of these days. You'll have to go down to Tucson and party."

"I hear you. When things slow down here I'll go down."

"It probably won't happen then before I leave," Cord says.

"Oh yeah, I almost forgot about that."

"Yeap, three weeks from today, I'll be a civilian again."

"I bet you can't wait," I say. "You better not keep her waiting. I'm going to fill my glass back up and take a shower and get all decked out for the legs a-coming."

"Right on! I'll get another glassful before going up to the phone."

I run into the trailer and put on a favorite tune I used to play in the city before stepping out "hunting holes" for the evening in overly crowded disco joints. I shave and slip into the cleanest pair of Levis I have. The record is over and the beer is working on my empty stomach. After I dress, I lie down on my bed. Within seconds, I am out like a light as the hard weekend catches up with me. I don't know how long I slept, I just remember Cord waking me.

"Petretti, what are you doing?" he says.

"Oh, wow, man. I passed out."

"You better get up if you want in on the bush outside before Kyle blows it."

"My God, I forgot about the Arches coming."

"Well, they're here," Cord says, and leaves to rejoin the party.

Even though I hear him and answer, I'm still half-asleep and can't seem to move from the bed. It feels like I've been out for hours. Then it dawns on me, the Arches are here. I jump up and peer out the window, making sure no one can see from outside. There are only three of them.

"Is that all? Fucking Dennis!" He made it sound like there were fourteen stepping out with wet crotches. Anyhow, I put on a casual shirt, comb my hair, and splash on some lady-killing cologne. I expect to see the girls completely surrounded by our boys, sniffing their asses and drooling with sexual starvation. To my surprise, the center of attraction is the keg and the guys are behaving themselves. Most of the ones with steady girlfriends back home are playing Frisbee or kicking a volleyball around. I walk over to the keg first thing, fill up my NAU glass halfway, down it, and fill it up again until it overflows with foam. I catch the eye of the blonde who's checking me out and know what my next move will be. I walk over and stand next to her. She interrupts her conversation with Mike and we exchange smiles. Cord realizes her interest has changed focus. Maybe it was my sweet smell. He formally introduces us. "Steve, this is Ginny. Ginny, that's Steve, our Italian Stallion." I get slightly embarrassed by the introduction. I hope it doesn't show.

Ginny turns and introduces me to her two co-workers. "Kathy here, is our boss, and Andrea just came along for the ride."

"Hi, girls."

"What's your name again?" Kathy asks.

"Steve, and you're Kathy, and you're Andrea. How come you're the boss?"

"She's working on her Ph.D.," Andrea explains.

"Oh, yeah? Great. What school?"

"ASU," Kathy says.

"What are you working on Andrea?"

"My Masters."

"Far out, sounds good. You working on your Masters, too, Ginny?"

"No, I already got it from San Diego State."

"You look like a California girl."

"Yep, fun in the sun and all that stuff."

"Steve's from there, too," Cord says, tired of being ignored. "You're from San Diego, aren't you?"

"Well, not really," I reply. "I spent a lot of time down there and know a lot of people who went to school down there from L.A. I'm really from L.A., the San Fernando Valley. I don't consider L.A. and San Fernando Valley the same place."

"I live near San Fernando Valley," Ginny says.

"Oh, where? What town?"

"You know were Placerita Canyon is?"

"Sure do, we used to go gold panning up that canyon. I also remember when I was real little going to Frontier Days at the park up there."

"The park was washed out years ago."

"Could have been. I haven't been up there in a long time. How long have you lived there?"

"A few years, off and on. I have a house in the canyon."

"Where are you originally from?"

"Born and raised in Pasadena."

"You're kidding," I say. "You must know where Lake View Terrace is."

"Oh, yeah," Ginny says. "We used to go riding down there."

"Probably at the Hansen Dam Stables."

"That was it."

"You know that street you turn left on to go down to the stables?"

"Yeah."

"Well, if you turn right, you'll be in my neighborhood." Cord couldn't believe that we were both familiar with the same locations.

"How old are you?" I ask her.

"Twenty-five."

"Me, too. You must know the Van Halens. They're from Pasadena."

Ginny nods, "I went to school with them."

"No shit! I just met Edward Van Halen at a club in Sylmar right before I came up here. Their father played at this place where my mother and her husband went to a lot. It was called the Alpine Inn. It was a German style restaurant with an um-paa um-paa-paa band. Their old man played in the band. My mom and Al hung out there a lot. Al and Mr. Van Halen were from the Old Dutch country. They've known his old man for years."

"I never met their father," Ginny says. "The Van Halen band used to play at our high school, I remember."

"Oh, yeah, the whole family is into music. They are a very talented family. I remember seeing them for the first time at the Antique Mirror in Granada Hills. Man, I never thought they would have made it so big."

"I've seen them playing around Pasadena. I knew they had potential."

"That they did, and look where they are at today, the big time. I never thought I'd run into anybody in the boonies from near my home town."

"Really, we're stuck way the hell out here."

"Where?"

"Chavaz Pass. About ten miles up 87 and about seven miles in."

"Is that where you're digging up bones?"

"Yeah. The digging sites are out there and Kathy here is in charge of them."

"Is she a good boss to work for?"

"Yes, she's good people. We all get along out there," Andrea adds with a smirk.

I nod and tell her, "It's the same way here. We all have to get along or we'd be at each other's throats." I stop talking and stare at her throat, wanting nothing so much as to lean into her and nibble on her neck. The alcohol is affecting my libido. I snap back to reality.

"It's all girls out there, too?" I ask.

"Yep, we like it that way."

"How long are you going to be digging?"

"We've been up here a week and a half already, and..."

I interrupt. "Yeah, I've noticed when you gals come in for showers."

"...and will be going home next Friday," she continues.

I'm crushed. "So soon?"

"That's all it lasts for."

Cord puts in his two cents worth. "You were up here last year, weren't you?"

"Yes, I was. This is my third year."

"I remember you from last year, coming in for showers."

"It's a big venture coming in to get cleaned up. We try to make it every other day. I can't stand myself for too long without a shower."

"I bet the others can't either," I say. "Oh, excuse me. I guess I don't know you well enough to make comments like that."

"That's alright. You're probably right."

I change the subject. "I need a refill and I'm going to mosey around. Don't run off without saying goodbye."

"I won't."

She looks me right in the eye and I know I am in love again. Russ is at the keg and sees me coming. He has a shit-eating grin on his face.

"Uh oh, Petretti, what are you up to?" he smirks. "Looks like you're moving in to get your dick wet."

"Hey, I hope so. She's a doll."

Russ leans over to me and asks in a soft voice, "You got any smoke on you?"

"Yeah, and I'm ready to take a break and get high. Looks like the food will go on shortly. It will give me a chance to get the munchies. Umm, let's excuse ourselves and, uh, go for a ride."

"Sure," Russ agrees. "That's what I need to get into the party. You can tell me all about your new love affair, too."

"Let's go before it gets dark and I get too drunk. Then we can munch out on the food."

During the half hour we were gone the party just about doubled in size. Kids and dogs are running around. People are playing "keep away from the hounds" Frisbee. A lot of families have shown up. In fact, most of the overheads are there, even the Ranger. I cut my engine and coast up inconspicuously. I am sure everyone heard the rapping of the header as we approached the station driveway. Russ and I jump off the bike and rejoin the party. The steaks are on the grill, and the beans are still warm. I eat fast, making sure not to lose any time with that beautiful blonde beast. She looks a lot better to me than before we left. The sight of her skin-tight purple top fills my jeans with excitement when I sit down beside her again.

"Hope I wasn't gone too long," I say. I suspect my bloodshot eyes are giving away the purpose of my recent excursion.

"Some guy named Kyle was talking to me," Ginny remarks.

"Ole Kyle, uh, he's a peculiar person that Kyle is."

Ginny agrees. "Were you one of the ones who invited us to this party last week at that gas station?"

"Yeah. I'm surprised you remembered that."

"I remembered your motorcycle. I was going to say something before, but I didn't."

"I would of loved to have taken you for a ride," I offered.

"I can't now," she sadly declines.

Ginny must have been doing some drinking while Russ and I were away, because she seems a little friendlier and leans into me when she talks. Every time she does, it sends shivers all over me. I love her natural girly smells. She is so fresh and natural, her hair clean and shiny. I hope she is as turned on by me as I am by her.

I notice that Andrea keeps looking at us as we talk. She stands quietly and alone, and doesn't appear to be having a good time. I tried to talk to Andrea earlier but didn't get anywhere. Her answers were short, and she was not engaging in lengthy conversations with anyone. Dennis is happily occupied with Kathy and it appears she favors his company. Ginny glances over at Andrea, and with a simple body gesture Andrea relays a message to her.

"We have to leave," Ginny says. "Andrea is getting bored and wants to go."

"Are you bored?"

"Not in the slightest, but it's a long way back and we have to work tomorrow."

"On the 4th of July? Too bad. We're in the same boat. It's too early to leave. The party is just getting started.

"I know, but we really have to go."

"Will I see you again?"

"I'm sure you will. We'll be back in a couple of days to get cleaned up."

"I hope so. I want to see you again."

"You will."

Kathy comes over and asks Ginny, "Are you ready to go?"

"Yes."

"Andrea's been ready. No one was talking much to her."

"I've noticed," I say.

"It was really nice meeting you guys, and thanks a lot for inviting us to your party," Kathy says graciously.

"It was short, but sweet," Ginny adds.

"Well, next time you'll have to stay longer," I say. Then I have a great idea. "You guys can stay here tonight. We can accommodate you all."

"No, thanks. We have to get back to camp," Kathy says.

"Good meeting you, and we'll see you all later," Ginny calls as they head out.

We watch them walk up to their cars, laughing and bumping into each other like adolescent schoolgirls. My cock gets hard watching them walk away, and I realize, sadly, they aren't going to be around up here much longer. Dennis comes up behind me.

"You like that, don't you?" he says.

"I'm in love."

"I seen you two talking over there."

"You looked like you were doing O.K," Cord says.

"Yeap, we made an impression on them."

"Great, a good one, I hope," Cord says.

"They invited a few of us out to the excavation sites," Dennis remarks.

"They did?" I ask. "Me, too?"

"Yeah, you're included," Dennis says. "They don't want everybody out there. Only a few of us."

"Oh, you mean she picked out who was acceptable and who wasn't?" I ask.

"Yeap, she liked Wakeford, Aaron, you and me." Dennis says. "She said the others were too noisy and immature. She also said not all the girls out there would be interested anyhow, but we behave like we know what we're doing."

"I guess they're in a position to be choosy out here, all alone in the wilderness." But I have an afterthought. What did he mean when Kathy mentioned that not all the girls out there would be interested? I propose the perverted notion that there must be some lesbos on the digs.

"Yeap, I guess so," Dennis says.

"Oh, well, back to the party and reality."

It was an exclusive Blue Ridge Party with a better turnout than anyone expected. Even the Ranger showed up, and a small crowd hung around him all night. He is more popular than the girls, with the usual brown nosing for expected gains. Steve "Ozzie" Nickles is talking to the Ranger and coughs up a mouthful of beer all over him. Neff has to take his glasses off and wipe them without interrupting his conversation. Some are highly amused and others embarrassed for the Ranger.

Country Western music is the order of the evening. Pat and I try to put on some punk and new wave, but that doesn't sit too well with the others. In moments, we are hogtied by rednecks. Everyone is having a great time, with minor squabbles arising about whose stereo is the loudest. Marty is putting down Shirley, his girlfriend, most of the night, and the Cat operator's wife is flirting around, mostly with me. She grows attached to my cowboy hat and grabs my body a few times. This minor foreplay is beginning to worry me. Her husband is watching her behavior and her drink intake. If only she knew how horny I was. She probably does, which encourages her to continue her flirtations.

Darryl, Drifty and Mike retire early. Darryl got too drunk, too early. Drifty probably wanted to go jerk off. Mike had a depressing conversation with Janine over the phone. It seems she was going out with some other guy tonight, as she is not the type to sit around waiting for Mike to show up. She is young and wants to get out and party. The whole idea doesn't sit well with Mike.

A drunken mob tries to roust Darryl out of bed to shame him for being such a pantywaist at the party.

Dennis eggs them on, slurring "I..I..I'll give any, anyone five bucks if they can get this lightweight out of bed."

"Let's try the hand in the hot water trick," I suggest.

"Yeah, yeah," James agrees.

"Kyle, get some hot water," Dennis commands.

"Should I warm it up in the microwave?"

"No, asshole! Get it from the sink."

Kyle comes back seconds later. We try to keep the laughter down as we wait outside Darryl's door then quietly enter, talking in whispers.

"Get his hand out from under the covers," I direct.

"He's probably got a hold of his dick," Pat says.

"Here it is," says Dennis. "Stick it in."

Pat replies, "What? His dick or his hand?"

Darryl pulls his hand away and turns over, lying on his arms. James pulls the covers completely off.

"God, it smells in here!" I remark. "Pat, how can you stand sleeping in here?"

"I don't breathe when I'm asleep."

Dennis butts in. "I got an idea." He gets a book of matches out and places a few between Darryl's toes.

"That ought to work," I say.

Dennis lights the matches and Darryl immediately kicks them clear. **"Get the fuck out of here! Leave me alone!"** he screams.

"O.K." says Dennis. "Now it's ten dollars."

"Here, watch this," Kyle says. He pours the water over Darryl who doesn't even move.

"We'll try some beer," Dennis says, emptying his foam on Darryl's head.

"He's fucking out of it," I say.

Pat takes hold of Darryl's arm and Dennis his leg. They pull him onto the floor, in the process flipping the mattress over so it lands on top of him.

Darryl swings and kicks at his oppressors. He kicks the glass of beer out of James' hand and catches Dennis' ear with an open hand, forcing him to lose some chew out of his mouth. Pat's glasses go flying off his head.

"Hey," I say. "We better go before someone gets hurt."

"Yeah, really," Dennis agrees. "He's out of it. You lightweight, Darryl!"

As we leave the room, we tie his door shut.

"Hey, how am I going to get in?" Pat asks.

"Sleep outside," I tell him. "Drink some more and you'll never know the difference."

Dennis remarks, "We won't be doing much tomorrow. Bob says we'll be going out to the rim and doing standby."

"Far out," I respond. "We can really get shit-faced tonight."

We leave the trailer and rejoin the party. The second keg is nearly half gone already.

July 4

I'm still asleep when Darryl yells through the doorway to see if I want a beer, which he refers to as "breakfast in bed." "Sure, why not," I respond. Then I jump up quickly, remembering what we did to him last night. I figure he's about to pay me back with a good dousing in suds. On the other hand he probably doesn't remember what went on last night, so I reply jokingly, "Thank you, dear." He brings the beer in, no problem. I down it quickly and go out for a refill. We manage to get three glasses down, and one for the bus ride out to the rim. We're going to the historic Captain Crook Trail to restack sticks that were inappropriately piled from last years thinning. This trail stretches and winds along the whole edge of the Mogollon Rim.

You can tell from the hangovers and red eyes with bags under them where our heads are at for the day. What a way to spend the 4th of July! I'm used to having family get-togethers and barbecues on the beach where we'd wait for the sun to go down and then, with beach blankets spread out beneath sunburned bodies, we'd watch the sky light up with colorful fireworks.

The highlight of this morning is when Jim and James pay Kyle two dollars to eat a fly. Everyone gets a big kick out of watching the winged insect crunch between his teeth. There are a lot of ladybugs around, but Kyle won't eat one no matter how much money we get together. He says they're too bitter. He has taken this kind of dare before.

The number of ladybugs here is phenomenal. We don't see them at first, but the deeper we dig into the year old slash pile the more they fly out, like swarms of bees attacking a bear intruding on their hive. There are so many of them that they cover the pine needle strewn ground like flowing red lava. The ladybugs cover our arms, fly up our nose and get in our ears. They creep under our hardhats and struggle to death in our hair. It's a mystery to me why they are here in these numbers.

The bus is parked at the halfway point of our day's scheduled work and we hurry to reach it so we can break for lunch early. Touring the historic and distinctive rim is the highlight of our extended lunch. At the rim's edge, the forest thicket lays an umbrella of shadows on the underbrush. Only a few feet farther, the forest opens up as far as the eye can see, revealing, close up, the clouds that hover over the forest and desert plateau. We eat lunch at the edge of the Mogollon Rim with the Tonto 2,000 feet directly below our soles. Darryl tells us that if you throw a Frisbee out as hard as you can, the warm desert updraft will boomerang it 200 yards behind you. Of course we have to try it. He is wrong. The Frisbee goes in about 300 yards!

The mighty Mogollon Rim is a miracle of nature. It was the edge of the glacier that covered the Colorado Plateau during the Ice Age millions of years ago. The Colorado River carved its way through the softer, less dense portions of the glacier. That is how the Grand Canyon was formed. Here we are today on what was the cutting edge of a massive glacier. I sit dazed, just thinking about how the earth works.

A wide variety of vegetation grows along the rim. The lush forest is thicker along this portion of the Coconino, and displays a unique combination of high timber floral along with surviving lower vegetation, possibly the descendants of antique pollen and seed dispersal. A botanist would have an orgasm here. A fire in these parts of the woods would be devastating. The heat rising along the vertical face of the rim would be the closest thing to being in hell. The fuels that lay on top where we are working would torch forever.

I hear the faint strains of some good ol' rock and roll from a Phoenix radio station, so I make my way back to the bus to get an earful. Jim Cruz rigged an antenna that accounts for the great reception we're getting. All I want to do is catch a few z's to recuperate from my hangover.

I hadn't gotten a moment's rest when I hear the dispatcher on the airways, "4-20, 7-20, dispatcher." My heart skips a few beats and my breath freezes. Dennis jumps to his feet in one motion and grabs the mike, "7-20 copy." More silence. Then we hear, "4-20 copy." "Dispatcher, 7-20 copies, Moqui." Moqui tower is relaying our response. At times the towers have to operate as a repeater for units in a draw. "10-4," dispatcher acknowledges.

"10-4, Moqui," dispatcher continues, "4-20 and 7-20 report to Mr. Bates at the Horseshoe Reservoir."

"10-4: 4-20."

"10-4: 7-20."

"Dispatcher, 7-20, 10-4, Moqui," as Moqui relays the call.

The four of us sitting around the radio yell at the top of our lungs, "Bob, fire! We got a dispatch." Like flies to freshly plopped horseshit, guys appear from the thicket within nanoseconds. The trip that took an hour driving out is cut to 40 minutes on the return to the station. We are allowed 5 minutes to gas up and get what we need in the trailers.

We are the first to arrive and we find this Bates guy sitting at a fork in the dirt road. Fire camp will be sited along the Verde riverbank a few hundred yards ahead, but nothing has been set up yet. We stake out a shady spot near the water in the campground area. It's only five o'clock, so we jump in the water to cool off from the hot, sticky bus ride down. A few years ago they would have hung a Hotshot crew for swimming in fire camp. The stares we get from the other crews as they drive into camp indicate they have been taught never to engage in such activity. I know they are eating their hearts out with envy.

Camp still isn't set up. There's no overhead, no helicopters, no medical facilities, no work or food, so C-rations are on the menu for dinner. Most of the crew crashes out early, except for Paul. He's messing with his pack, re-adjusting and preparing his fire gear. If it were up to him, he'd love to work tonight. We are frequently awakened by the noise of trucks rolling in and crews getting settled. I can smell the foot and body odor from the crew who's bedded down beside us. I was happy to sense that there might be some black members in the crew. I was wondering if there were any black hotshots. What a way to spend a 4th of July!

July 5

The trucks keep rolling in all night. At first the noise wakes me up, but after awhile their idling diesels drone me right to sleep. I wake at 0730 hours to the hum of the generators. That's pretty leisurely for fire camp. My back is a little stiff from the hard ground. Crews are all over the place. Everyone here seems to have awakened at the same time. Most of them are getting ready for something, maybe for breakfast. I haven't heard any announcement on chow, so maybe they're going out to work. Then I see them strolling over to a chow line. We are up and headed for breakfast within minutes. As we walk by the full campground, other crews are trying to get organized, scurrying around preparing to go eat. It looks to me like they're spending way too much time trying to do stuff in a disciplined, military way. If you do things properly, what need is there for that? Besides, when your stomach is talking to you, it's the only thing you want to obey. As it turns out, the joke is on us and the other crews... we have barf bags for breakfast. Although, not all is totally lost. There is still the aroma of coffee brewing.

Coffee isn't the only thing brewing. Heat is boiling up in the desert this morning, but luckily we aren't on the day shift. The campground slowly empties out leaving Happy Jack and our crew behind for the night shift. It's already too hot to go back to sleep. Jim and Kyle don't waste any time hitting on the girls. First, some Indian women then the Y.C.C. (Youth Conservation Corps) camp crew. Last on their hit list are the timekeepers. To their surprise, one of the cuties keeping time is none other than Sandy from our own office. Yes, even clerical workers go to fires. They aid in logistical support. Sandy is miserable here. She is a real sweet lady, though a bit grumpy at times. A full-figured person, she is sweating heavily and complaining.

Those remaining in our sleeping area are reading or trying to nap. We camp out by a river stemming from a reservoir spillway. A couple of guys find some hand fishing line and try their luck at fishing. Sluggo lures a craw daddy up the bank. Most of us stay cool by wading a bit, until the fire camp safety officer makes everyone get out of the water. Supposedly, the current is too strong. When he's through issuing orders, he nails up "No Swimming" signs all around.

Pat then gets silly on us by deciding to mock authority. Along with his gym shorts, he puts on boots, hardhat and goggles, gloves and fire shelter.

"No water," he says. "This how you put out fires with no water." He stands by a campsite fire pit with a serious look on his face, as if he was making an instructional film. "Now all you happy campers out there listen up. You pick up some cold dirt and mix it thoroughly with the hot ashes." He demonstrates a few times with exaggerated motions. "Yes. It's the Smokey the Bear approved method of extinguishing your personal campfires."

Koval and I walk upstream to the spillway of the reservoir. Littering the rocks above the waterline we find driftwood and dead, dried out fish. We discover a walkway behind the cascading spillway water. Graffiti decorates its walls. The cool mist from the waterfall, along with the slight breeze passing through the walkway, actually gives our overheated bodies goose bumps. We stay away as long as we reasonably can, and then head back. The harsh sun leaves only a vague remembrance of the refreshing mist behind the falls and the crash of the water on the driftwood piled around its rocks.

Back at the camp, we choke down rations for lunch instead of gut/barf bags of food. I am still very hungry since I had only coffee for breakfast, but I just can't handle another ration. Luckily, I find some sack lunches that a crew had left behind. I feel like a scavenger.

By now most of the crew is napping. The sun is directly overhead when we get notice that, positively, we are on the night shift. I manage to get a little shuteye while shooing off annoying flies and wandering ants. There are plenty of them, but the beads of sweat rolling off my body feel like a whole lot more of those creepy-crawlies.

Dinner is catered in and the pork chops and mashed potatoes hit the spot. Afterward we march out to the heliport with the Happy Jack crew. We are the only two night crews going out. Both crews are shuttled up to one of the highest peaks in the area. From the helicopter we can see, in the far distance, smoke from the Castle Ridges fire that we left a couple of days ago. The sun is sinking almost directly behind an undisturbed column of smoke. Some white streaks of jet exhaust add to the spectacle before us. But as soon as everyone lands we have to forget about beautiful sunsets and concentrate on mopping up and improving the line.

Our two crews bump around each other along the snake-like fire line. Everyone has his headlights on. From a distance we must look like solemn monks lined up, holding lit candles for a midnight funeral.

Although our main duties for the night haven't even begun, I already feel weak from lack of sleep over the past few days. The sector boss is waiting for us at some creek just south, so we go on ahead leaving Happy Jack to tie into the ravine. We will follow down later to start burning out. On the way to our assignment we notice a rattlesnake moving down the side of the mountain. It is in a moon shadow and difficult to spot. His rattle lets us know we are trespassing in his territory. He looks as scared as we do. He may have never seen a human before. He is at full alert. A third of his body is extended straight out, supported only by his own muscles. We all pass slowly as he stares at us with obsidian eyes, his forked tongue testing the air.

As we move down the ravine bed and into a canyon formed by two big ridges, the vegetation becomes denser. As hot as it still is and as bright as the desert moon is, I can't help but feel that the shrubs and the few trees are going to offer cooling shade. But coolness comes from a different source, a natural spring that seems to come out of nowhere. There is a refreshing pond at the creek head surrounded by mossy rocks and coated with a layer of algae. Some of the guys are leery about drinking the water, but eventually one, then another, and then all partake of the unexpected refreshment. Soon the pond is as busy as a public swimming pool in the heat of summer. It's a beautiful spot, an oasis in the middle of nowhere. The contrast of the bright moon in the dark sky makes me feel like I am living in a photographic negative.

I had never seen anything like this in the desert, and suspect it isn't a common occurrence. I wonder if anyone has ever been to this spot before. The only conceivable people might be Indians, perhaps a hundred years ago or more. It seems like this place shouldn't even exist in the desert, for further on down the canyon the water, shrubs, and trees disappear and cactus pops up again.

We travel eastbound. The northern aspect is decorated with small shrubs and occasional trees. The southern aspect is mostly bare with a few cacti, confirmation of how devastating the direct desert sun is.

We meet up with the sector boss where the creek reappears, but the vegetation isn't as plentiful here. We are to wait until Happy Jack catches up with us. From here on down we are to burn out along the creek bed. We all rest on the rocks near a small waterfall just below.

I know it's going to be a long night, so I mix the coffee and cream substitute that comes with a C-ration into one canteen for a little help during the next hours. I sip the cool caffeine mixture while I look out past the opening of the canyon to the flat desert below. I want to nod out, but I know it would only make things worse when we get back on our feet again.

Dennis makes off into the brush to see how far the blackened area reaches. A few minutes later he yells down, "Bob, I'm about 75 yards up. It's heavily brushed and hard to get around up here. There's a game path, though, that we can follow when we start burning."

Bob calls, "O.K., come on back down."

The sector boss speaks up and says, "We'll start as soon as Happy Jack gets here. We'll let your crew do the burning and Happy Jack can follow up and patrol for spots."

When Dennis comes back down he and Bob stick three or four fuses together in tandem, and are ready to go. When Happy Jack shows up the sector boss wants Bob to light a trial spot before engaging in a full-scale burnout. The burning index is still a little high due to the low humidity, and the sector boss wants to be careful not to let anything get out of control.

Dennis is instructed to proceed halfway up and light a small area on fire for observation.

Satisfied with the trial burn, the sector boss radios to fire camp our intent to have a full burnout along Professor Creek. Dennis goes up to the game trail and lights a line of fire. As soon as he is a couple of chains ahead, Bob torches-off the lower section at the creek side. The burn out starts slowly, but shortly afterwards, when Bob's lower half meets with the already burning upper-half, it becomes a blazing inferno. The crackling of the fire and the gusts of flames appear to run wild, but are actually as tame as we intended them to be. The flames grow immense in the dry desert brush. This was the 4th of July show we came to see, a day late. The fire will burn nicely up the steep mountain then extinguish itself three-fourths of the way up the canyon side when it reaches the previously burned area.

Slowly we move down the creek bed as the fire now seems tame enough, and danger spots are minimal. Some of our guys gaze at the fiery show as they contour the opposite hillside, patrolling for spots. All are moving along at a steady pace, never slow enough for a rest, but always progressing down the creek bed.

The whole mountain seems to be on fire, lighting up the other side like red filtered, bright sunlight. The darker silhouettes of passing Hotshots with tools in hand serve as foreground to the flames across the canyon. Communication is minimal. Each of us is alone with his thoughts. When watching the blaze gets boring our own musings provide the entertainment that keeps us awake.

As we walk down and around the switchbacks new view sites are constantly presented: creek patterns of flowing water and mini waterfalls, new rock formations, some straight up and some with a more gradual slope.

Everyone is exhausted as morning draws near. My knees are weak from constantly clunking downwards, putting all my weight on each foot carefully so as not to twist an ankle. Stepping down short waterfalls and on slippery rocks are additional ankle twisting hazards. I can feel the water in my canteens sloshing and shifting its weight, at times keeping my fatigue wracked body off balance. At one point, we climb a small ridge where we can look up and down both sides of the creek, and get a view of the fire on both sides and in front. It's a great spot, and we stay there for a while to rest a little and watch the fascinating flame patterns.

As people nod out, I keep an eye out for scorpions and other creeping insects while watching the flames settle down. I must have fallen into a dream state where time and place was suspended, because all at once, I am aware of the sounds of the creek and it snaps me back. I have no idea how much time has passed. I have been lost in thoughts about the million and one other places I would rather have been, and even a few about why I was here now. It was an interesting introspective experience.

July 6

One by one headlamps are extinguished as the morning sun peeks out over the eastern horizon. Staying awake is a hard part of this detail, but our continual momentum helps. It is noon when we finally reach the spike camp at the bottom of Professor Creek. The sun once again brings our body temperatures to one hundred plus. Warm sack lunches and used paper sleeping bags await us here. Some of us are too tired to eat. We lay our bags over the rocks in the creek bed. Though overhanging tree limbs along one side of the creek bank offer little shade, we crash there, clad only in our briefs.

As soon as we get horizontal the zzz's start rolling. Not even the heat disturbs us. The plan is to get four hours of rest before relocating to base camp. The fire boss eliminates the second shift for the east zone.

Some time must have elapsed when off in the distance a crackling noise intrudes itself on my dreamland. Though it sounds like a brush fire, none of us moves a muscle. Eventually the crackling becomes louder and whiffs of fresh smoke pique enough curiosity so that Bob and a few others decide to determine its origin. Surprise! The brush near our heads is on fire! Bob bellows out, "You guys better wake up before you get burned." People shake themselves awake to find a fire moving toward them a few yards away with the potential to get far worse. Everyone is rousted up, the sounder sleepers are kicked awake, cussing.

Guys are running around in their briefs and boots with armloads of gear. Some guys, who had found shady spots in the brush to sleep, come running out of the bushes. It pisses all of us off when we learn that a California Prunie crew was burning out somewhere on the other side. Supposedly, they lit off the wrong side of the hand line we had put in earlier right before we reached spike camp. We quickly find other spots among the rocks to lie down in. We're not going to raise a finger to suppress *this* fire.

Once again we are rousted from a sound sleep when the copters land in the creek bed. The ring of rotors sounds like thunder as it throws dirt in our faces. Crews and supplies are being lifted out. Spike camp is being demobilized. Though we are the last to go, most of us still can't get any sleep. Some just soak in the shallow creek to keep cool. Others get a little shuteye by putting their earplugs in.

Tired and spacy as we are, dinner at base camp tastes great. We gobble it down before turning right in for sleep. We are happy to hear we might be de-mobbed in the morning. One more day in this heat would drive us crazy.

July 7

The road home is hot and boring with one usual stop at Cordes Junction. A few sleep on the way, and most of us are wearing as few clothes as possible. There's no way to escape the heat. Air blowing in from the open windows feels like a massive hair dryer. Every so often you have to sit erect to let the sweat dry between your bare back and the plastic seat. Skin just peels off the seat, and when it dries, it leaves a residue of crackling salt deposits. As we reach higher altitudes, the sweaty seats became chilly and windows are pushed closed. We are to arrive at Blue Ridge in enough time to casually retool and achieve fire readiness again.

We pull into the station just in time to hear a chorus of "Mail Call". Bob and Dennis jump off and walk into the office. The bus motor is killed, but the ignition pop of the exhausted bus startles Russ while he is busy assigning minor chores to various people. Moments later Dennis comes trotting out with a handful of mail. We can tell something is up by the way he's scurrying, so we stop the chatter. Along with the mail he brings a message, "Turn on the F.S. radio. There's a fire on Penduck Mountain. We've been dispatched to the Wallace Fire."

Cheers ring out and the F.S. radio is cluttered with fire talk. Someone comments that if the radio had been on all along, we could have gone directly to the fire. That isn't so. We have rules that state we have to return to the station before being re-dispatched. Before we leave Dennis feels it necessary to say, "You guys got five minutes to retool with fresh tools and get what you need in the trailers. And hurry up, I don't want to see any stragglers or we will leave you. We don't need eighteen men to travel to one of our forest fires."

Bob jumps, tight lipped and disgusted, on the bus as it starts to roll away. He wanted to be dropped at his house on the way to the hotshot trailers. I'm sure he was hoping to see his wife for more than five minutes. I run in and grab some clean socks, a clump of cheese, kosher dill, and some stash. We drive by Bob's house again and Bob meets his wife outside. They kiss quickly and Bob jumps back on. No one makes any immature noises while they kiss, as we all empathize with what Launa must go through each time he gets called away. As tired as we are, the crew has never responded with more excitement to a fire, because this one is in our own forest. With the possible exception of Paul, all of us would rather fight fire in the timber than in the desert. Paul doesn't care where he gets to fight fire, just as long as he gets to.

Flagging along the highway indicates the turn-off and location of fire camp. The fire camp site is barren except for abandoned vehicles and buses. Mormon Lake and Flagstaff Hotshots are already there working on the south end of the fire. Blue Ridge and Happy Jack are to situate themselves on the opposite ends of the fire. We leave the fire camp just as the Happy Jack bus pulls in. Bob instructs them to follow us up the highway to where a fire official will lead us to the hot spot of the fire. It is there we are to start building line.

A fire official is waiting on Highway 180 and we follow him to the east side. Happy Jack will begin constructing line at this spot. Reamer is the line boss at this end of the fire. He is out running around, officially performing his duties. As the bus approaches him we cheer him on, singing "For He's a Jolly Good Fellow". When we see the look on his face we stop the foolishness. Reamer orders us to punch in a line where the cat had stopped. The fire is approaching the cat line and our immediate response is vital if we are to stop the flames from spreading. Smoke is rolling by, and any gusts will put us in a detrimental position.

This is really serious, and within seconds the whole crew is running toward the smoke and flames with tools in hand. We are to continue up the hillside to the other side and tie into the other cat line. It is a very hot line with tons of smoke. The surrounding air temperature is mild, but the closeness to the fire pushes the temperature up to desert heat. We soak down bandanas and use them as breathing apparatus to protect our lungs from the smoke. There are a number of very hot spots along the line where billows of smoke burn our eyes, and make them tear so much, it's difficult to see. My hard hat keeps falling off, so I have to use the chinstrap. I tuck one end of my bandana under the chinstrap and the other under the bottom of the goggles to try to keep the smoke out. It only helps a little.

I am now set to jam, and I hit the ground with sweeping blows. Sparks fly off the stones that lay under the duff. Hit and move up, hit and move up.

The whole crew is an awesome line-digging machine. Collectively we must have exerted as much horsepower as a D-9 Cat. A small gust of wind excites some flame and it bites my ass and nips my backside. I stand straight up, reposition myself, and return to the intense line digging.

We can hear Dennis up front yell to us to work harder to get out of the smoke. And that we do, hit and move, scrape and move. Reservoirs of sweat roll around inside my goggles and blur my vision. Sweat drips off the bill of my hard hat. I can feel a stream of sweat roll down my spine and into the crack of my ass. I am sure glad my asshole is as watertight as a duck's.

Someone else up front yells, "Keep the mounds on the hot side of the line down to prevent spotting." Another voice tells the rear to make sure the roll trenches are put in, and to improve them as they move along constructing line.

James notices a hot spot and we quickly react, putting a small line around it. James' reactions are somewhat slower. The rest of the crew continues up the hill with undisturbed momentum. As soon as the spot is extinguished, we rejoin the crew.

Now we are out of the dangerous situation, the bulk of the smoke behind us. The line is still being put in, but as the momentum slows I can feel my arms throb with pain and fatigue. We reach the top of the hill and continue over. We can see the cat line from here and the sight of it creates a moment of instant relief. Minutes later the sawyers reach the cat line and Darryl lets out a rejoicing yelp that echoes in the smoke filled draw.

As dusk falls, I look up at the snow-capped San Francisco Peaks that dress the skyline through the remnants of leafless oak trees. A full moon is rising at the two o'clock position from Humphrey's Peak. The sky is powder blue and the foreground white from layers of smoke. I take a deep breath and goose bumps cover my body. I feel glad to be alive. I look at the peaks and the moon again. The beautiful vista forms a strange contrast to what we have just been through.

Aaron interrupts my enjoyment of this beautiful scene. "Hey, Petretti," he says, "quit daydreaming and get this line done."

Stunned, I reply, "Sorry, I was just captivated for a moment by the skyline."

"Yeah," Aaron says seriously, "it looks reeeaaall nice. I just want to get out of here."

We continue ahead and tie into the cat line. We all "take five" at the cat line to readjust ourselves and make sure we are still intact. I wring out my headband. The sweat forms mudpacks in the dry, fine dirt.

When we return to fire camp a lot more activity is going on. Out-of-state and Indian crews are around. Catering trucks and outhouses are being set up. These aren't meant for the Coconino crews, for we are going home.

The efforts of the four Coconino crews stopped the fire at three hundred and twenty acres. Crews are being brought up from the desert fires. They will be the ones to mop up this mess. We all hail ourselves with intermittent chanting of, "We stop 'em, you mop 'em". We know we performed well, and our personal pride serves as reward for our work. This was OUR forest. Not any useless desert, but God's country, my new home.

July 8

I awake with my head in my armpit. The reek from it must have awakened me. It's time to get up for work, but my body is too tired to move. Cord comes in, drying himself off. "Is there any hot water left?" I ask him sleepily.

"Yeah, but Cruz just jumped in."

"Anyone after him?"

"Not that I know of."

"Boy, I stink, I'm going in next."

By the time I get my turn the shower is running out of hot water, so I turn the water off while I lather up. It is going to take a lot of scrubbing to get clean and I want to save what's left of the hot water to rinse off. Kyle bangs the door and it opens, "Petretti, come on, we got a fire."

"Shit, just what I needed."

"Hurry up! Everyone is on the bus."

"Sluggo, too?"

"Yes, Sluggo, too."

I run out of the trailer dripping wet with soap still in my hair, half dressed with clothes in hand and shoeless. I am the last one on the bus. This fire is at Blue Ridge campground just seven minutes away. We are at the turn-off towards the reservoir when we get the 10-19 call. There are plenty of mixed emotions about this dispatch. A citizen reported the fire. We cruise the campground anyway. Then I notice Darryl isn't aboard.

"Where's Darryl?" I ask.

Cord replies, "His parents are up from Tucson and camping on his land. He went to see them."

"That jerk missed a dispatch," Joe says. "He's always after us about missing a dispatch."

Cord counters sarcastically, "Hey, his parents are in town."

"That's no reason to take off. He could have seen them after work."

"Are you going to stop him from seeing them? Maybe he hasn't seen them in a while, you asshole."

"Fuck off! He shouldn't have left."

"You fuck off! He could if he wanted to."

People are listening to the argument and Joe and Cord are standing now with veins popping out of their necks. It's time for someone to step in. Drifty takes the challenge.

"Hey, you guys, cool it."

"Hey, you cool it," Joe snaps.

They both sit down. Gus looks at me and we smile at each other. I thought I was going to catch a fist while just minding my own business. Tempers are on the rise. Then it gets quiet again.

We return to the station and sharpen tools. Bad moods are very much in evidence. People just mind their own business and keep busy. Right after lunch we are called again. People hustle around and get on the bus. It is another local fire in the district. Halfway there we are 10-19'd, again. The tankers got there in a hurry and didn't need any help.

Another argument breaks out about how someone moved Paul's pack, and now he can't find his canteen. Smith has to get up and tell Paul in a stern voice to settle down. He practically yells it in Gus' ear. I look at him and smile as we did earlier. We both shake our heads. I say melodramatically, "Watch out. Tempers are flaring."

Darryl returned mid-morning from visiting his parents and is with us for this trip. I lean over to him and whisper, "I love it when the human will breaks down. You get to see what people are really made of."

"It's like a split personality in people. You know a Dr. Hyde and Mr. Jeckle," he responds.

"Uh, a Dr. Jeckle and Mr. Hyde?"

"Yeah, something like that."

"Fascinating. This crew is becoming more and more interesting," I say, and he agrees with me. "I've been meaning to ask you. How's the folks?"

"They're fine, thank you," he says.

"I'll have to meet them. I bet they're a couple of real nice 'guys'." That doesn't amuse him one bit. I guess it's time for me to shut up. No one is in a joking mood now or for the rest of the day.

July 9

All day while thinning I imagine how nice it would be to get laid by Ginny before she leaves the sites. I know this is their last week of digging. Just the thought of it makes me horny. Later, back at the Ranger Station playing volleyball, I start hoping like crazy that they come in for showers today. I'm too distracted to concentrate on the game, instead I'm checking out every car that turns into the station. The guys know, too, who I'm waiting for. After missing a couple of easy setups I figure it's not my day to play volleyball, so I let a spectator take my spot.

Kyle comes by and asks, "Hey, Petretti, where are you going?"

Darryl answers for me with a goofy laugh, "He thinks he's going to get laid."

"Is he going out to the sites?"

"Yeah, he's never been there before either."

"Should I go along?"

Some offside Hotshot asks, "Hey, can I go, too? Can I go?"

I turn around and flip them off. I get an "ahhhh" from the peanut gallery. Darryl is sitting in his chair at the trailer. "If they were coming, they would have been here by now," he advises.

"I know," I say. "That's why I'm leaving now. I'm going to check it out."

I run down to the trailers to clean up a little and put on fresh clothes, and bring my jacket for some possible late night traveling. I ride out without even looking at the volleyball court. A small fishtail expresses my hurry for what I hope will lie ahead.

The turn-off is 10 miles down Highway 87 and then another 8 miles on a dirt road impossible for a standard passenger car to navigate. The girls' camp is easy to find, but when I get there the place looks deserted. There are about a dozen or so tents set up, from single occupant to 8-person sleepers. Their bright colors clash with the more subdued greenery of the shrubs and junipers. A lot of cars and trucks are parked around. As I walk about I see big dog food bags, dirty dishes, big water drums, and hanging laundry. I remember what Dennis said after the Arches left the party. Why were they so choosy about which guys could come out here? The camp looks pretty normal to me. I doubt that the girls are far from here as none of the cars are locked. In fact, one Blazer's door is open. I walk over to shut it. Who's going to steal anything out here? I ride around looking for the actual digging sites, but can't find any. On the other side of a ridge you can tell that this spot is the noted Chavez Pass.

Looking outward from this ridge, the whole northeast opens up in front of you toward Winslow. It is so beautiful, nearly picture perfect open rangeland for miles. It would be the ideal lookout for discovering anything approaching. The Indians must have had it made here. I think about how a brave might have checked out the same sunset coloring hundreds of years ago at this very spot. Two different sets of eyes, very different culturally, would be experiencing the same aesthetics. The skyline reveals a breathtaking spectrum of color: light blue punctuated by white clouds, with darker tops and luminescent orange bottoms, many shades of violet and purple, and the dark-as-night eastern horizon.

Suddenly a chill hits me. The clouds behind are collecting and it is time to head back, disappointed and without the sexual release I hoped for. I ride back to the camp and leave a note on Ginny's car telling her to be sure to get hold of me when she comes to the station.

July 10

Instead of P.T., we empty the bus to ready it for some weekend repairs in town. At 4 P.M. as we walk up to the volleyball court, someone notices that Ginny's Volkswagen Rabbit is here and brings it to my attention. That means Ginny's here, too! I walk with the others to the court, but don't participate in team selection. Good thing, because shortly after, Ginny comes up to her car. I make my way over only to be interrupted by Cord, who is about to leave for Tucson.

"Headed out again?" I ask.

"Yeah. This will be my last time going down before I take off for good."

"That's right. Only a couple more weeks."

"Yeah, I guess I just can't wait."

"You don't sound as excited about quitting as you were a couple of days ago."

"Well, I tried to get a hold of Janine, but she wasn't home. Or maybe she's not answering the phone. But I don't understand it, her parents should have answered the phone."

"Maybe they all stepped out for dinner," I suggest.

"Naw. I think she went out with the other guy. She kinda hinted around last night that she might not be home when I got there tonight."

"Was she going out with Kathy again?"

"No, I think it's this guy she met last weekend in some bar. He asked her out and she said she would go."

"You gotta expect things like that. You here, and her down there. That's the problem I had in leaving L.A. My girlfriends were not going to wait around for me. I know Castleberry isn't. It eats at me. Sometimes it pisses me off."

Cord nods in agreement. "I know, but what gets me is that she just can't wait for a couple of weeks until I get home."

"Maybe she realizes that, and wants to get some action before you get home permanently. Speaking of action, I've got to hit up on Ginny before she takes off."

"Go for it. I'll see you later."

"Yeah, see you later, hope things work out. Hey, is this going to be another Cord Week?"

He doesn't say anything, just shrugs his shoulders as he lets his clutch out, dispersing a few pebbles under his tires. "Bye," I call after his departing figure. "Watch out for them critters."

Cord leaves and I move on to better things. As I approach Ginny I can see her hair is still wet from the shower. She matches my smile with hers.

"Hi," she greets me warmly.

"Hello, I missed you yesterday. I came out to see you, but no one was around."

"I got your note."

"That's good. I was afraid the wind might have blown it away."

"I got it. I went out to party and the others went to Winslow for groceries." She gestures towards the office. "I've got to use the phone."

"Good. I'll walk over with you."

We talk all the way there. She bumps me a few times and brushes her arm against mine for a cheap thrill, or by accident. I get jazzed over it, enough for a half hard-on. Some outsider is on the phone so we sit and talk some more. She tells me right off that she is getting married this fall. That sure drains the blood from my dick! She gets talking about how she likes working with her shirt off.

"Do others go naked, too?" I ask with ill concealed curiosity.

"Not naked, just topless."

"No kidding? There was a rumor around here that all you girls run around naked out there."

"Well, it's not totally true, we just like to get tan since no one's around to get too excited over bare breasts."

I lean into her and pull her top away with my finger to check out her full body tan. She doesn't try to stop me and lets me peek while her nipples stand erect. She just smiles at my expression. "Just keep it confidential," she says.

"Yeah, I will. Otherwise you'll have every Hotshot and tanker out there with binoculars."

Her call to her boyfriend is brief and not very intimate. When she hangs up, she tells me that the girls are having a going away party Friday night. Kathy warned her not to let us know about the party, but she figures it is O.K. to tell me. She doesn't know where they are going to have it, so we make arrangements for her to leave a note by the phone on the bulletin board. I suggest that they could have it here at the station, but that hits a sour note with her. She quickly says no because their parties are the quiet type. While we talk, Ginny's car pulls up with Ellen at the wheel. Goodbyes are short and the girls take off. Still, the future sounds promising.

Half the crew left for the weekend and it is fairly quiet at the trailers. It's time to do some drinking. I return to the trailer and grab a six-pack from the fridge. Then I attempt to find out what the heck Darryl is up to. Dennis comes barreling down in his car and skids on all four tires directly in front me. I just stand still, daring him to hit me, but his initial judgment is good and he halts a few feet from me. He smiles at me like he knows exactly what he was doing all along. That smile also telegraphs that he's been drinking.

He says, "I see you're still here. You're sticking around this weekend."

"I'll go up tomorrow," I answer. "I had some business to take care of."

"I'd offer you a beer, but I see you already got some. I was going to show Darryl some new toys I got. Hey, I saw the Arches driving down the highway. Did you see them?"

"Yeah. I talked to the blond somewhat. That's what business I had to take care of."

"What was her name?"

"Ginny."

"Oh, yeah."

"They kinda invited me, and probably you, too, to their going away party."

"When's this?"

"Friday. They didn't want anyone to come, but Ginny said I was O.K., and Kathy probably wouldn't mind you coming either."

"I doubt I can go, there's something strange about those girls anyways."

"Yeah, I found out some things about those girls." Without giving up any clues I change the tone of the statement. "Uh, about their work habits."

"Oh yeah? What?"

"I wish I could tell you, but I promised I wouldn't tell anyone. Maybe I will later, after they leave."

"It probably won't surprise me any."

"Oh, maybe not. Time to change the subject. What do you got to show Darryl?"

Dennis pulls out an awesome looking short gun and cocks it back with a loud CHINK.

"Wow! What's that?" I ask.

"Like I said, just a toy."

"Darryl will get a kick out of it. Come on, let's go."

Dennis grabs a canvas bag and his glass of beer and follows me back to the trailer. Darryl is sitting there by himself with a glass of wine and three empty Old Style cans on the table, like he was expecting us. He could have been there all along and I didn't notice him.

"Slide show tonight," Darryl comments.

"Fuck the slide show," says Dennis. "I got something to show you."

Darryl focuses his eyes on the army green canvas bag and his eyes open wide. He knows that Dennis only keeps certain goodies in those bags. "Ahh, what do you got in there?" he asks.

Handing him the bag, Dennis says, "Check it out."

Without looking Darryl asks, "How much?"

"About $300."

"Nice, real nice. With a bunch of these we can set up our own army here at Blue Ridge."

"The Blue Ridge Mercenaries," I say. "Now, that's a scary thought."

We sit for a spell, drink beer and talk about the army, war, and killing pimps, dope dealers, and child rapists. We are silenced by the sounds of footsteps up the stairs. The door swings open and Cord is standing there.

"Where did you come from?" Darryl asks.

"Fuckin' shit!!! God damned truck blew up on Zane Grey highway on the flat part before Camp Verde."

"Blew up? Like, what happened?" I ask him.

"It sounded like a rod. As soon as I heard the banging I turned it off."

"You didn't walk back here?" Dennis asks.

"No, an Indian that works at Happy Jack brought me all the way to Blue Ridge," Cord replies.

"Was he coming this far?" I want to know.

"Nope, he was going to Happy Jack. Went out of his way. A real nice guy."

Darryl asks, "So where's your truck?"

"I left it there, off the highway so no one would fuck with it. Uh, Dennis, can I ask you a big favor, a real big favor?"

"You want some help?"

"Yeah, I would like to tow it back tonight. I'll give you gas money and all the beer you can drink, and anyone else who comes along."

"Yeah, no problem," Dennis says. "Darryl, Petretti, come along."

"I'll go," I offer.

"I'm drunk enough," Darryl decides.

Dennis pleads, "Come on Darryl, you pussy."

"Darryl doesn't have to go," says Cord. "We can probably only fit three in your cab anyway."

"Yeah, and I can handle it," says Dennis.

"Great. Thanks guys, thanks a lot," Cord says sincerely, a sentiment you don't hear very often from him.

"I will need to stop at the Wells to get gas," Dennis tells him.

"I guess we better get going before he closes," Cord adds.

Darryl warns, "You better hurry. He closes in fifteen minutes."

"I think I've even got a tow rope in the back of my truck, left over from when James needed a tow," Dennis says.

"Dennis' Towing Service," I pronounce.

"I should go into business," he says.

We drink all the way down there and all the way back. Cord elects to ride in his truck to keep it under control. Cord must think we're crazy for weaving and crossing the yellow line, when we weren't actually driving right on top of it.

"It's kinda quiet in here," I say.

"Why don't you put in a tape?" Dennis suggests.

"Why didn't I think of that before? I'll find something." I look through his selection, mostly music from the sixties, bands I haven't heard for a long time. One in particular catches my attention, "Venture's Greatest Hits." Sounds good. Ah, "Pipeline" is on here. I haven't heard that in a long time, probably not since grammar school. I remember we played that song at our grammar school Sixth Grade Culmination. We weren't allowed to call it a graduation. It was our Principal's pet peeve at Fenton Elementary. Speaking of peeves lets pull over and do one. Cord might need to go, too."

"I almost forgot I had that tape," Dennis says thoughtfully.

"You don't hear about them anymore," I remark.

"You don't hear much of any good music anymore. I mean, really good music. Just listen to how... how..."

"Dramatic?"

"Yeah, how much of an impact the beat has. The music today just doesn't move you like it did before."

"You know, you're right. You're really right. There's something about this music that moves you," I say.

"It brings back a lot of memories," says Dennis.

"Memories, yeap, a lot of memories." My heads a-bobb'n with the music. "This reminds me of my grammar school days, right before I went to junior high."

I get pretty drunk at this point and find it hard to remember exact conversation, but I know we talk about music, one of my favorite subjects.

Music has always been a part of man, ever since he could make repetitious noise with some object. The Greeks thought highly of music, strummed lyres and blew flutes. Their gods were into music, too. Eros, the god of love, had his flute to influence those in love through their souls, for music can drastically alter moods and feelings. The variety of styles in which musicians and composers create, never fails to deliver its spell, to entertain and impress us.

Yet, the pleasure we get when we listen is only a small part of the influence music has on us. Music is absorbed in our subconscious minds, more so when we listen quietly, less if we are dancing to it or otherwise physically active. To be absorbed in listening, is to leave behind conscious thoughts of personal problems, politics, love, and the physical world. Even if your attention wanders and you find yourself drifting in and out, your subconscious still registers the harmonies and rhythm. It never ceases to perceive.

Both conscious and subconscious activity accompanies everything we do. They are stored as memory, and stem from different sources in the brain. Subconscious memory is the larger of the two, and can be reached at times through introspection. The conscious memory is triggered by one's sensual perceptions. The key to greater awareness is to develop a way to draw information from both sources.

Music can often do this. It has a way of digging into the subconscious, a place where feelings are stored. Listening to music from one's past evokes remembrances of events and emotions from the time when that music was a factor in your life. These could be solemn memories, nostalgia for a youthful past or special flights of thought that have value to you alone. Music can spark an energetic state, feelings of personal or national pride. It can give one shivers from a wellspring of deep feeling about a first love, a first conflict, the beginning of a war, the high points and even low points of one's life. It's almost as if the information is programmed in the music especially for you, and when you put the card into the computer, personal information comes up.

I believe the majority of the music today is not doing this. The funked out disco releases too much physical activity. The disco rhythms move the body, not the soul. The lyrics are meaningless, the beat the same. A person cannot be inspired and moved by meaningful lyrics when he or she is moving about putting a bedroom rap on a wet one.

The music of the sixties provides a full "computer readout" for the memorable events and changes of that era. If someone were to play a score from that past, you could probably recite the world events taking place at that time, and even what you were doing then. The disc can serve as a deliverer of a posteriori knowledge. In some cases, it can serve as an abstractor of apriori knowledge, such as a moral worth, or a philosophical insight. And this is probably true for even the most unaware people among us.

Repetition is the key to our survival on this earth, and this can be easily seen by our love for the repetition of music. Repetition within our environment is how we survive on this planet. Call it a form of Darwinism. Man conforms to his environment and repeats successful actions to survive. If we didn't conform to our environment, we would perish and become extinct. This is the key to the nature of man. Man's behavior must adapt to his environment to survive. Drugs are a synthetic form of repetition in the chemical equilibrium of our metabolism.

I guess I've been rambling on because Dennis stops me in my tracks. "Hey, you are getting too deep for me."

I focus my attention on the present. "Damn!" I exclaim. "We're at Little Springs already!"

"Time flies when you're having fun."

"Or, when you're in heavy conversation." We feel a tug on the truck.

"Damn," Dennis says, "I forgot all about Cord. Man, we've been so into talk... uhh what do you call that babble shit, psycho ologies or something like that."

"Philosophy, I guess you mean."

"I've been weaving a lot."

"You sure he's still back there?"

"Yeah, I can feel him back there. It scares me though. I completely forgot about him and I'm drunk, real drunk." He shakes his head in disbelief. "We're lucky we didn't get in an accident, or something. It would have been funny if we would have seen him pass us up."

"Like you see someone's tires fall off, and the guy sees them rolling by him, passing him up."

"Yeah. Ha, ha!"

When we got back to the station Dennis and I am jazzed enough from our talk to keep on partying. Cord is discouraged enough just to go to bed, but not without thanking us again. We want to pick up where we left off so we stumble back over to Darryl's trailer. All is dark inside.

"Darryl," Dennis calls, "Where are you?"

"Come out, come out wherever you are," I say. "He's probably in bed."

"Well, let's get him out."

"Darryl, we want to see slides, come on out and show us some slides."

We go into his room and turn on the lights and stereo. Darryl doesn't move. Dennis pulls the covers off him and Darryl moans loudly, "Leave me alone."

Dennis doesn't want to leave him alone. "Come party with us some more."

"No, I can't. I'm too drunk."

Dennis pulls him out of bed and onto the floor again. "Come on, Darryl, you owe us. Get up and drink with the men like we used to do."

Darryl still doesn't budge.

"Let's get an egg and smash it over him. That will get him up," I suggest.

"Go get one," Dennis directs.

I get two, one for each of us. Darryl is sitting up on the floor by now, drooling slightly. "Leave me alone," he moans. "I already threw up."

"Good," says Dennis. "Now you're ready to go again."

"No way. Leave me alone."

"If you don't get up we'll crack these eggs over you," I threaten. He doesn't move, just sits there with his eyes closed.

"O.K." Dennis says. "Here goes."

"He really doesn't believe us," I comment. "Here goes, Darryl."

Dennis smashes his egg over Darryl's head. I do the same. He still just sits there.

I step back a little. "I think he's mad."

"Yeah, the egg is starting to fry on his head. We better cool him off." Dennis pours the rest of his beer over Darryl's head, then grabs my beer and repeats the process.

I find this hilarious. "Egg and beer shampoo," I hoot.

Dennis says, "Darryl, are you ready to get up now?"

All of a sudden Darryl jumps up and starts swinging wildly while imploring us, "Leave me alone! Leave me alone!"

An open fist catches Dennis on the ear, but Dennis is laughing so hard and is so drunk he doesn't even feel the contact. Darryl runs out of the room, through the living room, down the hall to the back door, struggles to open it, finally does open it, and runs out the back door.

Dennis laughs, "He's a party pooper. Come on, we'll watch some slides. He'll see us playing with his stuff and he'll come back."

Knowing Darryl and his ways I say, "Let's lock the doors so he can't sneak up on us."

The film projector is already set up, so we proceed to watch the slides. After a while the room starts to spin. I say, "I'm going outside to look for Darryl." I go outside, look around for a while and call his name, but he doesn't appear. All of a sudden I don't feel so good, and a whole sixer of beer comes up all at once, smelly and foamy, in a massive blast. Part of it lands on my pant leg and shoes. I give up the search for Darryl and go back into the trailer.

Dennis is still sitting there with his head down and his hand on the remote control, changing the pictures automatically with one hand, paying no attention to what he is doing. His chew can is in his other hand, but the contents have spilled on his lap. The smell of chewed tobacco is sickening and I dry-heave all the way back to my room, which I stumble into almost by accident. I stand by my bed and reach out to pull my covers back. "**Arrrrgggg**," a screaming body flies out of my bed. I jump back in fright, hitting the wall on the other side, and slide down to the floor. It's Darryl! He runs out naked, screeching with laughter. I sit there with my heart beating wildly. He scared the total shit out of me. Wow, what a concept, opposing orifice projectiles! Good night.

July 11

I remained on the floor where Darryl left me until sometime early this morning, when I found my way to my bunk. It was too high for me to attempt to get into last night with my head spinning. This morning Darryl wakes me up early, laughing as he did when he ran out hours ago.

"Scared the shit out of you, didn't I?" he cackles. I nod affirmatively. "Teach you to fuck with me, huh?" I nod again. "I was hiding under the trailer. I saw you walk around looking for me. Then I took a shower in Paul's trailer and jumped into your bed."

"That's why my bed was wet. I thought maybe I had pissed in it." I reach to feel it. It's still wet.

Darryl finds this hilarious. "Ha! Ha! Ha! Dennis is still in the chair. He spilled his chew on himself. He fell asleep holding his spit can, and it all spilt out on his lap."

"I know, it made me sick enough to dry-heave. I had to leave."

"Is that why I heard you throwing up before you came in the room?"

I nod. "My stomach hurts, worse than Bob's sit-ups. My head hurts. My whole body hurts."

"Serves you right. Ha, ha, ha!"

"What time is it?"

He leaves, laughing, without even telling me the time. I sleep it off a couple of hours longer, collect myself and head for town without talking to anybody. Talk is cheap, but I am broke this morning. I am drawn into the Widowmaker by the sight of familiar vehicles in its parking lot. I swear to myself that I won't drink anything.

Inside, Drifty greets me. "Hey, Treddie."

"Hey, Drifty."

"Just the man I want to see."

"What for?"

"My truck broke down and I need to go to the house so I can pick up my car. I'll even buy you a beer."

"Sure, no problem. The only problem will be if I have to drink anything right now."

"Partied too much at the station again?"

"Yeah, too much. Come on, I'll tell you all about it. Oh, you got any pot?"

"Got a little at home."

"Great. I'll exchange my beer for a couple of bongs. I think that's what I need to ease this hangover. As much as I puked last night, my stomach still hurts."

On the way over to Drift's house I interrupt my description of the night's partying when I notice a white cloud of smoke to the west. The mass of it makes me think it's a fire, but Drifty reassures me it's only the Navajo Army Depot blowing off bombs, something they do regularly. The bombs are left over from World War II. They keep them stored there and explode them almost every day.

After a short buzz over at his house I feel like having a beer. We agree to return to the Widowmaker for a brew and a game of pool. That white smoke is still hanging around and it looks even larger now. Drift says if it were the explosives at the depot the smoke would have dissipated by now. We walk back to the Widowmaker to see if anyone has heard of a fire. Aaron and Russell are sitting in the same chairs they were in when we left.

"Hey, you guys seen the smoke outside?" I ask.

"Naw," Russ says. "Is there one?"

"Yes, it could be a fire," Drifty tells him.

"Shit!" Aaron exclaims. "That's all we need." He and Russ jump up and follow us outside. "Damn, sure looks like one."

"More so now, it was all white before. See the darker smoke there, that wasn't there before?" I ask.

"NO SHIT!" Russ cries.

"It definitely has gotten bigger," Drifty says. "We noticed it when we left an hour ago."

Russ says, "I'll call the dispatcher, maybe he knows what it is all about."

We walk back into the bar and notice that the bartender is on the phone. "That could be our dispatch now," Russ suggests.

"NO SHIT?" I respond. We approach the bar.

"Hey, any of you guys on the Blue Ridge Hotshots?" asks the bartender.

"Yeap."

"Someone named Darryl Atchison wants to talk to one of you."

Russ says, "I'll take it." He goes to the call, listens and quickly hangs up. "Let's go, were all meeting at Nob Hill Ranger Station."

Drifty asks, "Does that mean we're dispatched?"

"What do you think?"

"What about the bus?" I ask.

"I've got to pick it up at the dealers. Aaron, come with me, you can drive me over. Drift, can you go back to the house and get my gear in the living room?"

"Sure, I've got to get mine, too."

Aaron adds his request. "Drift, get my boots in my living room."

"What about my gear?" I ask.

"Darryl is bringing the six-pack with all the gear in back. He knows you're here," Russ replies.

"Far out, more money. I got pockets that go jingle, jangle, jingle."

I find my way to Nob Hill and, one by one, the guys who were in town start to show up. My brother-in-law Dave even shows up, but the emergency situation prevents us from any lengthy conversation. We assemble in the bus and wait for the rest of the crew from the station. The smoke is building and the excitement growing. People are running all around the station. Forest Service trucks and equipment are leaving in convoys. By the time the remnants of the crew finally appear, we're about the last ones to leave. Once again we are on our way, never to see another full day off.

A few of the guys were in Phoenix, and they are still missing, but we have enough to roll on. Mike Cord isn't too happy about the dispatch. He would rather have been in Tucson. James, on the other hand, is very happy. He has one of his peculiar smirks on his face. I go over and sit next to him to inquire about his elevated state of joy. "What are you so happy about?"

"Man, if you only knew what I'm going through right now."

"You look like you're on something."

"On something isn't the word for it!" He laughs, but tries to hold it back. "I'd say I'm rather fucked up. You know, of the tripping kind."

"What'd you eat?"

"Uh, about five grams of 'shrooms."

"Oh my God! You must be blazing!"

"I'd... I'd... I'd say that." He laughs again, slaps his face to stop the stutter. "I was in the aspen grove, had just eaten the buggers. Darryl drove by lookin' for me, so I thought I was busted. I tell you, I really didn't expect this to happen. I wanted to have a nice trip today, but this ruined my whole day. Or made it."

"Man, I wish I were in your shoes," I say enviously. "You're going to have a good time on this one."

"No, you don't. I was blowin' it on the way up. You know, tryin' to keep straight. Cord was trying to make me laugh."

"What was he doing?"

"Nothing. He was just looking at me, man. I was so squished in the back seat of the six-pack. Four of us were cramped in there, in that there back seat. I told him what I did and he never let me alone. Then there was Darryl's driving. Just the fact he was there made me want to laugh. You know, that thing about Darryl that makes you laugh?"

"I know what you mean. There's a particular thing I get when I eat 'shrooms. I get what I call the "Stickys." You know, that feeling when everything seems to be real close to you, like sticking to you. You never seem to have enough room. You keep pushing things away."

"Yeap, that's it. To start off with, I have claustrphobia."

"Holy shit." I laugh and return to my seat.

Cord leans up to me and says, "Did he tell you what he did?"

"Yes. Poor guy."

"After last night I need to be tripping to handle all this."

"Oh yeah, almost forgot what had happened, in all the excitement." Wow! How soon I forgot what happened last night. And to think this might be the last fire that I have with Michael J. Cord. I wonder what he's thinking about and feeling right now.

We turn onto the dirt road that leads us to the Metz Fire. Lots of smoke fills the draws. Driving is slow, as it is hard to see where we are going. The road is flagged along the way.

We squad up and ready to march down a freshly excavated cat line to back fire into the head of the fire. There is a distant roar inside the cat line from the fire and from busy cats plowing and unearthing mineral soil. Some of us with fuses commence to burn. Reamer is once again our sector boss. Without any recognition from us about his heroics, he runs into the trees with extended fuses, heading straight for the roar of the fire, and soon vanishes in the thick smoke.

A few crewmembers are behind the line patrolling for spots. Reamer can be seen a couple of chains away setting off the bulk of the backfire. The pillar of smoke and the crackling of the roaring fire are coming closer and closer. The vacuum created by the fire, the Venturi effect, draws the backfire right into the main fire. Like an explosion, the two fire heads converge. The roar peaks as the intensity of two identical but competing energies explodes, the synergy emitting the force of two bombs going off, mushrooming cloud masses to the heavens. Wow!!! I only hope James gets what I imagine he must be experiencing now. To me the thundering clashes and the fiery upheaval recall the great Norse Gods of Aasgard, and Thor's horseplay in the heavens of Scandinavia. The only thing that isn't going on, is the ground shaking experience of an earthquake. Yes, I lived through the 1971 "Big One" in Smell A.

When the fire head tapers down and the roar subsides, it seems almost too quiet. We are literally fighting fire with fire, right here in the lush vegetation around us. If it had failed to do the job, we'd all have been incinerated. I doubt that the cat line could have stopped the inferno that approached us in this high timber stand of pines. Amazing how such a simple theory can have such favorable results!

Now you can hear the crackling of cooled embers. The smoke and ash particles never really reach us. They were sucked up in the mushrooming effect. We continue to scout for spots while we let the burned-out area cool down. James is still smiling with the intensity of a Jimi Hendrix experience.

His evening's entertainment was nothing he planned for. An unidentified crew that has been working behind us congratulates us for our great work in stopping the only uncontrolled and most explosive, dangerous portion of the fire. The overhead had been very skeptical that it could be stopped here. They saw it all, too. I do believe that we got an "Atta boy!" for our efforts.

We rest for a couple of hours and watch the fire cool down. I can feel fatigue set in from all the work we have recently endured, not to mention the heavy drinking. Both add up to a severe handicap. The hardest part is still ahead... staying awake all night. This was supposed to have been our day off.

Cord strolls by and we talk about his Janine some more and swap stories about our girlfriend problems. We mop up all night when things get cool enough to tackle. We pull it off in small groups and by ourselves. We hit logs and stir ashes. Most of the men talk all night to stay awake. I'm sure that at one point I fell asleep standing up, leaning on my shovel.

July 12

After what seems like endless hours, to our relief the day finally dawns. Patches of smoke continue to rise as an Indian crew takes over our duties. Smoke in a pocket of the terrain cuts visibility to about twenty feet, so the bus cautiously creeps its way to fire camp where we can eat and rest. We have to rest four hours before we can be released. Once we got fed and take time to find some shade away from the noisy generators, there are only two hours left for actual sleep.

It's miserable not getting enough food and sleep. It leaves your emotions out in left field and gives you a nauseated, spacy feeling. You can't think even if you try to. You operate like a robot. Your mind and body go into survival mode. It's as if you're on a drug that you don't want to be on, and you just can't shake it off. It's a drugged out feeling just short of actually going delirious. You want to reach that threshold, but something keeps you short of going over the edge. I call it delirium.

As we drive back to Nob Hill, a western lookout tower on the Kaibab National Forest calls in a smoke. She sounds so excited it must be her first spot. A Coconino tower then picks it up. From out of nowhere a bit of excitement energizes the apathetic crew. The dispatcher wants to know if the Coconino crew was released from the Metz fire. Our 10-20 was at the Nob Hill Ranger Station parking lot. At that time all four Coconino crews are dispatched to the new fire. Large loads of slurry are ordered. A few guys jump for joy while others speculate on the size of our new encounter. We catch up with two other crews on the freeway and it turns into a road race to the off ramp. The race obliterates all thoughts of what we had been through on the Metz fire. We are no longer tired. Like a slap to a newborn, we are ready to deal with our new reality.

Slurry planes are already circulating above the smoke. Thankfully the fire is a lot smaller than it sounded on the radio. The fire is in the some housing units, with structures in danger. The Hotshot buses pull in and the two crews split up, each going in a different direction. Slurry is dropped above the edges, and sprinkles of over-spray dot our clothes. From out of nowhere a lead plane flies over the treetops. Someone up front yells, "Hit the dirt! Slurry drop!" and bodies along the hand line hit the ground like dead weights. You can feel the clumps of slurry pelt your back, and the over-spray rain down as a grand finale.

"Everyone up now, get this line tied in." This is the first time we get slurry dumped on us in a full-force drop. It was like an honor to be covered with slurry. The stench of ammonia, tingling burning eyes, and the irritation of our exposed weathered skin doesn't even bother us. Work needs to be done after our impromptu shower, and all go back immediately to digging lines.

The line is a little cooler now, for the slurry retarded the fire spread. We tie in short sections of line and bump around the other crew until we tie into the road. Some of us take off looking for spots. Others hold the line along where we just dug, and along the dirt roads that grid the units. The grid formations of the dirt roads serve as excellent firebreaks.

Luckily, I take off for spot patrol, for there are four more slurry planes that need to dump their full loads. The fire is stopped at a couple of acres,

and the planes cannot land with slurry in their bellies. The planes are to unload the slurry wherever they see fit along the line. They resume where they left off, along the road. About five of our guys are standing in a group, unaware of any more drops, as the radios give no warning. A plane flies low, along a cold edge of the fire, and drops a hundred foot wall of jelled red mass right over the unsuspecting Hotshots. They run in all directions trying to escape the red globs. Those watching the spectacle laugh heartily, but it is not so amusing for the men getting slurried. They are lucky they didn't get hurt. The impact of an unsuspecting slurry drop can knock you off your feet, knock the breath out of you, or even give you a concussion. The stuff is heavy! You can tell by all the trees sagging from the weight of it. Some are leaning at a 45-degree angle. Others have their tops snapped off. One nearby tree topples, crushing a cab and shattering the windshield of a tanker parked in the path of the slurry drop.

When everyone collects his senses we muster back at the buses. The buses and other nearby vehicles are thoroughly splattered with slurry. Where bus windows are open the seats and contents directly within are splattered with slurry droplets. We have to take a little time before we leave to clean off the mess. My motorcycle helmet is covered with the stuff. It was bungeed underneath the overhead rack.

July 13

For the rest of the world, tomorrow is Friday, the last working day of the week, but for a Hotshot, the next day is our Monday. We are reminded of this when we are dropped off at Nob Hill Ranger Station. Tonight after work, I go over to my sister's house instead of going back to the ranger station. I enjoy a home cooked meal, take a nice, warm bath, and go to sleep early. I wake up in the morning to the smell of a new house. I had forgotten that I went to her new home. Doug is still on the Metz fire. I guess they are continuing to mop up over there. We only left there yesterday, but it seems like weeks ago. With all the action we've had in the past couple of days, I forgot about the party tonight with the Arches. Thinking about it inspires me to drive back to Blue Ridge this morning. Paychecks are also waiting there for some of us.

About half the crew takes a few hours of annual leave at the end of the shift to cash their checks and buy some groceries. As soon as we get our hands on our checks, we take off. I give Pat a ride up on the back of my bike, the Mongolian Marauder. We make it to the Widowmakers happy hour, where Pat finds a ride home with someone else. Just as well. I don't want to cut short anyone's fun. However, I want to take off and get back before dark so I can make sure I connect up with Ginny and the other Arches for the party.

It's been dark for twenty minutes when I pull into the station. The note is there just like she said it would be. The directions are simple and familiar. I am to meet them at the campground five miles down the road. I get ready and hustle out there with two six-packs and what little stash I have. The campground is full to capacity. I start to get nervous because I can't locate the girls anywhere. I circle the campground four times and lose hope of seeing them. They must have gone elsewhere. They probably were forced to change their plans, and left without me. On the way back to the highway, I notice some Forest Service flagging, which could be theirs. I stop and shine my headlights on it and I'm relieved to see that is so. There is a message right on the flagging, "We will be down the lookout road about two miles. Look for us." The excitement builds in me. I have a notion good times are ahead.

Sexually fanaticizing, I ride down the rough, dark, rocky road. For two miles I see nothing. Then I notice what appear to be reflectors. I continue moving slowly ahead and the reflections turn out to be the taillights of a VW Rabbit bearing Ginny's California plates. I don't see anyone as I pull up, stop, and turn off my bike. The silencing of the headers echoes throughout the forest. It takes awhile for my eyes and ears to adjust to the silence and darkness of the night forest. Out of the darkness, I gradually perceive some bodies sitting around. I could have sworn they weren't there before! There are three, no, four of them. I believe they are glad to see me, but not as happy as I am to see them.

The girls have open sleeping bags laid out over the pine needles and duff. They have shit eating grins on their faces. I tell them about my difficult time finding them. They tell me others were here, but are now gone. They giggle when I remark that others must have had the same problem finding the spot. For some reason I am left out of the joke. They all stare at me like I am out of place. Ginny motions me to sit next to her. I start to relate some fire adventures from the last two days, but the girls seem uninterested. I babble away and notice Ginny is the only one listening to me. In fact, she is staring right into my eyes. She places her hand on my arm and it stops me in the middle of a sentence. By now I have a pulsating hard-on. It was time to get down to business, so I lean over to kiss her. She wraps an arm around my back and gives me a long, experienced kiss.

Meanwhile, the other girls are still talking about something. I have my arm around Ginny and we are both holding on tight. Suddenly a hand grabs my hard-on. At first I figure it's Ginny's, but something is different. I stop the wet kiss and look down. Kathy's hand is stroking my bone! I smile at Kathy and she smiles back. I turn back to Ginny. Wordlessly she leans into me for another seductive kiss. As I lean backwards with Ginny, Kathy starts to undo my pants and pulls my pants down. She barely starts to insert my penis into her mouth when I come. Ellen and the other girl just wonder what the stir is, and then begin to get involved in the action. Soon everyone is partially undressed, wrapped up in an orgasmic labyrinth. The girls take off all my clothes and really work me over. They do a nice job on themselves, too. I must have come four times, a first in one setting. I really enjoy the girls, and they also seem to enjoy themselves, uh, with each other. I've had a lot of strange experiences in L.A., but I would never have guessed I'd experience anything like this in the middle of nowhere.

We stop back at the station so the girls can use the bathrooms. We are still feeling pretty high. I hug and kiss them all and say goodbye, not knowing if I will ever cross paths with them again. I stroll down to the dark trailers. Everyone is asleep. I lie in bed thinking about tonight's action, the best sexual experience I ever had. I am almost afraid to fall asleep for fear I'll remember this as just a dream. When I do, my stiff pistol is ready to go through it all one more time.

July 14

I wake up in a panic, not sure if last night was a dream or real. Surely it was too fantastic to be true. I check my genitals for some kind of proof, hold my hand to my nose and inhale the funky fragrance of sex. The post sex glaze is still crusting my penis and I think there might be a faint aroma of juicy crotch on my facial hair. Was it masturbation or hot, lesbian orgy sex that I recall? I check the bed sheets to see if it could have been a wet dream.

The whole day I am lost in my own world, a sad one, and very different from the way I was feeling last night. It was similar to that feeling you get at the end of spring semester. That feeling I used to get when my family traveled around the country. Or when we'd be at a campground for a couple of days and then move to another campground hours away. I used to enjoy meeting people at the various campground spots. I'd get acquainted, find friends to play with, and go exploring the grounds with them. Friendship came easily to me, but when it was time to say goodbye I always had a lump in my throat. Girls had the most effect on me. I was never allowed to get too friendly with girls sexually, but I found my own personal ecstasy just talking to them. The love I felt was as deep as if I had been intimate with them. Over the years I developed a whole group of female pen pals. Each time we said goodbye I felt a little heartbroken about leaving someone I had shared great times and adventures with. Today I wonder where all my old pen pals are, people I haven't written to or heard from in years. Pregnant, married, or even dead, they all carry on without me.

I can't tell you what we did for work today. The trailers are silent tonight, everyone still replenishing their store of valuable sleep.

July 15 and 16

The next two days a belated monsoon season hits hard. Lighting strikes all over the dry forest and starts one fire after another. All three tankers at Blue Ridge are busy responding to two and three fires a day. Even the old men at the station are called into action for these fires. The crew is split up. Timber and recreation people go out in three man strike teams. We are dropped off and, in most instances, left to search out a single smoldering tree. The towers are calling in smokes left and right, north and south. Some trees are literally blown apart by lighting. A streak several inches wide of bare wood stretching to the ground marks the path of lightning to the ground, splinters of wood can be seen hundreds of feet from the ignited tree. The lightning hits in the most unusual and hard-to-get-to places. Each fiery strike has to be sought out and extinguished.

The radio stays active with calls from the moment the towers sign on until very late at night. Some of the teams have to spend the night at small fires. There are too many fires to name, so numbers are assigned instead. It is not uncommon to have to hike two to three miles with chain saws and piss pumps. This is where navigation experience plays an important part. Trees are no longer useful to navigate by. With so much random fire damage, they all start to look the same.

Towards the end of the second day of this fiasco, the Hotshots are dispatched to the Cherry fire on the Prescott. Lucky for us, all but six of the crew was at the station and as soon as the fire is contained, those six are advised to return. The tankers will check up on the fire tomorrow. We wait at the station until everyone shows up. Last minute phone calls to frustrated, waiting girlfriends back home are made. We, the Hotshots, know that we will be getting dispatched while we are all spread out on lightning fires.

Don Read, a timber marker, will make this road trip with us. He is in the right place at the right time, with his fire gear close by. He was at a lightning strike earlier with a couple of fire prevention technicians. Don traveled with the crew often the last two years. The crew boss would call him when they needed somebody to fill out the crew. He didn't mind one bit, it was extra money for him.

We are on the road again, going towards the setting sun, jamming down the highway to Waylon Jennings. "I've always been crazy, but it's kept me from going insane," echoes throughout the bus. Listening to the merriment, you'd never know that we were overworked from all the hours we've put in lately. Most of us are acting crazy, maybe just silly from fatigue. Reserve adrenaline keeps us going. The conversation in the bus certainly is jovial.

"Hey, Kyle, how much do you charge to eat a cow's pussy?" Cord asks.

"He's thinking about it," Pat says.

Jim remarks, "You know Kyle, once you get past the smell, you got it licked."

"Frailsen, there's some women, look!" Gus shouts, pointing to some cows grazing around a stock pond.

"Arrgh, let me at 'em," James says in a pirate's voice as he lunges towards the window.

Darryl interjects, "Hey, you want to know something about Kyle? He can't stand anyone to touch his neck."

Joe reaches over and grabs Kyle's neck. Kyle quickly jerks away. He has a childhood fear about hands around his neck.

Joe says, "Oh, yeah," and reaches up again, grasping Kyle's neck with both hands. Kyle stands up and swings his fist at Joe. Lucky for Joe his extended arms parry the blow which just brushes his shirt. Kyle looks dead serious. Trying to ease the situation, Cord says, "Kyle, look!" He grabs his own neck, screams and kicks, pretending to strangle himself. Cord stops when Kyle shows no change in expression. Kyle is still grim, but everyone else is laughing his head off.

Now the stereo starts to act up. Darryl puts his headlamp on like a miner and crouches in the front of the bus to investigate the problem. In another part of the bus, James passes around an arrowhead that he found on a lightning strike. Jim shows off a piece of pottery that he had found. Jake asks, "James, where did you find the arrowhead?"

"Oh, by Jack's Crossing hiking into the lightning fire."

Koval ends this conversation by saying, "You know there's a fine for picking up artifacts on the job."

Darryl diverts his attention from the tape deck and adds, "Oh, yeah, something like that." This arrowhead situation dealt with law and order, so he has to say something.

James responds, "Hey, I risk my fuckin' neck fighting fire, least they can do is let me keep this here arrowhead."

"James, you're going to jail, son," Wakeford warns.

"Darryl, did you fix the tape?" Aaron asks.

"Nope, it ate it up. Too bad. No more Waylon."

Private conversations now take over. Paul and Joe argue, but no one pays attention to them. It turns into a small elbow push and shove for the aisle space. A strap is hanging down from the racks over Gus's head. He lifts his arm and cups his palm, making it look like a cobra about to strike. He makes several thrusts towards the strap. Darryl forms a snake with his arm and calls it *his* S&W Python. He makes some snake-like strikes towards Gus. Everyone then gets in on the act with his own "snake". All at once Gus is under attack from a dozen hissing pythons striking his body. He ends up lying in the aisle as the busload of "pythons" retreat in victory.

Aaron sits up on the back of his seat watching the nonsense. He would never participate in such silliness. Don Reed just sits quietly, too unfamiliar with most of us to get involved. He is probably having second thoughts about traveling with us. Jake enjoyed a good laugh at the snake attack, but also was reluctant to participate. Jim passes out cookies he got in a care package, a gift from a girl, to a few guys. Paul begs to have one to increase his sugar intake. Bob stands up and rolls up a map. Most of us pretend not to see him. He puts the rolled up map in some brackets Jake had just made and mounted above the windshield. Unbeknownst to Bob, he gets a cheer from us, as does Jake for his craftsmanship.

There is still a ten-ring circus inside the bus. Trash is constantly being basketed, and a game almost develops until someone hits Aaron on the shoulder with something moist, and it flops into his lap. Aaron puts a stop to it with a verbal threat. Bob is still fiddling with the new map holder trying to ignore all the commotion going on behind him. At times I wonder how he puts up with us when we are like this. Darryl is still watching him. He then notices something different.

"There used to be a Playboy foldout up there," Darryl remarks.

"Put one of Kyle's up there," Cord suggests.

"Why?" asks Kyle. "So you can beat off to it?" He laughs nastily.

"Kyle, you're stupid, man. Real stupid," Paul says.

"Fuck off, Wakeford," Kyle responds.

Paul reaches up and flicks Kyle's ear. Kyle just ignores it. The bus passes an old man pulling a couple of horses with backs piled high with camping gear. "Look at that old man," Koval says. "He must be a prospector."

Sluggo rolls down his window and yells out, "Hey, where's the gold mine, ol' timer?"

Soon afterwards a Ford pick-up truck full of high school girls drives by. This, naturally, brings on some gestures and crude remarks. Sluggo initiates them by calling, "Hey, Kyle, there's some girls for you."

"Ahh, just the right age. The younger the better."

"Kyle, you're a pervert," Joe says.

"They're a Hotshot crew going to the Cherry fire," Cord quips.

"I'd like to pop their cherries," Koval murmurs.

"Yeah," I say. "The Beaver Hotshots from Beaver Valley."

"Where's that?" Sluggo asks.

"Nowhere, stupid, just nowhere," Darryl snaps back.

"If it was up your ass, you'd know where it was at," Cord adds helpfully.

"Just around the corner from your pussy, you pussy," carols Koval.

I add, "Better yet, the Youngblood Hotshots." That was a dud and I get slapped upside the head for it.

"Well," says Sluggo, "how am I supposed to know? They do have all girl crews. I know, I've seen 'em."

"Them are Indian crews," Koval tells him.

It has been almost an hour since we left the station. Most of us have now settled down into sleep, others carry on small conversations. After some time Darryl decides to wake up all the sleepy heads. He walks up and down the aisle like a streetcar conductor, barking out destinations, "Thirty miles to Presssss-cott, thirty miles to Prescott."

I open my eyes to see what Darryl is yapping about. He's standing up, smiling, like he's the Cheshire cat. Someone eloquently states the feelings of all when he says, "Darryl, SHUT THE FUCK UP!" Drifty throws an apple core that hits Darryl in the neck. Darryl turns around quickly, but everybody plays innocent. Everyone laughs again after miles of silence. That act brings some life back in the bus.

Water, that ultimate life-giving element, is evident now in the form of rain. There are white, black, and dark gray clouds above, with patches of darkening blue sky peeking through. Lightning flashes in the distance, while streams of filtered sunlight peek out on the horizon from a half exposed sun. Someone points out a full spectrum rainbow amid the multi-colored clouds and gets a chorus of "oohs," "ahhs," and "bitchens".

Darryl is still standing in the aisle and continues his annoying announcements, "Last chance for napping."

To this Aaron responds, "You wake us up to tell us that? I'd still be napping if you hadn't opened your big mouth."

Some guys check their gear, finish getting dressed, and confirm their fire-readiness. We settle down to save our energies. Pieces of elk jerky are passed around made from a warm road kill someone had come across on the highway. A McDonald's sign is spotted fifteen miles outside of town. We are all hoping we can stop to get some chow. Bob refuses, shaking his head "no". We all have a sour reaction to this, as if we were *supposed* to stop there to eat and get the latest Happy Meal toy. More blue patches appear in the sky, and the clouds slowly dissipate as we travel westward.

With blue skies and increased visibility, we start looking around for smokes before the sun sets. Sluggo is sure he spotted one, but he's told it is only a cloud. Sometimes clouds and waterdogs, misty cloud inversions, are difficult to distinguish from smokes viewed from a distance.

Cord uses his announcer voice to advertise Sluggo's poor visual judgment. "Yes, friends, here we are spotting for smoke... ah, wait, Sluggo thinks he spotted something. A smoke, maybe? Is it? Is it? No! It's just a cloud, folks, just a cloud. A false alarm." He continues, in his regular voice, "Yes, folks, we done it again, another false alarm. This Cherry fire is probably another Forest Service overkill, I sure don't see any columns of smoke."

To play along in spotting things, I get all excited and say, "Look! An elk!" Everyone turns and looks. It's an elk all right, but this one has four letters under it: B.P.O.E..

The radio is turned back on to a static-free station from Prescott. Houses appear more frequently now that we are entering town. A colonial style hotel with a pond and an overlooking weeping willow comes into view.

Paul calls, "Hey, Frailsen, is there a 'gator in that pond?"

"Naw," James replies. "They's only in the south. There might be some of them crocodiles, though."

"Yeah," says Pat. "I hear they grow them big out here."

"James, why don't you jump in and find out. I bet you'll make great 'gator bait," Drifty says.

We drive through town towards the airport. There isn't a thing we pass that we don't all set eyes upon. In turn, there isn't anyone in Prescott who has not eyed us. The sun is almost totally out of sight behind the horizon. It puts a nice hue on the panorama. The roads are still wet, and there's a pleasantly damp, woody scent in the air. It gives me the same aesthetic pleasure as the smell of an ocean breeze. As we near the airport, a slurry bomber flies low over the bus. Some duck their heads, jokingly remembering what happened last week at the Kline fire. We arrive at the airport and a bomber lands parallel to our route in. More slurry planes are lined up waiting to be washed off from a hard days dump.

Bob runs into the fire station aviation office, and some others disembark to stretch out. Minutes later Bob comes trotting back and jumps to the top of the step in the bus. "Let's go," he says.

Dennis asks, "Where to, Bob?"

Bob joyfully says, "Home, they don't need us anymore! Ah, 10-19'd again. Damn, fuckin' A."

The busload of Hotshots goes wild. After the crowd settles down Pat asks if we can get something to eat now. Bob agrees. Everybody on the bus, almost in unison, begins chanting, "Let's eat, let's eat."

I quickly go into my routine from the Presbyterian fire. "Who's hungry?"

Squad two in unison answers, "We're all hungry."

Squad one doesn't have a clue what's so funny. For some reason, Don Read thinks he might be responsible, and asks, "Is it because I am with you?"

I guess Bob thinks it proper to work himself up for a meal. He's already hyper from his untapped mental and physical energy. He gets Drifty into a nice half-nelson, and when Drifty's face is blue enough it's James's turn. Others take their cue from Bob, and soon everyone's choking everyone else. Kyle makes sure his neck isn't touched by anyone. It gets so out of hand that Laybe says, "Someone get the tranquilizer darts."

Aaron's been watching closely and observes, "Bob, Sluggo needs some help." Kyle is turned around in his seat trying to stop Sluggo with one hand in which both of Sluggo's hands are confined. Bob releases Darryl's neck, just short of him passing out, to attack Paul. He grabs him by surprise around the waist and swings him back in his seat. It's an all out battle to see who can get the best hold. Bob looks like he's winning, but Paul gets his feet under Bob and pushes him up to the next seat. Kyle keeps his distance in the seat in front until Bob lands, inches away from him, propelled by Paul's push. Bob is now face-to-face with Kyle, and says nonchalantly, "Oh, hi, Kyle," before he jumps back to get Paul.

Pat does a great Dick Lane or Howard Cosell imitation, calling the play by play. Dennis is viewing all this from the rear view mirror, weaving down the road. He sees a great opportunity to slam on the brakes. Paul and Bob go crashing into the back of the seat in front of them. Kyle must have thought they'd end up in his lap. It ends in deadlock, an even match. Both get backaches from the braking job. Dennis gets a hand for breaking up the fight, and says, "Oh, sorry to 'brake' it up, but we're here," as he pulls into the McDonalds parking lot.

The longest silence during the entire trip comes when we get pulled over by the Prescott police department for no taillights. Paul is driving and considers it a setup. Apparently, the fuse blew again. All we get is a fix-it ticket to show the overhead when we get back.

Once the cop is out of sight, we engage in a terrific, strategically aimed, spit-wad fight initiated with ice from the McDonalds drinks. It's the back of the bus against the front. We hide behind the seat backs with our hard hats on. Soon wet paper dots are all over the inside of the bus and the front windshield. The non-participants, Aaron, Jake, and Paul, become annoyed with our little war. They are getting hit in the back of the head, at times on purpose. Things get out of hand, as they always do, when Dennis and James run out of paper to spit and start to project chew through drink straws. This leads to the chucking of food, and then gallons of water emptied on people. We pull over to change drivers, and the fight immediately stops. It has lasted over an hour.

In all the fun we had forgotten about nature's needs. Everyone but one jumps off the bus to take a piss. This act of nature turns into a game as we see who had the longest stream. A couple of guys try to piss on each other. Taking that piss felt better than making contact in the face with a wet spit wad. We get back at the station at 2300 hours and go straight to bed, exhausted from all the horseplay. Besides, tomorrow is another workday.

July 17

Another workday. A lightning strike, held dormant yesterday, now requires work and another rude awaking by Dennis' truck. His locked brakes skid over the gravel. I hear the noise as background to my deep sleep, a part of my dream for all I know. But soon the heavy footsteps of Bob's shoes became louder, the door swings open with authority, and it's back to the real world. It is 6:30 A.M. and a new dawn is waiting.

Bob says, "We're going to Sedona, leaving right away. Let's get it together. Petretti, don't be the last one on the bus this time."

I mumble, "I won't," then say a quick prayer hoping it's not another "torcher" run like at the Presbyterian fire.

This fire is about one hundred and sixty acres, most of it cold. We walk through to get to the hot side. A nice cat line surrounds most of it. The Happy Jack 'Shots are also here. Some bushes are still burning as we poke around hot ashes, mopping up. We take care of the bushes the easy way, we just stand around and watch them burn themselves out. The whole day is relatively boring as we walk from one hot spot to another, stirring ashes and mixing them with dirt.

There are three highlights today. One, the fire boss comes by on a horse. Second, jet fighters (someone mentions their pilots are from the middle east, being trained here) fly low over our heads as they circle the crews, dipping a wing as they jet by. Lastly, Darryl shows me what a finger fuck is. For a fuck of this variety, you need a Cholla cactus, especially one that has been baked in the sun. Cut off the top and insert your finger down into the cactus in an in-and-out motion. The sensation is amazing. The cactus spear must have been at about 98.6 degrees. The sticky, milky, juices of the cactus feel alive. The cactus even appears to quiver a little. The only word of caution is don't lick your fingers on this one.

The day's work turns out to be pretty easy, that is, compared to the previous weeks. We never really over-exert ourselves. The crews on the fire have a great dinner at the Kings Ransom in Sedona. The food is tasty and plentiful. We get back at the station a little after eleven P.M. By the time we refuel and re-tool, we are off the clock at eleven-thirty. We all have our usual night routines. Some drink, some go straight to bed, and we party out at the P.T. course. It's about midnight and Darryl yells from the back porch, "Hey, you guys better get in here." He doesn't know our exact location so he yells in our general direction.

The four of us enter the trailer through the back door, probably reeking somewhat from our smokes. I pop my head into the bathroom to check my eyes. I overhear Darryl say, "Bob was just here, we're wanted on the Prescott." Whew! I was thinking we were busted. The short conversation continues.

"When?" Pat asks.

"I don't know. Bob went to get more details and is coming right back."

Cord speaks for a lot of Hotshots when he says, "Are we ever going to get a fucking break? I can't wait to get the hell out of here, one more week."

Just then Bob sticks his head in and says, "We're leaving at three o'clock. Be ready." Bob isn't too excited by the news. We all drink a couple more beers to ensure some sleep on the bus ride and, about one A.M., turn in to sleep in our own beds.

July 18

The next sound I hear is Dennis, barreling in an hour later, as hyper and excited as usual. He makes a loud general announcement, "Everyone up! We're going to the Prescott, we're leaving in fifteen minutes."

"We already know," Darryl says. "Bob came and told us earlier, around midnight."

"Darryl, Cain is working on the bus, he's trying to fix the taillights. Have everyone assemble at the shop."

"Yeah, yeah."

I put in my two cents worth. "Well, Cord, here we go again."

We drag our asses out of bed and make our way to the shop. As people roll out of the trailers, they aggregate in small groups, slowly walking towards the shop. We are out of the station by two-thirty A.M. and get to the Prescott Fire Station before dawn. Some Hotshots file out and find a place on the ground to sleep. Others, who never woke up, stay on the bus.

At the crack of dawn, a girl brings in our assignment and tells us what to do. We follow her, but it is apparent she doesn't know where she is going. We end up backtracking on a few dirt roads in search for a particular location that only she knows. When we realize we're totally lost, we see the Prescott Hotshot crew trucks. They are all lying around as if they had worked all night. No one knows if we are supposed to go out on the fire line, as some decisions hadn't been made yet. We take the opportunity to grab a couple of hours of sleep.

Paul rouses me from a dreamless slumber. "C'mon, we're going," he says brusquely.

"Where?"

"Back to the Fire Station."

"Ours?"

"No, theirs. These assholes don't know what the fuck is going on around here."

When we return to the Fire Station we hear a rumor, which Darryl confirms, that we are to be put on stand-by somewhere. Another girl is waiting for us at the station. Now we are to follow her. We motor up the mountain through forest pines, larger and denser than those below, until we reach an old schoolhouse built of rocks. The Forest Service owns this classic structure, and we are to stay here, on call, until they figure out what to do with us.

The granite and mortar schoolhouse in this serene forest setting is a beautiful spot. A rustic bathroom structure with pull cord toilets and hardwood floors is sited amongst the towering pines and huge granite boulders. The Prescott offers a lot for the mountain man and nature buff.

By afternoon the grounds look as if a massacre had taken place. Bodies are sleeping wherever they happened to fall. Under trees, on a log bench, between the boulders, in the sun or shade, bodies lie motionless in deep rest. Any and all of our spare time is utilized for badly needed sleep.

We are awakened once again by the noise of people assembling to eat. The tired, sleepy crew of Hotshots is loaded on the bus and is led by someone vaguely familiar to where food is being served. Lack of sleep does nothing to change our usual feisty behavior. We give the busboys and waitresses a hard time, but make up for it with extra-large tips. It's the least we can do for the entertainment we derived.

When we return to the schoolhouse, there's just enough sunlight to enable us to select a bed outside where we can sleep under the treetops and stars. Without saying good night to anyone, I go out like a light.

July 19

Sometime during the early night it starts to rain. It is characteristic of Arizona that rains are highly unpredictable. It must have sprinkled a little before I woke, for things were already pretty damp. I look around and notice a few people are scurrying about, grabbing their belongings before the light rain becomes a downpour. I gather my stuff, too, and run inside, and soon everyone makes a dash to the shelter of the schoolhouse. Inside, almost everyone is awake. The ones who were disturbed by the sudden rain are finding places to lay their bags. I get all set up, ready to crash were I am, then notice I am missing a boot, probably dropped outside. I make a mad dash and find it by my old resting place. As fast as I can, I re-enter my bag to resume my sleep. Dennis and a couple of others are still up playing cards. I hear them in the background as I feel myself settling once again into dreamland, but just before I nod off I hear Dennis address me.

"Good night, Petretti."

I pretend to be asleep because I don't want to answer. "Goodnight, Petretti," he says again.

"Aaarrrggg," I mumble, to avoid further discussion. Seconds later I leap out of my sleeping bag in one motion, screaming as quietly as possible to avoid waking others. I stand up and quickly scan the room, my eyes fixed on Dennis, who is laughing hysterically. Koval and Sluggo are also dissolved in laughter. The three of them put four prehistoric looking June bugs in my bag when I went to retrieve my boot. I am frantic! They are laughing. None of us can catch our breath... the pranksters from laughing so hard, me for being scared half to death by their prank. After I get control of myself I laugh with them about my own fears of bugs. I return to a disturbed sleep.

Not much later, the lights come on. I squint from the discomfort it causes, but as my eyes adjust I see Bob and a Forest Service person standing in the doorway.

"Everyone up! Let's go! We're going to Horsethief camp."

It's eleven o'clock. I have only been asleep for about an hour. My eyes sting even more as I become increasingly awake. I assemble my things and make a move for the tool cage at the rear of the bus. I assemble a bed back there and curl up in it, hoping to get some sleep.

The three hour drive seems to go on forever as I drift in and out of sleep. Most of the time we are on a very bumpy road. In the rear of the bus, I feel it the worst. Lightning flashes light up the sky at five-second intervals and give me a glimpse of the mountainside near the bus. I know there is trouble ahead of us. All that lightning will torch off a multitude of fires.

We arrive at our destination at two A.M. I remember waking up when someone opens the back door. The details of it don't interest me. Bones and muscles aching, I just roll under the bus with my bag. From here I gain a few more hours of poor sleep.

Everybody is awakened at 0500 hours for a gut-bag breakfast and to be airlifted to the fire line. Our assignment is to burn out and hold the fire along the south flank. I am tired, dead tired, as we march up the canyons to our starting point. From there we go by copter up the mountainside. As we fly, I get an uneasy, irritating sensation in my crotch. I reach down and scratch it through my pants. Because it's hot and humid, I figure the problem is jock itch, and plan to inspect it the first chance I get.

That chance happens when we reach the top of our assignment. We have to wait here for the go-ahead from the line boss. I reach down my pants to give myself a good scratch and feel bumps that I assume is a rash. I concentrate my itching in an area with the most bumps. Then something happens that shocks me. One of the bumps dislodges, snagged under my dirty fingernail. Bewildered, I quickly retract my hand to inspect the object. I use another nail to dig it out and cannot believe what I see. I undo my web belt, take off my vest, and dash for the nearest bush for confirmation of my discovery. I unzip my pants, pull them down, and there, to my horror, lots of tiny creatures running all over me, having a field day in my pubes. I pull another "bump" off and take a closer look. Sure enough, it's a *crab*!

I quickly think of my medicine sitting back at the trailers next to my aspirin and vitamins. I was so glad I opted to keep the lotion. I discovered I had crabs the day I left for Blue Ridge for my physical. It was the black girl I screwed two weeks before I left. Valerie. Oh yes, Valerie. Sweet young Valerie.

Valerie was the "clean room" girl at Litton. Oh, but she was so nice! She had the softest, smoothest skin I ever felt. She had always had a crush on me, and we had a fling shortly before I left for Blue Ridge. We started messing around at the bowling alley, a little grab ass, then some kissing. I always thought that kissing a black girl was going to be odd. I was worried what other people would think of it. But it wasn't odd or weird. Well, maybe a little at first. When it gets your dick hard, what else matters? She was a great kisser. I just kept my eyes closed and got into it.

We were on a Litton bowling team. What made this team special was that we were on second shift, the four P.M. to twelve-thirty A.M. duty. We would meet at 0100 hours at a Woodland Hills bowling alley and bowl 'til dawn. We'd bring our own alcohol because they quit serving at one-thirty A.M. It was a lot of fun, and great to have company sponsored events for the second shift. Second shift life is unique in the L.A. area. There are a whole community of people who are out and functioning at those hours. When the second shift workers get off work they go out and party. I loved that lifestyle, mostly because I was on a different schedule than the rest of the assholes in Smell A. You travel in different directions for work. You don't have to wait in long lines at the bank or grocery store. It's the good life!

(Author's note to reader. The next four paragraphs are more of my corporate bastard babble. You may skip it if you're inclined.)

Everyone on day shift tries to get things done on their lunch breaks, and wastes a lot of time standing in line. Then they wait some more on the streets and freeways, getting to and from work. If they do things after work because they couldn't get them done at lunch, they still wait in lines.

What is it with lines anyway? There is more to life than waiting in lines. Now the corporate bastards have people wait in/on lines, telephone lines while they have you on hold. You are put on hold, press numbers, enter account numbers that they always ask for again, on the telephone lines, waiting, just waiting. Yes, that cyber line we are waiting in. It is corporate policy to make you wait ten to twenty minutes to accomplish anything over the phone. They already have it pre-calculated that a consumer's life is so busy that we aren't going to wait twenty minutes to get a ninety-five cent overcharge credit. That, multiplied by millions on a contract or monopolized service on a bill can put millions in the corporate bastards' pockets every month.

They brainwash consumers through advertising into thinking that you can't live without their product or scam. They get you locked into a contract that's too good to be true. Then they sneak in the extra bogus charges and mistakes. The mistakes are never in your favor because they are intentional. And our fucking voted representatives don't give a shit that we are being ripped off in that manner. They are not the ones subjected to the extra bogus service and late charges. Somehow they are immune to it, or the taxpayers pick it up. And what about the credit card late fees and charges? I always thought that my penalty was being charged interest. Do you ever think that we will have a corporate Holocaust? Do you ever think we will be reimbursed for all the money they stole from us consumers?

Include your elected officials in the Holocaust. They are the ones that allow this to happen by kissing corporate ass while their lobby money is flowing in your rep's pockets. FIRE YOUR GOD DAMN INCUMBENTS, YOU STUPID FUCKING CONSUMER GENERAL PUBLIC! You see that's how they think of the public. Holding candy to your face while their hands are in your back pocket. They know that we are ignorant. AND WE ARE!! Did I get a little crabby there? Now how did I get from black babes fucking me, to corporate America fucking me?

I guess there were a few eggs that the medicine didn't get earlier. The incubation period and the hot moist climate hatched these creatures. Who knows when we will be getting home? I don't know what to do... tell someone or keep it a secret. If I tell someone, like Bob, it might get me home sooner. This is an emergency. I can't go on with these creatures crawling all over me. Before I come to a decision I hear Bob calling me.

"Petretti! What are you doing over there. Taking a shit?"

For lack of something better to say, I reply, "Ahh, yeah, right."

"Come on, we're starting to burn out now. Get your gear on and watch for spots."

"Coming, boss." I snicker to myself. "I am pinching one off right now," I say, removing another crab from my privates and crushing him between my fingernails until I hear a vigorous crack. This is just too much. Why me? Oh, God, why me? Haven't I been through enough lately? This is all I need. Every chance I get, while watching for spots, I pick off as many crabs as I can, crushing them between my dirty, sooty, fingers, making sure they're dead. I feel their crunching bodies lose life between my fingers, as the embers do under my shovel. I do not cherish the idea of sharing my body with crabs. Even though I am so involved in my new tragedy, I am still aware of how tired I feel. My eyes burn as I watch for spots.

As the shift wears on, it appears we will only do a single shift here. Thank God! I can't wait to get home and get the lotion on me. The hike down the draw leads us to a helispot where we will stage for the flight home. On the site is a very old house, pitted with bullet holes from passing hunters and target shooters. It looks like a picturesque backdrop for photos. I get the idea to take a snapshot of someone standing in front of the structure with a blindfold on. We make it look like a firing squad scene. Pat volunteers for the shot. We then pose for a crew shot in front of the rustic wall. All this is a distraction to keep my mind off of the itching that is driving me crazy.

When the helicopter arrives we quickly check in and embark the ship. I can't wait to get back home. The itching is building up real bad. On the bus it is hard to hide the fact that I have something going on in my crotch as my hand is down there scratching all the time. Joe wonders what the hell is wrong with me. I inadvertently pull up one of the crabs. I can feel it between my fingers, moving around, trying to escape for its life. Joe looks over at me and asks what's wrong. I just look at him and reply, "Have you ever seen a crab?"

"No, I can't say that I have," he says cautiously.

"Well, do want to see one?"

"No, not really."

I decide to make a general announcement. "Hey, does anyone want to see a crab?"

That drew a crowd of curious onlookers. I have the crab in my fingers. I squeeze him enough to make sure he's stunned, instead of crushing him with my nails. "OK, are you ready?" I slowly open up my compressed fingers. "Look. There he is, a real crab." I no sooner open them up when the little guy leaps like a kangaroo. Everyone jumps back in unison to get away from it.

"Where did that thing go, you bastard?" Joe asks angrily.

"Wow! That thing took off," Drifty says.

From left to right:

Russell Copp;
Paul Wakeford;
Mike Cord;
Jim Cruz;
Bob Smith;
Kyle Penick;
Greg 'Sluggo' Leveque,

Knelling;
Jake Brookings;
Aaron Sobel;
Dennis Savage;
John 'Gus' Gustafson;
Darryl Atchison;
Yours 'Mad Italian' Truly;
David 'Drift' Grimwood;
Joe Rudd;
Pat Laybe;
James 'Gator Bait' Frailsen;

and not shown,
Marty Lankford.

As expected, everyone is mad at me for letting those things out. I didn't realize they'd make such a big deal out of it. I sat by myself all the way home. Ahhhh, a seat to myself, wallowing in my own misery.

July 20

It is a keep busy day at the station what with retooling and getting fire ready. James Bedlion tries to get us administrative leave, but the supervisor's office won't approve it. He ends up trying to get it for half day. If this fails, we will take a few hours of our annual leave. Most of us need to get groceries and do banking and other errands in town. Cord wants to take Saturday off, so he can arrange suitable transportation to get back to Tucson. He's considered leasing a truck and towing his Dodge in order to take everything back in one trip. His last few days of work are going to be a Cord Week. The main reason he wants off is because Janine and Kathy are going to be at a party in Flagstaff this weekend. He wants to attend that instead of the district party our station is throwing. Even though he'll be back in Tucson next week, he insists he's going to the Flagstaff party.

Janine has been on his mind a lot. He was worried about the attitude she would have when he returns to Tucson to be with her all the time, rather than just the occasional weekends. He tells me some of this while we're in the shop, sanding tool handles.

"Hey, I should practice my going away speech," he says.

"Where you going?" Sluggo asks.

"I'm leaving Tuesday right after work for freedom and civilian life."

Sluggo remembers. "That's right, you are leaving."

"No shit, where the hell have you been, SLUGG-O?"

Cord turns around and jumps up on the table in one leap, and says in an echoing, public announcer's voice, "My friends... friends... friends, today... today... today, is a memorable... moment... moment... moment of the infamous departure time... time... time of my personal freedom... dom... dom... dom."

Everyone laughs on each repeat echo. Behind him, out of sight, Russ is ready, with the shovel handle he's been sanding, to jab Cord in the ass. Unaware, Cord continues, "On this occasion I wish to thank... thank... yike!"

Right in the middle of the echo Russ planted the shovel handle in Cord's butt cheeks. "Shut up, Cord, and get back to work," he says. "Do your speech making on your own time."

We are all still laughing at Cord's surprise when Russ says, "All the rest of you better hurry up and get this work done if you want to get off early today to go to town. Bedlion just approved three hours of administrative leave."

"All right!" is the delighted response to this news, as the sanding continues.

Cord jumps off the table and comes over to me with a question. "Are you going up to Flag?"

"I have to. I got to put my check in the bank and get drunk tonight."

"When are you coming back?"

"Tonight, probably."

"Can I get a ride with you up to town?"

"Well, I'm taking my bike up, you know. You can ride with if you want."

"I forgot about that. I'd rather not. Darryl's driving up right after work, I can ask him for a ride. I don't think anyone else is going with him."

"James is going up, too, probably."

Cord doesn't seem too pleased about that. "I'll go ask Darryl," he says, and leaves to look for him.

I return to my sanding. "I think he's over by the gas house," I yell. Kyle hears me but doesn't turn around.

"What's by the gas house?" he asks.

"Darryl."

Kyle nods. "Oh, yeah. He's there."

Later that afternoon up in Flag, I sit at Shakey's F.A.C. (Friday Afternoon Club) getting drunk, hoping to see someone I know, but trying to avoid people I didn't want to see. Darryl and Cord will probably stop by as we had made tentative plans to meet here. I wait and wait, but eventually lose hope of meeting them. There's not much time left in happy hour. I've still got my eye on the door when Cord finally shows up. He knows the guy collecting money at the door, so he gets in for free and comes over to where I'm sitting.

"Say, Tred," he says.

"Say Bleed. What it is?"

"You should see what I got!" he says with excitement.

"Did you solve your lease-a-truck transportation problem?"

"No, I got something better."

"Something better? You got hold of some smoke?"

"No, nothing like that. I just bought a '68 Bronco."

"You did? Great! Was it what you wanted?"

"Yeah, except for the price."

"How much was it?"

"Twenty-four hundred dollars. He wouldn't come down any more."

"That sounds alright."

"Yeah, I guess so. What sounds better is a beer. Let me get something to drink before the prices go up, and then I'll show it to ya."

"Sure, take your time." I scan the crowd. "Hey, where's Darryl?"

"He's probably still over at the Widowmaker."

"He doesn't like it here."

"No. He thinks there's too many scum people here. We'll take a ride over there in the Bronco a little later."

"Sounds good," I say. "Maybe we can get something to eat, too. You better get your drink, you don't have much time left before happy hour is over."

Cord waits in line with an inebriated crowd to get up to the bar. He looks over at me to see if I'm still there and shakes his head with impatience at having to deal with a lot of nudging from this bunch. I soon lose interest in his efforts to check out a beautiful brunette in line that I've seen in here before. Cord walks up, notices who I'm looking at and says, "Wow, she's nice! Nice tits, nice cleavage."

"Yeah, real nice. I've seen her in here before."

"I never have," Cord says and drops the subject. "Boy, it's been kind of a hassle today. I'm not sure I did the right thing by getting the Bronco."

"What year did you say it was?"

"Sixty-eight."

"A sixty-eight for twenty-four hundred bucks?"

"Yeah, I think I paid too much for it."

"You were going to lease a truck otherwise, weren't you?"

"That's what I should have done. I never spent that much money on one purchase before."

"Leasing one would probably cost you more money in the long run. You were talking about buying a Bronco anyway. Now you don't have to get one when you get down to Tucson."

"Yeah, now I can go to that party tomorrow night and show Janine my new toy."

"Take her for a ride and let her be the first one to get laid in it," I suggest.

"I'd like to, at least one more time. She'll probably be on the rag. I'll just take Kathy for a ride if Janine don't want to go. She probably don't want nothing to do with me anymore. Hey, maybe I'll get both to go for a ride and get a nice threesome going in the Bronco."

We interrupt our conversation to check out a newly arrived piece of ass. Feeling good, Cord says, "There's one of Janine's friends, the one that's having the party." He starts to leave and I say, "See you later."

"Oh, I'll be right back, I just want to get an update on tomorrow night."

After a short social visit Cord returns with an empty glass and a smile on his face. "Well," he says, "are you ready to jam for awhile?"

"Yep. Let's go look for Darryl and see if he wants to go out to eat with us and catch a buzz."

"You got some smoke?"

"I've got a little stash."

"Great, let's go."

I leave my bike parked out front and we take off in Cord's new Bronco. We try a test drive on some dirt roads, and then look for a secluded place to get high. We end up nearby at his friend's ranch. Cord sometimes crashes out in their barn. It is cool to get high there, so we do.

After the smokes, the munchies set in fast, and we decide to get something to eat. Darryl isn't at the Widowmaker, in fact, he's nowhere to be found. In hopes of meeting him we have dinner then go to Shakey's for the night.

There isn't much of a crowd there, and the band hasn't started to play yet. We order a pitcher and sit a bit back from the action, but still close enough to see the band play. We talk a lot... of good times this season, girlfriend problems, and we toast to probably our last weekend of partying together before Cord goes back to Tucson. We make plans for the coming winter to get together in Los Angeles to party.

Meanwhile the place is filling up fast. While we were talking, the band almost finished their first set. We never noticed, we were so engrossed. We order a third pitcher and sit back to check out the crowd. When the band breaks, we walk around looking for some female conversation to excite our hormones.

Mike goes his own way, and when I got back to our seats, he is sitting a couple of tables away rapping to two cute girls. The band is playing again, and trying to talk to a girl by yelling in her ear over the music isn't my style. Cord dances with each of the girls in turn, while I just sit and watch. He waves to me again and this time I make the trip over to his table. As I sit down, he leans over the table towards the girls and says to them, "This is my friend, roommate, and fellow worker. His name is Steve." He completes the introductions by leaning back to me and yelling in my ear, "That's Fargo, and this is Katharine." I smile and wave with the music. The band takes another recess, so it's my time to get to know the girls.

They have been friends since Junior High in a Chicago suburb. They wanted to go away to school and settled on NAU, knowing little about the area. They are young, pretty, freshman girls, but the blond is the cutest. Her personality is real nice and it makes talking to her easy.

They want to see more of Flagstaff, and listen eagerly as we tell them about all the beautiful local sights. We even offer to take them up to the peaks in a couple of months to see the Aspen trees turn colors. They get pretty excited about that. I invite them out to our district party, but they have other things going on that night. It appears the mountains turn them on. We see this as an opportunity to use that to our advantage. Cord gets their phone number and we arrange to contact them for a date. Things are looking promising and Mike has forgotten about Janine for the moment. The band starts and I ask Fargo to do a little bop with me. We dance up a sweat and sit back down. We all talk a lot and enjoy one another's company. Just when the girls start to get a little drunk and loosen up, they decide to leave. They accept a small acquaintance kiss and thank us for our politeness.

I turn to Cord. "Well, it looks like I got something in the bag for next week."

"I don't know what I'm getting excited for," he says. "I'm not going to be here."

"I'll be here, you'll have to let me copy that number down."

"Sure, you can keep in touch with them, and maybe I'll come back up for a weekend to go hiking with them."

"Yeah, that's what you should do. Especially, if Janine gives you a bad time down there."

"You would have to mention her," Cord says. "I had forgotten about tomorrow night."

"Well, don't start worrying about that now. Think about what you're going to do next time you see Katherine. I'll be thinking about what I'm going to do with that blond. They looked a little inexperienced."

"Yeah," Cord says. "They did. They could very well be virgins."

"I think I'm in love. She sure was a cutie."

"Yeah, well, best of luck, I'm not going to be here."

"You'll be back," I say.

"You're probably right. Are you about ready to go? I still have to go back to Blue Ridge tonight."

"You're going to drive all the way down and back again tomorrow? I thought you were going to stay in the barn tonight."

"I was, but I only brought one pair of clothes and I don't have a sleeping bag with me. Besides, there are some things I want to get done tomorrow. I want to do a little packing. I'll come back up in the afternoon."

"I guess I'm about ready to leave, too. I'm getting tired and I met my bush tonight already. I'll go back in the morning. I don't like driving back this late at night. Just assume to do it in the morning. My sister knows I'll be over tonight."

"That's a good setup you got there. Yeap, it's convenient. I'll finish this beer and go."

We stand outside by the Bronco and talk some more about tomorrow night. "So you don't know if she's going to bring this other guy or not?" I ask Cord.

"No, sure don't. I'll probably beat him up if he comes. I don't think she'll do that anyway."

"Well, if she does, you got Kathy."

"Yep, we almost got it on before. Janine and Kathy get uptight about it."

"Uptight about what?"

"When I start scamming. When it's on someone else, Janine gets jealous. She can do all she wants, but when I start scamming, she gets weird."

"How do you feel when she flirts around?"

"It gets me mad, but I try not to let it get to me. I know she goes out with guys in Tucson when I'm up here. But you can't let things get to you. It's hard not to, I know, but it will only drive you insane. It's not worth it." He takes a deep breath and heaves an exaggerated sigh. "I better go, it's not getting any earlier."

"You have a long way to go."

"I'm used to it by now. Well, buddy, have fun if I don't see you tomorrow." Cord extends his hand and I shake it hard, putting my left hand over his.

"Drive carefully, and don't worry about tomorrow, have a good time anyway."

"I intend on it."

"That's the attitude, see you later."

"Later, Tred."

July 21

The ride back down to work isn't bad at all. Neither is the hangover. I came and went from my sister's house without even seeing them. That's what makes it so nice. I can come and go as I please, enjoying lodging for my individual active schedule. Besides, the price is right.

As we muster up in the shop, it's obvious that it's going to be an easy day, as long as we don't get dispatched to a fire. I'm not sure where in the rotation we are for off forest dispatches. The pessimists are saying that we're going because we have our District party tonight. That's why it's an easy day. Some preparations still have to be made. The District party accounts for most of the conversation in the shop.

We work around the station doing things to improve its function or appearance. I notice a couple of guys still cleaning off spit wads from the fight we had last week. So many of those suckers were flying around it's going to take forever to remove them all. In each task- circle talk is all about the party tonight. I had actually forgotten about it until today. Besides, around here, when you get your heart set on something, it usually doesn't happen. But hey, so far, so good. Things are looking up. Halfway through the morning, Dennis takes a few of the guys with him to set up the party site. It's going to be at some campground east of here, down Highway 87. Fleetingly I wonder what Cord is up to. James says he came in late last night, grabbed some clothes and took off. He didn't even turn off his Bronco. James mentions that he only looked out his window to see what the commotion was.

July 22 to 24

Most of us have a pounding hangover as we walk slowly up to the shop. We sufferers just managed to get ourselves out of bed a few minutes earlier. I don't have time to do anything but get my clothes on while going out the door. Sluggo and James bring up the rear, dragging their feet, their heads hanging low. Gus sips on his coffee from a cup the size of a German beer stein. If I had only got my butt out of bed a few minutes earlier I could have made some to help sober me up. Anything would have helped, even a glass of water. I still feel drunk, but at least my head's not spinning. Darryl and Drifty reek of stale alcohol. Or maybe it's my own breath I smell.

"Hey, Stevie." That's Sluggo's voice drilling through my throbbing head. "How do you feel?"

I turn around to answer him. "Sluggo, leave me alone. I feel as bad as I look, still shit-faced. Uh, I take that back, I feel as bad as you look."

"Look at this hair," James says, chuckling.

I turn around to look. I feel like making another comment, but trying to be funny is too much of an effort in my present condition. I'm not the only one in bad shape. Most of us are quiet, moaning inside from overdoses of beer and Dennis' Lord Calvert that we had polished off. I have a genuine case of alcohol poisoning.

Wakeford is a little cheerier, feeling no pity for any of us. At times like these he knows why he doesn't drink. All he has to do is look at us.

Bob is standing outside the shop watching the mob stagger their way to work. When he determines most of us are present, he goes inside. We gather in the shop. The stragglers stroll in at 20 minutes after, and Bob gets down on them for being late. It's his duty to do so. He is also one of the non-drinkers, and feels compelled to add to our suffering. He only gets amped out on caffeine. This is the day for the non-drinkers to have fun with us.

We are told to keep busy cleaning saws, straightening up the shop and the metal shop until he finds out what we're going to be doing today.

"Where's Cord?" Bob asks, looking around for him, "He only had yesterday off."

"He is on the extended Cord Week again." Koval answers with a chuckle.

"Petretti, was Cord here this morning?" Bob asks.

"No. I didn't see him. I'm still half-asleep myself. I could have missed him and not even known it." I can see that Bob is not pleased with my evasive answer. "I don't think he ever came in last night. I probably wouldn't of heard him if he did." That doesn't sound right, even to me. I clarify it. "For some reason it sounded like I slurred that."

"You're right, you were pretty shit-faced last night," Bob says, exhibiting his first half-smile of the morning.

"Still am. Mike probably had such a good time last night he didn't want to spoil it by coming to work."

"He's quitting in a few days," Aaron adds. "He's not likely to give a shit."

"He was here yesterday getting his shit together. He had his new wheels with him, a Bronco," James says.

"Yeah, I thought I saw him in that thing," Bob confirms. "Where's Dennis?"

No one wants to reveal his condition, but Marty just has to say something. "He was pretty drunk last night. He was so drunk that he could barely talk by the end of the night."

"It was that whisky he had," Darryl says. "That stuff will do it to you."

Bob starts to make his way out the door, pauses and says to Russ, "I'll call him at home when I find out what we're doing."

"Hey, Steve, how'd ya like that bear?" Darryl asks.

"Oh, yeah. I forgot about the dinner part. That bear meat was great. I didn't think that it would taste so good."

"It was very tasty and tender." Darryl, the connoisseur, says.

"Who cooked it?"

"Bedlion did. He even shot it. It was the best game I ever had."

"Yeah. That elk and deer was good, too. I've had them before. But that bear was definitely good."

"Home grown meat fresh from the hills of Blue Ridge."

People are livening up a little, now that we are talking about the party. Kyle gets that look in his eyes. "Hey, Marty, who was that chick last night?"

"She's a friend from Phoenix. She was with someone. Well, those guys that came up with her," Marty says.

Darryl jumps in with a question he's just itching to ask. "Does she always carry a gun around like that?"

"Most of the time," Marty answers blandly.

Darryl's just getting started. "What kind of gun was it? I was afraid to ask her. I didn't want to get shot if I looked at her wrong."

"I think it was a .357. I don't like to get too close to her with that thing on. She's crazy."

"That's what it looked like to me," Darryl concurs.

Kyle adds with his goofy laugh, "I bet she can blow your socks off in bed. Yuck, yuck, yuck."

"Kyle, you asshole," Paul chides, disgusted. "Is that all you ever think of?"

"He's got to," says Cruz. "He never gets pussy, just talks about it. When I talk about it, at least I get it."

"Sure, Cruz," Darryl says, calling his bluff.

Marty asks, "Kyle, what happened to those girls you were going to bring?"

"Lisa and Kim? Or was it Debbie and Kathy?" Kyle replies suavely. "I don't know who you mean."

"I don't really know either. The ones you say you live with."

"I didn't want to bring them. You guys would jaw around them and scare them off."

"No, Kyle that's what *you* do," Drifty accuses.

Joe jumps in with a comment. "Yeah, Kyle, you talk so much shit that you scare them off."

"They were probably dog ugly," Gus says, and laughs.

Marty jumps back in. "Yeah. Bedlion or Hopkins might recruit them for one of their hunting hounds."

"That's all Kyle goes out with is the four legged kind," Koval says, adding to the laughter.

Russ decides to step in before this gets out of hand. "Alright, you guys, put it to rest. Start getting busy." He turns to Joe and starts giving out assignments. "You, Sluggo and Pat. Clean up the metal shop. James and Drifty can clean up the laundry room. The rest of you clean saws and clean up in here. I'm going to see what's taking Bob so long."

He turns and walks away without another word. We abandon our cut down session and slowly make our way to our temporary assignments. I just stand there in the shop as people leave, wishing I felt more energetic.

"I definitely do not want to work today," I mutter.

"Hope we don't have to do much," James says.

"Maybe we'll just stay around here again," Gus remarks hopefully.

"At least for half the day, until my head stops pounding," I say.

The shop phone rings and I jump up to answer it. "Oh, no, looks like back to work time. Hello, shop here."

"Who's this?" Bob's voice on the phone sounds serious so I answer correctly.

"Petretti, sir."

"Where's Drifty?"

"He's in the metal shop cleaning up."

"Get him to change the oil in the bus."

"O.K., Bob. Hey, Bob, are we staying in today?"

"Don't know," he answers curtly.

"Do you think we are going thinning?"

"Don't know."

"I just remembered that Dennis might be over cleaning the Elks' campground. He said something last night about how he was assigned to clean up after the party."

"He's right here," Bob says.

"In the office?"

"Yes! Just tell Drifty to do that."

"O.K. Bye." I hang up the phone and wonder why Bob is acting so cold. I walk over to the metal shop to relay the message to Drifty. On my way back I see Russ heading towards the shop.

"What's going on?" I ask.

Russ acts like he doesn't hear me and goes right into the shop. I run up to door and catch it before it slams. I open it briskly and he turns around and looks right at me with glazed eyes. I just give him a big, toothy smile. Everyone else in the shop appears busy with clean up.

"Hey, listen up," Russ says, and takes a deep breath. "Hey, everyone, I got some bad news."

I quickly respond, "Don't tell me we have to go thin."

"No!" he replies sharply. "Nothing like that." He takes another deep breath and exhales it slowly. "Cord rolled his truck last night."

"You mean his Bronco?" I ask.

"Is he alright? Did he get hurt?" Darryl asks.

"He's dead. Dennis just went to identify the body."

Everyone freezes in his tracks and goes silent. All eyes are fixed on Russ as he continues, "Cole... Coleman found the Bronco turned over on his way to work this morning. He couldn't find the body so he got Dennis to help him. He was found..." Russ stops to collect himself, "...he was thrown out about a hundred feet."

"Where did he crash?" James asks.

"By mile marker 303, they said."

"My God! He must have been going to the party," I exclaim.

Russ continues, making an effort to keep his voice from breaking, "That's about all I know, is that he's dead. He's... dead." He stops talking and just stands there.

A sudden rush of horror strikes my body. My legs want to collapse under me, but I manage to stay upright. The atmosphere is thick with emotion, the room silent except for the ringing in my ears. Everyone just stands there, staring, motionless, silenced, and gasping for breath.

Into that troubled atmosphere Drifty appears, unaware and laughing. "Hey, Treddy, what did..." He stops in his tracks and notices the expressions on the faces around him. "What happened in here?"

Nobody moves. Russ turns to him, "Cord got killed last night."

Drifty doesn't move, but I do. The fresh air from the open door temporarily revived me. I ease my way to a chair to avoid collapsing. My head throbs with even more intensity than before. It becomes the only thing that exists, that horrid throbbing, accompanied by the ringing in my ears. I'm sure I'm not the only one who wants to burst into tears, but no one does. It's not the macho thing to do.

After a while I get up and walk outside. The pounding headache makes me realize I need to go down to the trailers for some aspirin. I want to cry, but someone follows me out the door. Paul is down in the bone yard. As I walk by he doesn't look up, but tries to keep himself occupied with some menial chore. Cord's death definitely got to him, too. Paul comes across as strong and mean, so you wouldn't think he has a soft spot. But this kind of tragedy touches even the hardest hearts. He left the shop early because he felt like the rest of us. We are all involved in this collective consciousness. Everyone's thoughts are on Cord's death, and each of us is experiencing it in his own way. It's what happens, too, when we are on an intense fire line, working for a common goal... to vanquish the fire.

Before we go out thinning for the rest of the day, I have to do one of the hardest tasks stated under, "and other duties as assigned" in my employee contract. I have to gather up all of Cord's personal belongings and lock them up in our room. This brings home to me in a very concrete way that Michael J. Cord is gone for good. Not just laid-off for the season, fired, or quit, but really gone. Dead. I slowly gather up his things from the common areas and put them on his bunk. I swallow hard as a tear drips off my cheek.

After a solemn afternoon of thinning, I feel compelled to visit the crash site after work. It should be cleaned up by now. Darryl and James follow me out there. I don't tell them what I have in mind. I don't have to. They are thinking of the same thing.

As I ride closer to mile marker 303, my heart begins pounding and my blood pressure rises. The throbbing is like the one my hangover gave me this morning.

We walk over to the debris scattered around the road and off the shoulder in the dirt. You can still smell the fresh rubber on the road from the skid marks. There has been no rain to wash off the scars of this casualty. An indentation in the earth marks the spot where the Bronco went off the asphalt.

I invite myself to speak up. "I wish we knew what happened. I hate to think he was lying here when I drove by, returning home from the party. I don't think he was, though. I would have seen something on the side of the road."

"The last person left the party about one-thirty and they didn't see anything," Darryl says.

"It must have happened pretty late," James comments.

"Or early this morning," I add. "He could have been driving back this morning and spaced the station and drove right past it. He was real tired and it could have easily been done."

"He was probably going out to the party," James remarks thoughtfully.

"Not so late at night," I say. "He didn't want to go out to the party. If it were real late he would have stopped at the station to see who was there. He wouldn't have driven twenty extra miles to find out that no one was out there."

Darryl remarks, "I don't think he fell asleep at the wheel, he's driven back from Tucson many times with little sleep."

"Yeah," I say. "As Hotshots we are more or less conditioned to stay awake for long hours. He probably got in a fight with Janine and had her on his mind. That could have made him miss the station. Girls will do that to you. They can really mess with your head. He had her on his mind the night before. Something must have happened at the party in Flagstaff to upset him."

Darryl points to the indentation. "Look here. Here's where he went off the road on the other side. It looks like he tried to correct himself and went off over here."

We all agree that the direction of the skid marks indicate that this most likely happened. "He must have been hauling ass," James says.

I nod. "That could of happened. He could only go fifty-five miles an hour in his old Dodge, and wasn't used to the power he had in the Bronco. They're not known for stability. They tip very easy."

"It looks like he rolled twice," James says.

Darryl asks, "Where did the body land?"

"Look over there by the fence," I say, and start to walk over towards the fence. A peculiar smell catches my attention. "Hey, come here, come here! Stand right here." I quickly motion them over to middle of the southbound lane.

Darryl responds as if I had found something significant. At the same time James makes a discovery. "Look! Something!" He calls, then sees the look on my face and comes over to where I'm standing in the middle of the road.

"What is it?" Darryl asks. He looks around the asphalt. "I thought you had found something."

"It's the smell of death," I say. "It's that unforgettable smell of death."

James picks up the pace when he hears me. "I don't smell nothing, either." He walks away shaking his head as if I was trying to pull one over on him.

I stand my ground. "It was here, I know it was here. I'm not making this up." I get a sudden chill and want to shake like a drenched dog. "This is where he must of actually died. This very spot, about this high."

"How do you know?" Darryl asks suspiciously.

"I know." I go over to smell the place where the Bronco landed in the dirt. There's no funny smell there.

James calls, "Come over here." He is standing by the fence pointing to the ground. "This is where his body landed. See how the ground is? There are no weeds here. He bounced here and went up right into the fence."

The fence is mangled for about fifteen feet where his body rolled along. Pieces of his blond hair and shards of his clothing are snagged in the barbs. I recognize the fabric as pieces of the sweater he was wearing when I last saw him in Flagstaff. That alone sends another cold rush through my body.

"Look!" I say, pointing in a circular motion around the indentation in the dirt. "There's no blood where the body bounced, or even where it finally landed. I know for a fact that dead bodies don't bleed. He died back there where that smell was. He didn't feel a thing while he flew in the air."

Darryl notices something in the grass. He bends over very slowly and picks up a watch. "Look, it's still ticking," he says wryly. We look and he's right. Too bad, maybe we could have told what time the accident happened. He stares blankly at the watch for a few seconds. "Janine gave this to him last Christmas."

"You should give it back to her. Look here, I see some money laying around." I pick it up and hand it to Darryl.

James is over on the other side of the fence. Something has his attention there. "Hey, look at these tracks. Looks like elk."

We hop over the damaged part of the fence, careful not to disturb the fragments on it. "Sure does," we both agree.

"There's a bunch of them around here," James says. "Looks like they were curious and checked out what happened."

Darryl has another idea. "They probably were the ones who caused the accident."

"That's what I was just about to say," James agrees.

"He must have swerved to avoid hitting them. It's at a bend. He could have seen them too late to react."

"That doesn't explain him driving past the station," I say.

"True, but the elk caused him to go off the road. I've seen it lots of times around here."

"Plus the fact he was going too fast."

"Yeap. I guess it all adds up and contributes to Cord's death," I say. "Dammit! Why did *he* have to die?"

Before we wrap up our little investigation and head back to the station I go over to where I smelled that odor to see if I can find it one more time. I don't detect anything. I only got eerie feelings.

I figure getting good and drunk is in order. My supply is too low to support the objective, so I go get beer at Clint Wells. I am surprised to see the wreckage of Mike's Bronco there. I guess Bruce was the one who got the Bronco this morning. It looks like it went through a war zone. Still intact, but obviously rolled. The only broken glass was on the passenger side door. That doesn't sit well with me. I go in, buy my beer, and quickly leave without saying a word to Bruce.

Back at the trailers I grab a cold beer and take a shower. Under the spray I can cry aloud. I am alone at last, where no one can see or hear me, and I can give vent to my deep emotions. Up here, you know, showing your feelings is not the macho thing to do. As the tears flow freely, I wonder who else is doing the same.

July 24

We awake to another strange day at the station. It looks like we might get tomorrow off. Only six of us go out thinning. The rest of the crew stays at the station keeping busy. I'm glad for the opportunity to be doing something. We head out to Long Lake to find an obscure place to thin, new surroundings for us to work in. We work slowly as we are all still depressed. When we break for lunch, we gather around the vehicles parked at the campsite around the lake. Out of the blue Darryl asks, "Have you been thinking about Cord?"

"Yeap." I stop a moment to gather my thoughts. "Quite a bit. More so at night when I'm trying to sleep. I scare myself just thinking about him while I'm trying to go to sleep. I've been going around looking behind doors, and I'm hearing things in the trailer."

Russ, who has been eavesdropping, chuckles a little. Darryl ignores him and says, "Yeah, I've been talking to him lately."

"You have?" I exclaim. "He talked to me Sunday night."

"Naw," says Darryl. "You're crazy."

"No, really, I'm serious. That's how I know how he died. He told me how it happened. That's how I came to this theory. He told me."

"What theory? This is the first I've heard of this."

"This is the way it figures out. Remember Dennis was saying he flew out of the passenger side and wasn't wearing his seat belt."

"Yes, I do."

"Well, when the Bronco went off the road on the left side and right off the shoulder, the front end dipped and his body was on a different plane of relativity. The theory of relativity is applied here. Have you heard of the example about this dog traveling in space at a rate of ninety percent of the speed of light? Now this flea on the dogs back is traveling at twenty percent of the speed of light. How fast is the flea really traveling, twenty percent or one hundred ten percent of the speed of light?"

"I don't know," Darryl says. "It sounds tricky."

"The flea is only going twenty percent because he is moving in relation to the dog and the dog is moving in relation to the earth. The flea doesn't move in relation to the earth because the earth doesn't exist as far as the flea is concerned."

"So?"

"Well, listen! When the Bronco went off the road and Cord's body left the seat, he ceased moving in relation with the earth, while the vehicle still was. The vehicle and the slant of the road shoulder would have brought the passenger side of the window to Cord's body that was now suspended in mid-air inside the cab. His body was motionless while the Bronco dipped down at the front left, which would have made him appear to fly out the window on the passenger side. But it was impossible for him to have been thrown that far by going out the window."

"My theory goes on like this. After he exited through the passenger side he was still alive. The way the motion of the Bronco continued off the side of the road, he was outside the Bronco, and the front end dug into the ground where we saw the indentation just off the pavement. Then the right back end went flying and it batted him over to where we saw his body landed before it went into the fence. You saw how far his body traveled down to the fence. It had to be a great force that hurled him that distance. Just flying out of the window wouldn't have put him there by the fence where we were looking. He had to be batted by the back end as it whipped around as the left front end anchored itself in the ground. That exact place where I smelled that weird odor was probably the very same place he was when the Bronco batted him and went off the road. The bronco was violently in motion, but his body wasn't, until it was batted away by the right rear section."

Darryl steps in and says, "What if he broke his neck inside the cab?"

"Could have on his way out the window," I say. "There was no time for him to have been bouncing around inside."

"Do you really think that's the way it happened?" Darryl asks.

"I *know* that's the way it happened. It's the only way it *could* of happened, the only logical way. Besides, I told you, he told me that's the way it happened."

"Who told you?" asks Russ. "Oh, I know. You really believe that shit? Huh?"

"Yes, I do. Do you think that I could have thought of that all by myself? He told me by putting the thoughts into my head. Remember I told you of that odor I came across. It was head high. I didn't smell it anywhere else. Not on the ground where his body landed or anywhere. Something got absorbed when I inhaled it. You couldn't smell it could you?"

Darryl answers, "No, I couldn't smell a thing.

"Well I couldn't either, after the first time." I sit back and get serious again. "Well, it's a distinctive smell... the smell of death. I've been told that it is because when people die a sudden death, the body excretes a lot of fluids: urine, shit, come, sweat, and fear. You know, adrenaline. Hey, have you ever smelled an epileptic? They have an odor right before they convulse."

"No, I don't think I ever have," Darryl says. "I've never been around one while they was in convulsions. It's also said that they get a kinda fruity taste in their mouth right before they convulse."

"Well, maybe so, but this smell was very pungent and a very distinct odor. I've smelt it before where I've seen three people die in a head on collision in rainy weather. I know I smelled the same thing there about head high. You don't forget that smell once you have experienced it. There's something else about Cord's odor that intrigued me. It's like there was a source of data or thoughts stored on that smell. Somehow when he died he emitted thoughts along with the excretion of bodily fluids."

"I don't believe that," Darryl says.

"No, listen, I'll make a believer out of you. When you die the soul has to go somewhere. I believe that it kinda gets dispersed into the atmosphere. But like the same way it stays in the body, that is, around the space the body takes up. It could be in your toes, head, or anywhere, or everywhere within your body. It's encapsulated in the body."

"Yeah, that seems logical," Darryl acknowledges.

"If it does, then why can't the soul enter into a rock or a tree, or anything that has matter and things that have form? Now, the air around the body has ions and particles from the body it just came from. They are floating around outside the body in a gaseous form."

"Uhmmmm," Darryl muses.

"You could say that his soul was entrapped in that smell, still lingering in the exact place he died. You see, the soul leaves the body upon death, and when it does, it somehow recognizes the ions or cloud of moisture and fluids from the mass it had just escaped. In recognizing it, it grasps a hold of the fluids, encapsulating it, just like it did in the body. You know the body is made up mostly of fluids. So it encapsulates itself around the dense mass of mist composed of sweat tears, come, urine, shit, and spit that just left the body. By doing so it keeps the mist intact. You know, encapsulating it. It keeps it from wandering just as the soul wants to wander off into the heavens."

"So keeping the cloud intact has the appearance of a ghost," Darryl comments.

"That is where I think ghosts come from. It's a strong willed person that is most capable of encapsulating the body fluids after it leaves the body."

Darryl adds a thought. "Have you heard about people dying and entering back into their body? People who have done this and lived said they saw themselves being operated on or saw themselves gathered around by a bunch of people gawking over their body while they were lying in the street dying. Do you think Cord was out there watching us that day?"

"Not impossible. In order for him or any of those people to have seen what they claim they saw they had to have a body with eyes, ears, and touch to have perceived anything. You need senses to perceive something. The body is an instrument for the mind. It's a sensing instrument that carries messages to the mind. In particular, messages of sight, sound, touch, smells, and tastes. Of course we can't forget the common of these senses, commonly called, the common sense. Hey, that rhymed. Pretty neat, uh?"

Darryl enjoys this and remarks, "It sounded funny, but you couldn't have said it any better."

"So if a soul can't actually see or hear things, what were these people experiencing? I say they are only imagining what they think they saw. If anything, they probably felt something that instilled pictures or images in their heads. Cord felt us there but he didn't see us. I am sure he waited for us. Well, he did because that smell was Cord, or what was left of him."

"Do you think he'll be at the funeral?" Darryl asks.

"No. His soul went somewhere in a million places."

"Is there a place where they all go, the souls, that is?"

"Well, if you want me to get religious, you can say they all went to heaven, or hell if was an evil soul. The soul is a very powerful thing. It's more powerful than we think. There's no reason why it can't keep together as an identity and enter into a rock or tree or anything that doesn't have a soul."

"You're talking now about reincarnation."

I had to think about that one. "Well, no, not really. Reincarnation infers that it goes to a higher form of life. In India, for example, it's the cow, that's why the fucking things are sacred and protected. They don't even eat them with all the starvation there. They are afraid they might eat their own mother or cousin. Not just kidding, I think the real reasons are that the cows are more valuable to them alive than dead. You see, when you kill a cow, it can't produce milk. Milk is one of their main sources of nutrition. And the shit? I hear they can make houses and use it for fuel."

Darryl laughs heartily. "I didn't know that."

"Don't quote me on that, but I think it's true. There could be a form of reincarnation of some sort. It stands to reason that there is some sort of reincarnation. It's weird though, how civilizations of long ago have thought of these things before, and that I think of them now almost the same way, but thousands of years later. Something had to be true about the matter."

"No wonder there is so much confusion about God," Darryl says.

"Yeap, there is. If God does have something to do about it, it would probably be that he's the one that specialized the soul to be assigned to the human body. There is something about the reproduction of the egg and sperm and the formation of the specific chromosomes. The human soul can read the chromosomal message. The wandering soul can pick up and hone in on, and attach itself to the newly formed cellular life form. It's not necessary that one's individual soul is absorbed into a particular egg and sperm, but collectively the souls of many that have been dispersed all around. Or how about this? You heard about people reflecting about an earlier life? They get flashbacks from a period in the past. Maybe these are particular souls that didn't wander around but rather stayed together. Wait a second I'm getting off the subject."

I look around and everyone there is listening to me. So I continue. "God's the one that puts the characteristics into human life forms. The dog soul enters into canine bodies and the cat soul into feline bodies. They all have their specific chromosome code to help God find the home for each soul. Yes, animals have souls, too. Consequently, creatures can effectively work in dualism with their own body and soul.

"Boy, I really got off the subject. Going back to where I started out, I think that's why Cord's soul was present in the roadway when we were there inspecting the crash site. That smell was part of his body and part of his mind. His mind talked to me, sent me messages on how he really died to share with everyone who gives a shit about him." I had to stop and take a breather. "Fascinating stuff, uh?"

"Yeah. What about sound that can travel around from one place to another?" Darryl inquires. "Is that how, like, the soul travels around?"

"Now you're thinking. You could be right. Think of it this way. Sound needs air to travel through. Remember the soul needs a matter form to truly exist as a functioning thing. Air is matter with less density, we just don't see it. We feel it, and know its effects. Sound travels through the matter from one place to another." I hold up my hands to demonstrate. "Sound can travel from one place to another, but it needs air to travel through. Even then you need two most important ingredients. You need a perceiver of audible things before you can carry it out, and you need the sound itself, or a source."

"You might have heard of that famous philosophical example: If a tree falls in the forest and no one is around to hear it, does it make any sound?"

"Yes," Darryl replies quickly.

"Nope, the answer is no. How can anything be heard if nothing is around that is equipped with senses to perceive that certain audible noise it makes?"

"I don't believe that, it's got to make noise." He adds, "Maybe if you put instruments out there they can measure sounds and sound waves."

"Yes, its a sensing thing. It senses and it is sensitive to sounds. The body is just an instrument itself. In fact, that's exactly what it is, a sensing instrument that serves the mind."

"O.K. How about radar? It travels through space."

"You're right, but it's controlled by instruments from the beginning, to only be perceived by its own kind, some device out there to pick up the radar. A matched set, a specific sender and a specific receiver."

Darryl smiles a big, toothy grin.

"Darryl, think of it like temperature, hot and cold. The soul is like heat. Heat can only be transferred through matter. It's never lost. It goes from one object to another. Haven't you ever crushed an ember between your fingers? It goes out when the heat is transferred from the ember into your fingers. Your fingers get hot, don't they?"

"Yeah," he says reflectively.

"I think it falls under the laws of thermodynamics. Well, you're just killing the ember. You took the energy source away and it died. You drained the life from it. The energy source was absorbed in your fingers. It wasn't lost, but rather transferred. Just like the soul can be transferred in the same way maybe, but it's characteristic only allowing it to be transferred into human bodies."

"Well, when something dies, where does that energy go? Are you then saying that it goes into the air we breathe? What if I had a bug in my hand?" He shows me the little insect he just found. With his thumb and forefinger he proceeds to crush it. "Now where does the energy go?"

"All you are doing there is ceasing a biological chemical reaction. You're stopping a cause and effect chemical reaction by interrupting the respiration process. That's what kills people, when the respiration and circulation process fails. You're taking away the causes, and only the energy released is from the last effect from the cause that you just willfully eliminated. That's a famous argument for the existence of God. He was the creator of the first cause. He put everything in motion so that if everything should stop you'll have the energy he used to originally put the first thing in motion."

"I don't know. It all seems strange... so crazy. Cord's death is crazy."

"Yeah, but what happens if no one ever dies? Eventually everything would die. I don't know. I could be full of shit."

We must have been talking for about an hour. Russ didn't say anything because he was captivated and just listened. He didn't want to interrupt us.

July 25

I wake up rather early this morning. I know I don't have to, but I am still feeling pretty uneasy about the last few days. I lie there in bed for a while, thinking. Not liking where my thoughts where taking me, I get up to make some coffee. I get my coffee and pull out my bills. I guess it's time to pay some of them. Looking through them I come across a letter from a friend I've been writing to, Kelsey Ueame. She is a beautiful Hawaiian babe that I lusted over at Litton G&CS. I read it again. It reminds me that she and a friend are going to be in Las Vegas this week. That inspires me to get out of town for a couple of days. Energized, I quickly rise, get ready, and hit the highway. The letter said something about them staying at the Four Queens, and that is where I find them. They are surprised to see me and I have the impression that I caught them off guard.

We buddy around the town the rest of the afternoon and evening. As much as I always wanted to make love to Kelsey, it feels like the farthest thing from my mind. I am feeling too solemn to pursue that kind of activity right now. My creepy crawling crab catastropy had also suppressed my libido. I hope she doesn't think I don't like her. I can't discuss Cord's death with the girls. I crash out on the floor in their motel room without making any advances. I just want to prepare myself for an early departure in the morning. Some time during the night, I called the Coconino dispatcher. We have moved to first on the list to go off forest again. I hope Kelsey will forgive me for not making passionate love to her. Gee, I could have even pursued a threesome. I get up early and head back to Flagstaff.

Stay tuned for part two, "Hotshots: The Big One."
Due out Jan. 2003.

Bill had many wonderful memories of his time as the Crew Superintendent. He enjoyed the camaraderie, the challenges, the work ethic, and was especially proud of the reputation the crew had for getting things done. He always felt that he was able to make a difference in the working conditions and the needed recognition for Hotshot Crews when he attended the Regional and National Hotshot meetings. Even after he left and moved on in his career, I know that there were times he wished he was still a Hotshot.

After his death in April of 1998, he was given the great honor of being recognized as one of the eight Charter Members of the Arizona Firefighters Hall of Fame and was inducted in September of 1998. That was a great honor, but I know that he would be even more pleased by this book and the recognition you have given him by this dedication. On behalf of Bill, his family, friends, and myself,

   Thank You.
Sharon Krushak, Sept. 21, 2002
P.S. One thing about his passing – at least he got to meet Jerry Garcia.

AUTHOR'S NOTES TO MY FELLOW HOTSHOTS

You know I wanted to print this book with the Hotshot in mind. He reads a lot on the road. He moves from place to place. He hurry ups and waits. He pulls his book out of his back pocket and reads in-between movements and at times during moments. Consequently, to have printed this in a standard pocket size paperback would of meant a lot of paper waste from trimming. Nevertheless economy, efficiency, and conservation wins. Sorry about that guys, you can still undo a button in your shirt and tuck it in there. That way, it is not going to be a pain in the ass.

Some proceeds of this book and all future Hotshots series books will be put in a Federal Firefighter Relief Fund to aid the families of those who have died in the line of duty.

Front cover design by Steve Petretti,
a collage of tee-shirts and photographs.

Back page photograph:
Sunset on the Arizona Strip
taken by Steve Petretti 1979
a scene from "Hotshots: Season's End."

SAVE OUR PLANET

Save our Children.
Hug your kids and tell them you love them.
Support the family.
Make Love not Money.
Quit your job and invest in your kids .

Did you know that AT&T is one of the biggest porn distributors in the world. Get rid of their long-distance service and sign up with EXCEL COMMUNICATIONS WITH A PLAN OF $.05 PER MINUTE AND $5.00 A MONTH. NO RESTRICTION OR MINIMUMS, 24/7. LOTS OF PLANS TO CHOOSE FROM.

WWW.EXCELIR.COM/THANKS TO COMPARE PLANS AND SERVICES AND TO SIGN UP.

OR CALL 1-888-ORDERXL USE GLOBAL REP ID# 9567506114

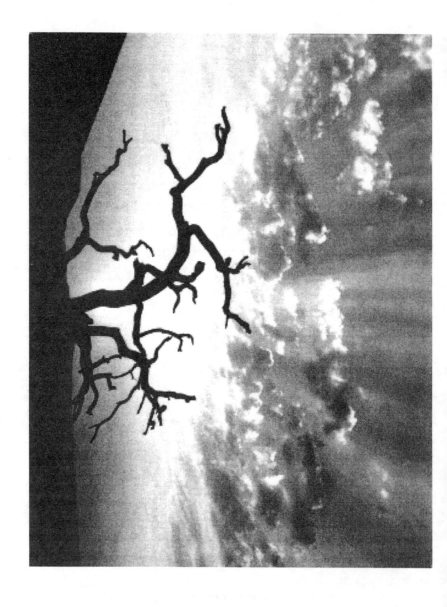